To Margaret
with deepest love & appreciation
of your part in the Felt St. Mission

Noel.   March 1948

GOLDEN BELLS

HYMNS FOR YOUNG PEOPLE

703 PIECES

NEW AND ENLARGED
EDITION.

LONDON:

CHILDREN'S SPECIAL SERVICE MISSION,
3, 5, & 7, Wigmore Street, Cavendish Square, W.1

PREFACE.

More than thirty-five years have passed since the first edition of "Golden Bells" was issued, the special purpose of this book having been to put "the songs of Zion" into the lips of boys and girls. That God has graciously accepted this effort to spread abroad His praises is evidenced by the widespread appreciation won by the book, nearly four million copies of which have been circulated.

"Golden Bells" will always be regarded in a special sense as linked with the founders of the Children's Special Service Mission. But for some time past it has been felt that the great expansion of the work in many lands should be reflected in a new edition which would cover a wider field and embrace the latest and best of the wealth of new hymns and tunes. The Committee have therefore prepared this revised edition, a special Sub-Committee of C.S.S.M. Workers having been appointed to undertake the compilation, and the result of their long and earnest labours is now placed before the Christian public. Numerous suggestions from workers and friends were carefully considered, and many hundreds of hymns and tunes reviewed, with the result that it is believed that the final selection of 703 pieces, which comprise this volume, will ensure its being established in the near future as a popular, comprehensive, and representative collection of old and new Hymns for Young People.

Nearly four hundred of the hymns appearing in the former edition are retained in the new volume, while over three hundred numbers appear in "Golden Bells" for the first time, including many well-known favourites, together with a number of new hymns. A large proportion of the old favourite tunes have also been retained, and many added which will be welcomed. The references to alternative tunes are a feature that will be much appreciated. While the boys and girls may still claim this book as their special hymnal—and it will be more useful than ever in Children's Services, Sunday Schools, Bible Classes, &c.—the collection will also appeal to all hymn lovers.

The Committee desire to place on record their deep gratitude to E. J. Bellerby, Esq. Mus. Doc., for his most valued services, so freely and graciously rendered, in the preparation of the musical portion of this Hymnal. Many tunes received his revision, and many more his approval, but it is only fair to Dr. Bellerby to state that he was not responsible for the selection of the tunes, some of which the Committee desired to insert rather for their recognised popularity than for their artistic merit. Special thanks are also due to the Rev. E. H. Gladstone Sargent, Cecil J. Allen, Esq., and William Perkins, Esq., for their assistance in seeing the music proofs through the press. A pleasing feature of the preparation of this work has been the very willing help given by the compilers of other hymnals, and to such the Committee express their gratitude; as also to the great number of friends who have, in varied ways, helped in the compilation of this volume, which is now sent forth with the earnest prayer that it may be graciously used of God to the blessing of many souls, and to the extension of Christ's Kingdom among the young throughout the world.

The Committee gratefully acknowledge the kindness of authors, composers, and owners of copyrights in granting permission (in many cases freely given) to include hymns and tunes, noted below. Every endeavour has been made to trace the owners of copyright, and should any infringement have been inadvertently made, the Committee tender their apologies, and will gladly make any necessary corrections in subsequent editions.

Where no name is given in the second column the author or composer is understood to be the owner of copyright.

HYMNS.

AUTHOR.	OWNER OF COPYRIGHT.	NO. OF HYMN.
Ainger, A. C.	Society for Promoting Christian Knowledge	611
Aitken, Canon W. H. M. Hay		553
Armitage, Mrs. E. S.		644
B. E.	Mrs. H. C. Dixon	383
Baker, Sir H. W.	Proprietors, Hymns Ancient and Modern	130, 478, 591
Bellerby, Dr. E. J.		455
Bennet, Rev. Norman		508
Bennett, Lucy A.		154

AUTHOR.	OWNER OF COPYRIGHT.	No. OF HYMN.
Bickersteth, E. H.	Canon S. Bickersteth	91, 181, 338, 612
Blanchard, G. B.	Wesleyan Methodist S.S. Dept.	646
Blatchford, A. N.	Rev. Rudolph Davis	26
Blunt, A. G. W.	Mr. Reginald Blunt	695
Bonar, Horatius	Rev. H. N. Bonar	29, 224
Bourne, W. St. Hill	Proprietors, *Hymns Ancient and Modern*	437
Boyd, M. R.	Mr. Frederick P. Wood	451
Breck, Mrs. Frank A.	Mrs. H. C. Dixon	462
Brooke, Stopford A...	Messrs. Macmillan & Co., Ltd., and Mr. Stopford W. W. Brooke	500
Burroughs, Right Rev. E. A., D.D.	The Lord Bishop of Ripon	86
Burrow, S. E.		431
Burton, H.	Messrs. Morgan & Scott, Ltd.	258
Butler, Mary	National Sunday School Union	675
Chapman, J. Wilbur	Mrs. H. C. Dixon	129
Charlesworth, Vernon J.	Gipsy Pat Smith	344
Cherry, E. Gilling	Messrs. Morgan & Scott, Ltd.	547
Codner, Elizabeth	Mr. W. Wood for Exors.	259
Cousin, A. R.	Messrs. Auld & MacDonald, W.S., for Exors.	141, 559
Crosby, Fanny J.	Messrs. Morgan & Scott, Ltd.	46, 278
Deck, H. L. Richmond	Mrs. H. L. R. Deck	315
Deck, Mary A. S.	Mrs. A. C. Walton	564
Dennison, Dorothy		50
Edwards, M. Betham-	Exors. of Rev. W. Garrett Horder	670
Ellerton, J.	Oxford University Press	606
Elliott, E. E. Steele	Mrs. C. M. Wyley	109, 113, 178
Farningham, Marianne	Messrs. J. Clarke & Co., Ltd.	489, 628
Forrest, S. F.		326
Fox, H. W.	London Missionary Society	624
Frances, Grace J.	Mrs. H. C. Dixon	319
Francis, S. Trevor		138
French, Rev. F. Goldsmith		88, 297
Gill, T. H.	Mr. E. W. B. Gill	493
Goadby, F. W.	Mrs. Chater	131
Goodman, George		140, 160, 277, 372, 515, 523, 683, 703
Goodman, Montague		529
Gordon, Amy	London Missionary Society	614
Goreh, E. L.		74
Gould, S. Baring-	Messrs. A. W. Ridley & Co., Ltd.	525, 536, 605
Greenwell, Dora	Messrs. H. R. Allenson, Ltd.	471
Griffiths, Caroline	National Sunday School Union	97
Grimes, E. May	Mrs. E. May Crawford	409
Habershon, A. R.	Mrs. H. C. Dixon	303
Hankey, Kate	Messrs. Longmans, Green & Co., Ltd.	204, 444
Hardy, J.	National Sunday School Union	528
Hatch, W.	Mr. W. Hatch	188
Havergal, Frances R.	Messrs. J. Nisbet & Co., Ltd.	15, 147, 174, 176, 206, 246, 329, 333, 376, 417, 443, 459, 465, 466, 482, 484, 501, 530, 690, 691
Hedden, K.		19 (v. 3)
Hills, L.	Mr. R. Hudson Pope	28
Homer, C. G.	Mrs. H. C. Dixon	353
Hopps, J. Page	National Sunday School Union	659
How, W. Walsham	Rev. W. H. Walsham How	98, 143, 473, 696
Hudson, Anna	The Hall-Mack Co.	396
Hughes, Gibbard		251
Humby, F. H.		634
Jackson, E. H.	Mrs. F. S. Riggall	92
J——, G. M.	Mrs. H. C. Dixon	289, 623
Janvrin, Alice J.	Church Missionary Society	435
Johnson, Mrs. C.	London Missionary Society	621
Kelly, K. A. M.	Mr. Frederick P. Wood	161
Lloyd, J. W.	Mr. W. J. Lloyd	112
Luke, Jemima	National Sunday School Union	635
Lyne, J. L.	Mr. T. M. Leycester Lyne	375
Martin, S.	Mrs. L. Sweney Kirkpatrick	496
Mathams, Rev. Walter J.		548, 651
Matheson, Annie	National Sunday School Union	442, 673
Matheson, G.	Miss Jane Matheson	398
Maude, Mary F.	Mrs. Chevesse	331
Maxwell, Mary E.	Mr. W. J. Gibbs	421
McGill, J. Wakefield	Messrs. Pickering & Inglis	488, 616
Midlane, Albert	Mrs. M. E. Mill	220, 441
,, ,,	Messrs. Reid Bros., Ltd.	640
Morgan, S. C.	Rev. E. Tilson-Morgan	233

TUNES.

COMPOSER.	OWNER OF COPYRIGHT.	NO. OF TUNE.
Blunt, F. W.	Messrs. Novello & Co., Ltd.	605 (2)
Booth, Josiah	..	530, 675
" "	Church Hymnary Trust	204 (2)
Boyd, M. R.	Mr. Frederick P. Wood	451
Boyd, Rev. W.	..	538
Bridge, Sir J. F.	Proprietors, *Hymns Ancient and Modern*	437
Brinkworth, E. K.	National Sunday School Union	626
Brown, Arthur H.	Oxford University Press	600
Bullinger, E. W.	Miss E. Dodson	417
Burroughs, Right Rev. E. A., D.D.	The Lord Bishop of Ripon	86
Button, H. Elliot	Messrs. Novello & Co., Ltd.	531, 680
Caldbeck, G. T.	Rev. Canon S. Bickersteth	338
Caldicott, A. J.	Mrs. M. Mayne Caldicott	294
Calkin, J. B.	Messrs. Novello & Co., Ltd.	93
"	Messrs. J. F. Shaw & Co., Ltd.	111 (1)
Carrott, Livesey	Mrs. L. Carrott	234, 260, 520
Chadwick, G. W.	Messrs. A. S. Barnes & Co.	88 (1)
Challinor, Dr. F. A.	National Sunday School Union	656
Cooke, W. H.	Exors. of Rev. W. Garrett Horder	37
Craig, James A.	..	630 (1)
Crosbie, H. A.	Mrs. H. A. Crosbie	638
Cummings, W. H.	Messrs. Novello & Co., Ltd.	119
C. W. and E. M.	Messrs. Pickering & Inglis	488
Dale, R. F.	Miss M. Pickersgill-Cunliffe	447
Dobbs, J. S.	London Missionary Society	614
Duckworth, Francis	..	625 (2)
Dugdale, J. J.	..	223 (2)
Dugdale, L. Z.	..	88 (2)
Dykes, J. B.	Messrs. Novello & Co., Ltd.	259 (2), 484
" "	Proprietors, *Hymns Ancient and Modern*	558, 571
Elliott, J. W.	Messrs. Novello & Co., Ltd.	168, 363
Elliott, E. E. Steele	Mrs. C. M. Wyley	178
Excell, E. O.	Mrs. H. C. Dixon	462
Feilden, O. M.	Rev. R. H. Harvey	644
Fishwick, C.	..	345, 489
Forrest, C. H.	Mrs. C. H. Forrest	416, 477
Foster, Myles B.	Proprietors, *Hymns Ancient and Modern*	546
Gabriel, C. H.	Mrs. H. C. Dixon	353
Gaul, A. R.	Mr. C. A. Gaul	545
Gibb, W. O.	Mrs. Lena A. Gibb	461 (2), 643 (1)
Gibson, A. F.	..	515
Gilbert, W. B.	Messrs. Novello & Co., Ltd.	185, 657
Gladstone, W. H.	Messrs. Novello & Co., Ltd.	391
Gould, A. C. Barham	..	551
Gould, S. Baring-	Messrs. A. W. Ridley & Co.	605 (1)
Gounod, C.	Messrs. Novello & Co., Ltd.	457
Green, Rev. H.	South Africa General Mission	409, 413
Hancock, Charles	..	122
Harkness, Robert	Mrs. H. C. Dixon	301, 303
Havergal, Frances R.	Messrs. J. Nisbet & Co., Ltd.	174, 246, 690
Hervey, F. A. J.	Messrs. Novello & Co., Ltd.	563 (1)
Hopkins, E. J.	Messrs. A. Weekes & Co.	691
Hurndall, W. F.	Exors. of Rev. W. Garrett Horder	673
Husband, E.	Mrs. S. E. Bradburne	311, 616
Jackson, R.	Mrs. E. Taylor	3, 99, 108, 151, 340, 423, 594
Jamoneau, A. J.	The Epworth Press	578
Jewson, J. P.	Mrs. A. Sanderson	95
Jordan, C. Warwick	Mrs. Warwick Jordan	85
Kelly, K. A. M.	Mr. Frederick P. Wood	161
Kettle, C. E.	Messrs. A. W. Ford & Co., *Bristol Tune Book*	20, 188
Kingham, M. D.	Society for Promoting Christian Knowledge	611
Knowles, G. F.	..	146
Lahee, H.	Exors. of Rev. W. Garrett Horder	5, 406
Langran, J.	Messrs. Novello & Co., Ltd.	407, 408, 557
Larbalistier, P. G.	..	164, 296
Lehman, R. Frank	The Hall-Mack Co.	396
Lightwood, J. T.	National Sunday School Union	132
Lomas, G.	Exors. of Rev. W. Garrett Horder	84, 298, 450
Macfarren, Sir G. A.	Proprietors, *Hymns Ancient and Modern*	692
Maclagan, W. D.	Mr. Eric W. D. Maclagan	331
Main, H. P.	Mrs. H. C. Dixon	319
Maker, F. C.	Psalms and Hymns Trust	59, 232, 402, 431, 448
Mann, Dr. A. H.	..	491, 627 (2)
Marsh, C. H.	Mrs. H. C. Dixon	129
Matthews, T. R.	Messrs. Novello & Co., Ltd.	445, 473, 671

INDEX OF SUBJECTS.

Golden Bells

Hymns for Young People.

Section I.—Praise and Worship.

Laudes Domini.   6.6.6.6.6.6.   Sir Joseph Barnby.

1

Daily shall He be praised.—Psalm lxxii. 15.

1 When morning gilds the skies,
  My heart awaking cries,
    May Jesus Christ be praised!
  Alike at work and prayer
  To Jesus I repair:
    May Jesus Christ be praised!

2 To Thee, my God above,
  I cry with glowing love,
    May Jesus Christ be praised:
  The fairest graces spring
  In hearts that ever sing,
    May Jesus Christ be praised!

3 Does sadness fill my mind?
  A solace here I find,
    May Jesus Christ be praised!
  Or fades my earthly bliss?
  My comfort still is this,
    May Jesus Christ be praised!

4 When evil thoughts molest,
  With this I shield my breast,
    May Jesus Christ be praised!
  The powers of darkness fear,
  When this sweet chant they hear,
    May Jesus Christ be praised!

5 When sleep her balm denies,
  My silent spirit sighs,
    May Jesus Christ be praised!
  The night becomes as day,
  When from the heart we say,
    May Jesus Christ be praised!

6 Be this, while life is mine,
  My canticle divine,
    May Jesus Christ be praised!
  Be this the eternal song
  Through all the ages on,
    May Jesus Christ be praised!

Tr. *E. Caswall.*
A*

Diademata. S.M.D. Sir G. J. Elvey.

2 *And on His head were many crowns.*—Rev. xix. 12.

1 CROWN Him with many crowns,
The Lamb upon His throne;
Hark! how the heavenly anthem drowns
All music but its own:
Awake, my soul, and sing
Of Him who died for thee,
And hail Him as thy matchless King,
Through all eternity.

2 Crown Him the Lord of life,
Who triumphed o'er the grave,
And rose victorious in the strife
For those He came to save:
His glories now we sing
Who died, and rose on high;
Who died eternal life to bring,
And lives that death may die.

3 Crown Him the Lord of love;
Behold His hands and side,
Those wounds yet visible above
In beauty glorified:

No angel in the sky
Can fully bear that sight,
But downward bends his burning eye
At mysteries so bright.

4 Crown Him the Lord of peace,
Whose power a sceptre sways
From pole to pole, that wars may cease,
And all be prayer and praise:
His reign shall know no end,
And round His piercèd feet
Fair flowers of Paradise extend
Their fragrance ever sweet.

5 Crown Him the Lord of years,
The Potentate of time,
Creator of the rolling spheres,
Ineffably sublime!
All hail, Redeemer, hail!
For Thou hast died for me;
Thy praise shall never, never fail
Throughout eternity.

M. Bridges and G. Thring.

Lymington.　　　　　　　7.6.7.6., D.　　　　　　R. JACKSON.

Alternative Tune, EXULTATION, *No.* 20.

3　　　　*Hosanna to the Son of David.*—MATT. xxi. 9.

1 WHEN, His salvation bringing,
　　To Zion Jesus came,
　The children all stood singing
　　Hosanna to His Name;
　Nor did their zeal offend Him,
　　But as He rode along
　He bade them still attend Him,
　　And smiled to hear their song.

2 Then since the Lord retaineth
　　His love for children still,
　Though now as King He reigneth
　　On Zion's heavenly hill,
　We'll flock around His banner
　　Who sits upon the throne,
　And sing aloud, Hosanna!
　　To David's royal Son!

3 For should we fail proclaiming
　　Our great Redeemer's praise,
　The stones, our silence shaming,
　　Would their hosannas raise.
　But should we only render
　　The tribute of our words?
　No; while our hearts are tender,
　　They too shall be the Lord's.

John King

Miles' Lane. [FIRST TUNE.]　　　C.M.　　　W. SHRUBSOLE.

And crown Him, crown Him, crown... Him, crown Him Lord of all.

4　　　*King of kings, and Lord of lords.*—REV. xix. 16.

1 ALL hail the power of Jesus' Name!
　　Let angels prostrate fall;
　Bring forth the royal diadem,
　　And crown Him Lord of all.

2 Crown Him, ye martyrs of our God
　　Who from the altar call,
　Extol the stem of Jesse's rod,
　　And crown Him Lord of all.

3 Ye saints redeemed of Adam's race,
　　Ye ransomed from the fall,
　Hail Him who saves you by His grace,
　　And crown Him Lord of all.

4 Sinners, whose love can ne'er forget
　　The wormwood and the gall,
　Go, spread your trophies at His feet,
　　And crown Him Lord of all.

5 Let every kindred, every tribe
　　On this terrestrial ball,
　To Him all majesty ascribe,
　　And crown Him Lord of all.

6 Oh, that with yonder sacred throng
　　We at His feet may fall,
　Join in the everlasting song,
　　And crown Him Lord of all!

　　　　　　　　　　　E. Perronet.

4 **Diadem.** [SECOND TUNE.]   C.M. with Refrain.   JAMES ELLOR.

1. All hail the power of Je - su's name ! Let an - gels prostrate fall:

Let an - gels pros - trate fall: Bring forth the roy - al di - a - dem,

And crown . . . . Him,

And crown Him,   crown Him,   crown Him,   crown Him,
And crown . . . . Him,

And crown Him,   crown Him,   crown Him,   crown . . .

crown Him, crown Him,   crown Him, and   crown Him Lord of all.

. . . . Him,

Nativity. C.M. H. Lahee

Alternative Tune, LYNGHAM, *No.* 16.

5

Worthy is the Lamb that was slain.—REV. v. 12.

1 COME, let us join our cheerful songs
   With angels round the throne;
   Ten thousand thousand are their tongues,
   But all their joys are one.

2 "Worthy the Lamb that died!" they cry,
   "To be exalted thus!"
   "Worthy the Lamb!" our lips reply,
   "For He was slain for us."

3 Jesus is worthy to receive
   Honour and power divine:
   And blessings, more than we can give,
   Be, Lord, for ever Thine.

4 Let all that dwell above the sky,
   And air, and earth, and seas,
   Conspire to lift Thy glories high,
   And speak Thine endless praise.

5 The whole creation join in one
   To bless the sacred Name
   Of Him that sits upon the throne,
   And to adore the Lamb. *Isaac Watts.*

Mildmay. 6.5.6.5. Anon.

Alternative Tune, NORTH COATES, *No.* 473.

6

Jesus Himself stood in the midst.—LUKE xxiv. 36.

1 JESUS, stand among us,
   In Thy risen power,
   Let this time of worship
   Be a hallowed hour.

2 Breathe Thy Holy Spirit
   Into every heart,
   Bid the fears and sorrows
   From each soul depart.

3 Thus with quickened footsteps
   We'll pursue our way,
   Watching for the dawning
   Of eternal day. *W. Pennefather.*

Tours. 7.6.7.6., D. BERTHOLD TOURS.

By permission of Novello and Company, Limited.

7

Christ is all and in all.—COL. iii. 11.

1 My song shall be of Jesus;
　His mercy crowns my days,
He fills my cup with blessings,
　And tunes my heart to praise:
My song shall be of Jesus,
　The precious Lamb of God,
Who gave Himself my ransom,
　And bought me with His blood.

2 My song shall be of Jesus;
　When, sitting at His feet,
I call to mind His goodness,
　In meditation sweet:
My song shall be of Jesus,
　Whatever ill betide;
I'll sing the grace that saves me,
　And keeps me at His side.

3 My song shall be of Jesus,
　While pressing on my way
To reach the blissful region
　Of pure and perfect day:
And when my soul shall enter
　The gate of Eden fair,
A song of praise to Jesus
　I'll sing for ever there.

Fanny J. Crosby.

8. My Redeemer.

8.7.8.7.

JAMES McGRANAHAN.

CHORUS.

With His

Sing, oh sing, . . . of my Re-deem - er! With His
Sing, oh sing, of my Redeem-er, sing, oh sing, of my Redeem-er! With His

With His

blood . . .

blood He purchased me, He pur-chased me! . . . On .. the
blood . . . He pur-chased me, He purchased me! On .. the

blood He purchased me, With His blood He purchased me!

cross . . . He sealed my par - don, Paid the
cross He sealed my par - don, On .. the cross He sealed my par- don, Paid the

debt, . . . and made me free. . . .

debt, and made me free, and made me free, and made me free.

and made me free. . . .

Alternative Tune, HYFRYDOL, No. 158.

8

O Lord, my Strength, and my Redeemer.—PSALM xix. 14.

1 I WILL sing of my Redeemer,
And His wondrous love to me;
On the cruel cross He suffered,
From the curse to set me free.
Sing, oh sing, of my Redeemer! etc.

2 I will tell the wondrous story,
How my lost estate to save,
In His boundless love and mercy,
He the ransom freely gave.
Sing, oh sing, of my Redeemer! etc.

3 I will praise my dear Redeemer,
His triumphant power I'll tell;
How the victory He giveth
Over sin, and death, and hell.
Sing, oh sing, of my Redeemer! etc.

4 I will sing of my Redeemer,
And His heavenly love to me;
He from death to life hath brought me,
Son of God, with Him to be.
Sing, oh sing, of my Redeemer! etc.

P. P. Bliss.

Ephraim.   7.7.7.7.   H. T. LESLIE.

9

Thou shalt call His name Jesus; for He shall save His people from their sins.—MATT. i. 21.

1 CONQUERING kings their titles take
From the foes they captive make;
Jesus, by a nobler deed,
From the thousands He hath freed.

2 Yes, none other Name is given
Unto mortals under heaven,
Which can make the dead arise
And exalt them to the skies.

3 That which Christ so hardly wrought,
That which He so dearly bought,
That salvation, mortals, say,
Will ye madly cast away?

4 Rather gladly for that Name
Bear the cross, endure the shame;
Joyfully for Him to die
Is not death, but victory.

5 Jesus, who dost condescend
To be called the sinner's Friend,
Hear us, as to Thee we pray,
Glorying in Thy Name to-day.

6 Glory, to the Father be,
Glory, risen Lord, to Thee,
Glory to the Holy Ghost,
From the saints and heavenly host.

Tr. J. Chandler

Old Hundredth.   L.M.   G. Franc.

10   *Serve the Lord with gladness.*—Psalm c. ii.

1 All people that on earth do dwell,
  Sing to the Lord with cheerful voice;
Him serve with fear, His praise forth tell,
  Come ye before Him and rejoice.

2 Know that the Lord is God indeed,
  Without our aid He did us make:
We are His flock, He doth us feed,
  And for His sheep He doth us take.

3 Oh, enter then His gates with praise,
  Approach with joy His courts unto:
Praise, laud, and bless His Name always,
  For it is seemly so to do.

4 For why? the Lord our God is good;
  His mercy is for ever sure;
His truth at all times firmly stood,
  And shall from age to age endure.

W. Keith.

Rivaulx.   L.M.   J. B. Dykes.

11   *In the Name of the Father, and of the Son, and of the Holy Ghost.*—Matt. xxviii. 19.

1 Father of Heaven, whose love profound
  A ransom for our souls hath found,
Before Thy throne we sinners bend,
  To us Thy pardoning love extend.

2 Almighty Son, Incarnate Word,
  Our Prophet, Priest, Redeemer, Lord,
Before Thy throne we sinners bend,
  To us Thy saving grace extend.

3 Eternal Spirit, by whose breath
  The soul is raised from sin and death,
Before Thy throne we sinners bend,
  To us Thy quickening power extend.

4 Almighty Father, Spirit, Son;
  Mysterious Godhead, Three in One,
Before Thy throne we sinners bend,
  Grace, pardon, life to us extend.

E. Cooper.

Cantate Domino.   L.M.D.   Sir J. Barnby.

By permission of Novello and Company, Limited.

12   *Sing unto the Lord, all the earth.*—Psalm xcvi. **1.**

1 Sing to the Lord a joyful song:
  Lift up your hearts, your voices raise:
To us His gracious gifts belong,
  To Him our songs of love and praise.
For life and love, for rest and food,
  For daily help and nightly care,
Sing to the Lord, for He is good,
  And praise His Name, for it is fair.

2 For strength to those who on Him wait,
  His truth to prove, His will to do,
Praise ye our God, for He is great:
  Trust in His Name, for it is true.
For joys untold, that from above
  Cheer those who love His sweet employ,
Sing to our God, for He is love:
  Exalt His Name, for it is joy.

3 For life below, with all its bliss,
  And for that life, most pure and high,
That inner life, which over this
  Shall ever shine, and never die,
Sing to the Lord of heaven and earth,
  Whom angels serve and saints adore,
The Father, Son, and Holy Ghost,
  To whom be praise for evermore.

J. S. B. Monsell.

Evelyns. [FIRST TUNE.] 6.5.6.5., D. W. H. MONK.

13 *That in the Name of Jesus every knee should bow.*—PHIL. ii. 10, *R.V.*

1 IN the Name of Jesus
   Every knee shall bow,
Every tongue confess Him
   King of glory now;
'Tis the Father's pleasure
   We should call Him Lord,
Who from the beginning
   Was the mighty Word.

2 At His voice creation
   Sprang at once to sight,
All the angel faces,
   All the hosts of light;
Thrones and dominations,
   Stars upon their way,
All the heavenly orders
   In their great array.

3 Humbled for a season
   To receive a Name
From the lips of sinners,
   Unto whom He came;
Faithfully He bore it
   Spotless to the last;
Brought it back victorious
   When from death He passed.

18 Vespers. [SECOND TUNE.]   6.5.6.5., D.   H. A. PROTHERO.

Alternative Tunes, EDINA, *No. 25, and* HATHERLEY, *No. 223.*

4 Name Him, brothers, name Him
   With love strong as death,
But with awe and wonder,
   And with bated breath;
He is God the Saviour,
   He is Christ the Lord,
Ever to be worshipped,
   Trusted, and adored.

5 In your hearts enthrone Him,
   There let Him subdue
All that is not holy,
   All that is not true;
Crown Him as your Captain
   In temptation's hour,
Let His will enfold you
   In its light and power.

6 Brothers, this Lord Jesus
   Shall return again
With His Father's glory,
   With His angel train;
For all wreaths of empire
   Meet upon His brow,
And our hearts confess Him,
   King of glory now.
       C. M. Noel.

St. Hilda. 8.7.8.7., D. Sir J. BARNBY

14 *Hail, King of the Jews.*—MARK xv. 18.

1 HAIL, Thou once despisèd Jesus,
  Hail, Thou Galilean King!
Thou didst suffer to release us,
  Thou didst free salvation bring.
Hail, Thou agonising Saviour,
  Bearer of our sin and shame,
By Thy merits we find favour;
  Life is given through Thy Name.

2 Paschal Lamb, by God appointed,
  All our sins were on Thee laid:
By Almighty love anointed,
  Thou hast full atonement made.
All Thy people are forgiven,
  Through the virtue of Thy blood:
Opened is the gate of heaven,
  Peace is made 'twixt man and God.

3 Jesus, hail! enthroned in glory,
  There for ever to abide;
All the heavenly hosts adore Thee,
  Seated at Thy Father's side:
There for sinners Thou art pleading,
  There Thou dost our place prepare,
Ever for us interceding,
  Till in glory we appear.

4 Worship, honour, power, and blessing
  Thou art worthy to receive:
Loudest praises, without ceasing,
  Meet it is for us to give:
Help, ye bright angelic spirits,
  Bring your sweetest, noblest lays;
Help to sing our Saviour's merits,
  Help to chant Immanuel's praise.

J. Bakewell.

Zoan. 7.6.7.6., D. W. H. Havergal.

15 *Whom, having not seen, ye love.*—1 Pet. i. 8.

1 O Saviour, precious Saviour,
  Whom yet unseen we love,
O Name of might and favour,
  All other names above!
    We worship Thee, we bless Thee,
      To Thee alone we sing;
    We praise Thee, and confess Thee
      Our holy Lord and King.

2 O Bringer of salvation,
  Who wondrously hast wrought,
Thyself the revelation
  Of love beyond our thought;
    We worship Thee, we bless Thee,
      To Thee alone we sing;
    We praise Thee, and confess Thee
      Our gracious Lord and King.

3 In Thee all fulness dwelleth,
  All grace and power divine;
The glory that excelleth,
  O Son of God, is Thine;
    We worship Thee, we bless Thee,
      To Thee alone we sing;
    We praise Thee, and confess Thee
      Our glorious Lord and King.

4 Oh, grant the consummation
  Of this our song above
In endless adoration,
  And everlasting love!
    Then shall we praise and bless Thee
      Where perfect praises ring,
    And evermore confess Thee
      Our Saviour and our King.
        Frances R. Havergal.

Lyngbam. [FIRST TUNE.]

C.M.

T. JARMAN.

1. Oh, for a thou - sand tongues to .. sing My great Re-deem-er's

praise, My great .. Re-deem-er's praise! The glo-ries of .. my

God .. and King, The tri-umphs of His grace, The

The tri-umphs of His grace,

tri-umphs of His grace, .. The tri - umphs of His grace.

grace, .. The tri-umphs of His grace, The triumphs of His grace.

16   *I will praise Thee, O Lord, with my whole heart.*—PSALM ix. 1.

1 OH, for a thousand tongues to sing
  My great Redeemer's praise!
The glories of my God and King,
  The triumphs of His grace.

2 My gracious Master and my God,
  Assist me to proclaim,
To spread through all the earth abroad
  The honours of Thy Name.

3 Jesus, the Name that charms our fears,
  That bids our sorrows cease;
'Tis music in the sinner's ears,
  'Tis life and health and peace.

4 He breaks the power of cancelled sin,
  He sets the prisoner free;
His blood can make the foulest clean,
  His blood availed for me.

5 He speaks, and, listening to His voice,
  New life the dead receive,
The mournful, broken hearts rejoice,
  The humble poor believe.

6 Hear Him, ye deaf: His praise, ye dumb,
  Your loosened tongues employ;
Ye blind, behold your Saviour come;
  And leap, ye lame, for joy!

C. Wesley.

16 **London New.** [SECOND TUNE.] C.M. SCOTCH PSALTER.

1. Oh, for a thou-sand tongues to sing My great Re-deem-er's praise!

The glo - ries of my God and King, The tri-umphs of His grace.

Alternative Tune, SAWLEY, *No.* 370.

17 **Gerontius.** C.M. J. B. DYKES.

The second Man is the Lord from heaven.—1 COR. xv. 47.

1 PRAISE to the Holiest in the height,
    And in the depth be praise :
  In all His words most wonderful,
    Most sure in all His ways !

2 Oh, loving wisdom of our God !
    When all was sin and shame,
  A second Adam to the fight
    And to the rescue came.

3 Oh, wisest love ! that flesh and blood,
    Which did in Adam fail,
  Should strive afresh against the foe,
    Should strive and should prevail ;

4 And that a higher gift than grace
    Should flesh and blood refine,
  God's presence and His very Self,
    And Essence all-Divine.

5 Oh, generous love ! that He who smote
    In Man for man the foe,
  The double agony in Man
    For man should undergo ;

6 And in the garden secretly,
    And on the cross on high,
  Should teach His brethren and inspire
    To suffer and to die.

7 Praise to the Holiest in the height,
    And in the depth be praise ;
  In all His words most wonderful,
    Most sure in all His ways !

J. H. Newman.

Houghton. 5 5.5 5.6 5.6 5. H. J. GAUNTLETT.

18 *All Thy works shall praise Thee, O Lord.*—PSALM cxlv. 10.

1 OH, worship the King,
  All-glorious above;
  Oh, gratefully sing
    His power and His love :
  Our Shield and Defender,
    The Ancient of Days,
  Pavilioned in splendour,
    And girded with praise.

2 Oh, tell of His might,
    Oh, sing of His grace,
  Whose robe is the light,
    Whose canopy space ;
  His chariots of wrath
    The deep thunder-clouds form,
  And dark is His path
    On the wings of the storm.

3 The earth, with its store
    Of wonders untold,
  Almighty ! Thy power
    Hath founded of old ;
  Hath 'stablished it fast,
    By a changeless decree,
  And round it hath cast,
    Like a mantle, the sea.

4 Thy bountiful care
    What tongue can recite ?
  It breathes in the air,
    It shines in the light ;
  It streams from the hills,
    It descends to the plain,
  And sweetly distils
    In the dew and the rain.

5 Frail children of dust,
    And feeble as frail,
  In Thee do we trust,
    Nor find Thee to fail ;
  Thy mercies how tender !
    How firm to the end !
  Our Maker, Defender,
    Redeemer, and Friend !

Sir R. Grant.

19 *He that is our God is the God of salvation.*—PSALM lxviii. 20.

1 YE servants of God,
    Your Master proclaim,
  And publish abroad
    His wonderful Name ;
  The Name all-victorious
    Of Jesus extol :
  His kingdom is glorious,
    And rules over all.

2 God ruleth on high,
    Almighty to save ;
  And still He is nigh,
    His presence we have !
  The great congregation
    His triumph shall sing,
  Ascribing salvation
    To Jesus our King.

3 Let children acclaim
    Their Saviour and Friend !
  In songs to His Name
    Their praises ascend :
  In such a salvation
    How great is their joy ;
  In true adoration
    How blest their employ !

4 Salvation to God,
    Who sits on the throne ;
  Let all cry aloud,
    And honour the Son ;
  The praises of Jesus
    All angels proclaim,
  Fall down on their faces,
    And worship the Lamb.

5 Then let us adore
    And give Him His right ;
  All glory and power,
    All wisdom and might ;
  All honour and blessing,
    With angels above ;
  And thanks never-ceasing,
    And infinite love.

C. Wesley and (v. 3) *K. Hedden.*

Exultation.   7.6.7.6., D.   C. E. KETTLE.

By permission of the Proprietors of the *Bristol Tune Book.*

20   *The children . . . . saying—Hosanna to the Son of David.*—MATT. xxi. 15.

1 HOSANNA! loud hosanna!
    The little children sang:
  Through pillared court and temple
    The glorious anthem rang:
  To Jesus who had blessed them,
    Close folded to His breast,
  The children sang their praises,
    The simplest and the best.

2 From Olivet they followed,
    'Midst an exultant crowd,
  Waving the victor palm-branch,
    And shouting clear and loud;
  Bright angels joined the chorus
    Beyond the cloudless sky—
  "Hosanna! in the highest:
    Glory to God on high!"

3 Fair leaves of silvery olive
    They strewed upon the ground,
  Whilst Salem's circling mountains
    Echoed the joyful sound:
  The Lord of men and angels
    Rode on in lowly state,
  Nor scorned that little children
    Should on His bidding wait.

4 "Hosanna in the highest!"
    That ancient song we sing:
  For Christ is our Redeemer,
    The Lord of heaven, our King.
  Oh, may we ever praise Him
    With heart and life and voice,
  And in His blissful presence
    Eternally rejoice!
              J. Threlfall.

Crüger.　　　　　　7.6.7.6., D.　　　　　J. Crüger.

21　　　*His Name shall endure for ever.*—Psalm lxxii. 17.

1 Hail to the Lord's anointed,
　　Great David's greater Son!
Hail, in the time appointed,
　　His reign on earth begun!
He comes to break oppression,
　　To set the captive free;
To take away transgression,
　　And rule in equity.

2 He shall come down like showers
　　Upon the fruitful earth,
And love, joy, hope, like flowers,
　　Spring in His path to birth;
Before Him, on the mountains,
　　Shall peace, the herald, go,
And righteousness in fountains
　　From hill to valley flow.

3 Kings shall fall down before Him,
　　And gold and incense bring;
All nations shall adore Him,
　　His praise all people sing:
For He shall have dominion
　　O'er river, sea, and shore,
Far as the eagle's pinion
　　Or dove's light wing can soar.

4 O'er every foe victorious,
　　He on His throne shall rest,
From age to age more glorious,
　　All blessing and all-blest,
The tide of time shall never
　　His covenant remove;
His Name shall stand for ever,
　　That Name to us is Love.
　　　　　　　　　　J. Montgomery.

Leoni.   6.6.8.4., D.   Ancient Hebrew Melody.

My praise shall be continually of Thee.—PSALM lxxi. 6.

22

1 THE God of Abraham praise,
    Who reigns enthroned above,
Ancient of everlasting days,
    And God of love!
Jehovah! great I AM!
By earth and heaven confessed,
I bow, and bless the sacred Name,
    For ever blest.

2 The God of Abraham praise,
    At whose supreme command
From earth I rise, and seek the joys
    At His right hand.
I all on earth forsake,
    Its wisdom, fame, and power;
And Him my only portion make,
    My Shield and Tower.

3 He by Himself hath sworn;
    I on His oath depend :
I shall, on eagles' wings upborne,
    To heaven ascend.
I shall behold His face,
    I shall His power adore,
And sing the wonders of His grace
    For evermore.

4 There dwells the Lord our King,
    The Lord our righteousness,
Triumphant o'er the world and sin :
    The Prince of Peace.
On Zion's sacred height
    His kingdom still maintains,
And glorious with His saints in light,
    For ever reigns.

5 The whole triumphant host
    Give thanks to God on high ;
"Hail, Father, Son, and Holy Ghost !"
    They ever cry.
Hail, Abraham's God and mine !
    I join the heavenly lays ;
All might and majesty are Thine
    And endless praise.

T. Olivers.

Gratitude.　　　　　　　　　　L.M.　　　　　　　　　　Anon.

Chorus.—A - bove the rest this note shall swell, this note shall swell, this note shall swell,

D.C. for Chorus.

A - bove the rest this note shall swell—My Je - sus hath done all things well.

Alternative Tune (without Chorus), GALILEE, No. 625.

He hath done all things well.—MARK vii. 37.

23

1 Now in a song of grateful praise,
To my dear Lord my voice I'll raise;
With all His saints I'll join to tell,
My Jesus hath done all things well.

2 All worlds His glorious power confess;
His wisdom all His works express;
But oh! His love what tongue can tell?
My Jesus hath done all things well!

3 And since my soul has known His love,
What mercies has He made me prove!
Mercies which do all praise excel:
My Jesus hath done all things well.

4 And when to that bright world I rise,
And join the anthems of the skies,
Above the rest this note shall swell—
My Jesus hath done all things well.

S. Medley.

Monkland.　　　　　　　　7.7.7.7.　　　　　　　　　German.

24　　　*For His mercy endureth for ever.*—PSALM cxxxvi. 1.

1 LET us with a gladsome mind
Praise the Lord, for He is kind;
For His mercies shall endure,
Ever faithful, ever sure.

2 He, with all commanding might,
Filled the new-made world with light:
For His mercies shall endure,
Ever faithful, ever sure.

3 All things living He doth feed,
His full hand supplies their need:
For His mercies shall endure,
Ever faithful, ever sure.

4 He His chosen race did bless
In the wasteful wilderness:
For His mercies shall endure,
Ever faithful, ever sure.

5 He hath with a piteous eye
Looked upon our misery:
For His mercies shall endure,
Ever faithful, ever sure.

6 Let us, then, with gladsome mind,
Praise the Lord, for He is kind;
For His mercies shall endure,
Ever faithful. ever sure.

John Milton.

Edina.　　　　　6.5.6.5., D.　　　　　Sir H. S. Oakeley.

Alternative Tune, PRINCETHORPE, No. 223.

25　*Being confident of this very thing, that He which hath begun a good work in you will perform it until the day of Jesus Christ.*—PHIL. i. 6.

1 SAVIOUR, blessèd Saviour,
　　Listen whilst we sing,
　Hearts and voices raising
　　Praises to our King;
　All we have to offer,
　　All we hope to be,
　Body, soul, and spirit,
　　All we yield to Thee.

2 Nearer, ever nearer,
　　Christ, we draw to Thee,
　Deep in adoration
　　Bending low the knee:
　Thou, for our redemption,
　　Cam'st on earth to die;
　Thou, that we might follow,
　　Hast gone up on high.

3 Clearer still, and clearer,
　　Dawns the light from heaven,
　In our sadness bringing
　　News of sin forgiven;
　Life has lost its shadows,
　　Pure the light within;
　Thou hast shed Thy radiance
　　On a world of sin.

4 Onward, ever onward,
　　Journeying o'er the road
　Worn by saints before us,
　　Journeying on to God:
　Leaving all behind us,
　　May we hasten on,
　Backward never looking
　　Till the prize is won.

5 Higher, then, and higher
　　Bear the ransomed soul,
　Earthly toils forgotten,
　　Saviour, to its goal;
　Where, in joys unthought of,
　　Saints with angels sing,
　Never weary, raising
　　Praises to their King.
　　　　　　　　G. Thring.

The Blessed Name.   8.7.8.7., D.   Sir Joseph Barnby.

In Him re-joice with heart and voice, Whose glo - ry fa-deth nev - er,

Whose pro - vi-dence is our de - fence, Who lives and loves for ev - er!

By permission of Novello and Company, Limited.

26

Rejoice in the Lord alway.—PHIL. iv. 4.

1 A GLADSOME hymn of praise we sing,
    And thankfully we gather
To bless the love of God above,
    Our everlasting Father.
        In Him rejoice with heart and voice, etc.

2 From shades of night He calls the light,
    And from the sod the flower;
From every cloud His blessings break,
    In sunshine or in shower.

3 Full in His sight His children stand,
    By His strong arm defended,
And He, whose wisdom guides the world,
    Our footsteps hath attended.

4 For nothing falls unknown to Him—
    Or care, or joy, or sorrow;
And He whose mercy ruled the past
    Will be our stay to-morrow.

5 Then praise the Lord with one accord,
    To His great Name give glory,
And of His never-changing love,
    Repeat the wondrous story!
                        A. N. Blatchford.

Austria. 8.7.8.7., D. J. Haydn.

27 *Glorious things are spoken of thee, O city of God.*—Psalm lxxxvii. 3.

1 GLORIOUS things of thee are spoken,
　Zion, city of our God!
He, whose word cannot be broken,
　Formed thee for His own abode:
On the Rock of Ages founded,
　What can shake thy sure repose?
With salvation's walls surrounded,
　Thou may'st smile at all thy foes.

2 See, the streams of living waters,
　Springing from eternal love,
Well supply thy sons and daughters,
　And all fear of want remove:
Who can faint, while such a river
　Ever flows their thirst to assuage?—
Grace, which, like the Lord, the Giver,
　Ever flows from age to age?

3 Round each habitation hovering,
　See the cloud and fire appear!
For a glory and a covering,
　Showing that the Lord is near—
He who gives them daily manna,
　He who listens when they cry:
Let Him hear the loud hosanna,
　Rising to His throne on high.

4 Saviour, if of Zion's city
　I through grace a member am,
Let the world deride or pity,
　I will glory in Thy Name:
Fading is the worldling's pleasure,
　All his boasted pomp and show;
Solid joys and lasting treasure
　None but Zion's children know.

John Newton.

D

28 Singing.　　　　　P.M.　　　　　R. HUDSON POPE.

God will . . . fill thy mouth with laughter and thy lips with shouting for joy.—JOB viii. 21 *(marg.)*.

1. As through this world to a hap-pier shore　I　go　sing-ing,　The
2. In spite of the way so rough and long,　I　go　sing-ing,　Though
3. When things go wrong and I seem a - lone,　I　go　sing-ing,　For His
4. So on - ward, up-ward, homeward bound,　I　go　sing-ing,　—

pros - pect brightens more and more, And a thou-sand joys un-known be - fore Seem
hard the . . fight 'gainst sin and wrong, Tho' friends are few and foes are strong, The
arm of . . pow'r is round me thrown, — Bright with the joy He gives His own, A -
Sing- ing the Gos-pel to all a - round, — Sound-ing it forth till hearts re -sound ; In

flood - ing my heart till it's brimming o'er, And　I　go　sing - ing.
joy of the Lord, my strength and song, Still keeps me　sing - ing.
- long the way with bless-ings strewn, —　I　go　sing - ing.
heaven at last with the ransom'd crown'd, For ev - er　sing - ing.

CHORUS.

Sing - ing, sing-ing, I . . go sing-ing, Yes, I'm al - ways sing - ing ; Christ

holds my hand, by faith I stand, And as the hours are wing - ing, I press a - long with cheer - ful song, Sing-ing, sing-ing, sing - ing.

L. Hills.

29

Morningside.

11.11., with Chorus.

English Air.

CHORUS.

Sound His prais - es, tell the sto - ry of Him who was slain ; Sound His prais-es, tell with glad-ness He liv - eth a - gain.

29

Rejoice in the Lord.—PHIL. iii. 1.

1 REJOICE and be glad! the Redeemer has come;
Go, look on His cradle, His cross, and His tomb!
  Sound His praises, tell the story, etc.

2 Rejoice and be glad! it is sunshine at last;
The clouds have departed, the shadows are past.

3 Rejoice and be glad! for the blood hath been shed;
Redemption is finished, the price hath been paid.

4 Rejoice and be glad! now the pardon is free;
The Just for the unjust has died on the tree.

5 Rejoice and be glad! for the Lamb that was slain
O'er death is triumphant, and liveth again.

6 Rejoice and be glad! for our King is on high;
He pleadeth for us on His throne in the sky.

7 Rejoice and be glad! for He cometh again:
He cometh in glory, the Lamb that was slain.
  Sound His praises, tell the story of Him who was slain;
  Sound His praises, tell with gladness He cometh again.

H. Bonar.

Alleluia. 8.7.8.7., D. S. S. WESLEY.

Alternative Tune, LUX EOI, *No.* 542.

30 *Thine, O Lord, is the victory.*—1 CHRON. xxix. 11.

1 ALLELUIA! sing to Jesus!
  His the sceptre, His the throne;
Alleluia! His the triumph,
  His the victory alone.
Hark, the songs of holy Zion
  Thunder like a mighty flood:
"Jesus out of every nation
  Hath redeemed us by His blood."

2 Alleluia! Not as orphans
  Are we left in sorrow now;
Alleluia! He is near us,
  Faith believes, nor questions how,
Though the clouds from sight received Him
  When the forty days were o'er,
Shall our hearts forget His promise,
  "I am with you evermore"?

3 Alleluia! Bread of heaven,
  Thou on earth our food, our stay;
Alleluia! here the sinful
  Flee to Thee from day to day.
Intercessor, Friend of sinners,
  Earth's Redeemer, plead for me
Where the songs of all the sinless
  Sweep across the crystal sea.

4 Alleluia! sing to Jesus!
  His the sceptre, His the throne;
Alleluia! His the triumph,
  His the victory alone.
Hark, the songs of holy Zion
  Thunder like a mighty flood ·
"Jesus out of every nation,
  Hath redeemed us by His blood."

W. C. Dix

Zionwards.

Spirited.

S.M., with Chorus.

R. LOWRY.

1. Come, ye that love the Lord, And let your joys be known, Join in a song with sweet ac-cord, Join in a song with sweet ac-cord, And thus sur - round the throne, And thus sur - round the throne...

CHORUS.

We're march - ing
We're march-ing on to Zi - on, Beau-ti-ful, beau-ti-ful Zi - on; We're

march-ing up-ward to Zi - on, ... The beau-ti-ful ci-ty of God...
Zi - on, Zi - on,

Alternative Tune (without Chorus), ST. MICHAEL, *No.* 275.
Our feet shall stand within thy gates, O Jerusalem.—PSALM cxxii. 2.

31

2 Let those refuse to sing
   Who never knew our God;
   But children of the heavenly King,
   Must speak their joys abroad.

3 The hill of Zion yields
   A thousand sacred sweets,
   Before we reach the heavenly fields,
   Or walk the golden streets.

4 Then let our songs abound,
   And every tear be dry;
   We're marching through Immanuel's ground
   To fairer worlds on high.

Isaac Watts.

32 **Praise my soul.** [FIRST TUNE.] 8.7.8.7.8.7.   Sir JOHN GOSS.

Triumph. [SECOND TUNE.]   8.7.8.7.8.7.   H. J. GAUNTLETT.

32 *O Lord my God, I will give thanks unto Thee for ever.*—PSALM xxx. 12.

1 PRAISE, my soul, the King of heaven;
　To His feet thy tribute bring;
Ransomed, healed, restored, forgiven,
　Who like thee His praise should sing?
　　Praise Him, praise Him!
　Praise the everlasting King.

2 Praise Him for His grace and favour
　To our fathers in distress;
Praise Him, still the same for ever,
　Slow to chide, and swift to bless:
　　Praise Him, praise Him!
　Glorious in His faithfulness.

3 Father-like, He tends and spares us;
　Well our feeble frame He knows;
In His hands He gently bears us,
　Rescues us from all our foes:
　　Praise Him, praise Him!
　Widely yet His mercy flows.

4 Angels, help us to adore Him;
　Ye behold Him face to face;
Sun and moon, bow down before Him:
　Dwellers all in time and space:
　　Praise Him, praise Him!
　Praise with us the God of grace.

H. F. Lyte.

Venice.　　　　**S.M.**　　　　　W. AMPS.

Alternative Tune, HUDDERSFIELD, *No.* 446.

33　*Bless the Lord, O my soul, and forget not all His benefits.*—PSALM ciii. 2.

1　OH, bless the Lord, my soul!
　　His grace to thee proclaim,
　And all that is within me join
　　To bless His holy Name.

2　Oh, bless the Lord, my soul,
　　His mercies bear in mind,
　Forget not all His benefits:
　　The Lord to thee is kind.

3　He will not always chide;
　　He will with patience wait;
　His wrath is ever slow to rise
　　And ready to abate.

4　He pardons all thy sins,
　　Prolongs thy feeble breath;
　He healeth thine infirmities,
　　And ransoms thee from death.

5　He clothes thee with His love,
　　Upholds thee with His truth,
　And, like the eagle, He renews
　　The vigour of thy youth.

6　Then bless His holy Name,
　　Whose grace hath made thee whole,
　Whose loving-kindness crowns thy days;
　　Oh, bless the Lord, my soul!

J. Montgomery.

Sunshine in my Soul.

P.M.

Jno. R. Sweney.

Oh, there's sun - - shine, bless - ed sun - - shine,
Oh, there's sun - shine in my soul, bless - ed sun - shine in my soul,

When the peace - ful, hap - py mo - ments roll;
hap - py mo - ments roll;

When Je - sus shows His smil - ing face, There is sunshine in my soul.

34

*As the light of the morning when the sun riseth, even a morning
without clouds.* —2 SAMUEL xxiii. 4.

1 THERE is sunshine in my soul to-day,
   More glorious and bright
Than glows in any earthly sky,
   For Jesus is my Light.
      Oh, there's sunshine, etc.

2 There is music in my soul to-day,
   A carol to my King;
And Jesus, listening, can hear
   The songs I cannot sing.

3 There is spring-time in my soul to-day,
   For when the Lord is near,
The dove of peace sings in my heart,
   The flowers of grace appear.

4 There is gladness in my soul to-day,
   And hope, and praise, and love;
For blessings which He gives me now,
   For joys laid up above.

E. E. Hewitt.

Praise ye the Name. P.M. Anon.

For His love flow-eth on, free and full as a riv-er, And His mer-cy en-du-reth for ev-er and ev-er.

35 *Sing praises to the Lord, which dwelleth in Zion.*—PSALM ix. 11.

1 PRAISE, praise ye the Name of Jehovah, our God,
Declare, oh, declare ye His glories abroad!
Proclaim ye His mercy from nation to nation,
Till the uttermost islands have heard His salvation.
     For His love floweth on, etc.

2 Praise, praise ye the Lamb, who for sinners was slain,
Who went down to the grave and ascended again;
And who soon shall return when these dark days are o'er
To set up His kingdom in glory and power.

3 Her bridal attire and her festal array
All nature shall wear on that glorious day;
For her King cometh down with His people to reign,
And His presence shall bless her with Eden again.

H. Bonar.

B *

36 To God be the glory. 11.11.11.11.

W. H. DOANE.

REFRAIN.

Praise the Lord! praise the Lord! Let the earth hear His voice! Praise the Lord! praise the Lord! Let the peo-ple re - joice! Oh, come to the Fa-ther through Je - sus the Son; And give Him the glo - ry—great things He hath done!

36

Give unto the Lord the glory due unto His Name.—PSALM xxix. 2.

1 To God be the glory! great things He hath done!
So loved He the world that He gave us His Son,
Who yielded His life an atonement for sin,
And opened the life-gate that all may go in.

2 Oh, perfect redemption, the purchase of blood!
To every believer the promise of God;
The vilest offender who truly believes,
That moment from Jesus a pardon receives.

3 Great things He hath taught us, great things He hath done,
And great our rejoicing through Jesus the Son:
But purer and higher and greater will be
Our wonder, our transport, when Jesus we see!

Fanny J. Crosby.

Sanctissimus.　　　　　　　12.10.12.10.　　　　　　W. H. COOKE.

Copyright by W. Garrett Horder.

37

O come, let us worship and bow down.—PSALM xcv. 6.

1 OH, worship the Lord in the beauty of holiness!
Bow down before Him, His glory proclaim;
With gold of obedience, and incense of lowliness,
Kneel and adore Him; the Lord is His Name.

2 Low at His feet lay thy burden of carefulness,
High on His heart He will bear it for thee,
Comfort thy sorrows, and answer thy prayerfulness,
Guiding thy steps as may best for thee be.

8 Fear not to enter His courts in the slenderness
Of the poor wealth thou wouldst reckon as thine;
Truth in its beauty, and love in its tenderness,
These are the offerings to lay on His shrine.

4 These, though we bring them in trembling and fearfulness,
He will accept for the Name that is dear;
Mornings of joy give for evenings of tearfulness,
Trust for our trembling, and hope for our fear.

5 Oh, worship the Lord in the beauty of holiness,
Bow down before Him, His glory proclaim;
With gold of obedience, and incense of lowliness,
Kneel and adore Him; the Lord is His Name.

J. S. B. Monsell.

Infants' Praise. 7.7.7.7.

38 *Hosanna in the highest.*—MATTHEW xxi. 9.

1 CHILDREN of Jerusalem
  Sang the praise of Jesus' Name;
  Children too of later days
  Join to sing the Saviour's praise.
    Hark! hark! hark! etc.

2 We are taught to love the Lord;
  We are taught to read His Word;
  We are taught the way to heaven:
  Praise for all to God be given.

3 Parents, teachers, old and young,
  All unite to swell the song;
  Higher and yet higher rise,
  Till hosannas reach the skies.
      J Henley.

St. Theodulph.   7.6.7.6., D.   M. TESCHNER.

Verse 1 and Refrain after verses 2—6.

All glo - ry, laud, and hon - our, To Thee, Re-deem-er, King, To whom the lips of chil - dren Made sweet Ho-san-nas ring!

FINE.

Verses 2—6.

D.C.

39   *Out of the mouth of babes and sucklings Thou hast perfected praise.*—MATT. xxi. 16.

1 ALL glory, laud, and honour,
   To Thee, Redeemer, King,
   To whom the lips of children
   Made sweet hosannas ring!

2 Thou art the King of Israel,
   Thou David's royal Son,
   Who in the Lord's Name comest,
   The King and blessèd One.
   All glory, etc.

3 The company of angels
   Are praising Thee on high;
   And mortal men, and all things
   Created, make reply.
   All glory. etc.

4 The people of the Hebrews
   With palms before Thee went:
   Our praise and prayer and anthems
   Before Thee we present.
   All glory, etc.

5 To Thee, before Thy Passion,
   They sang their hymns of praise:
   To Thee, now high exalted,
   Our melody we raise.
   All glory, etc.

6 Thou didst accept their praises;
   Accept the prayers we bring,
   Who in all good delightest,
   Thou good and gracious King.
   All glory, etc.
                    Tr. *J. M. Neale.*

Nun Danket.   P.M.   J. Crüger.

40   *The Lord hath done great things for us; whereof we are glad.*—Psalm cxxvi. 3.

1   Now thank we all our God,
With hearts, and hands, and voices,
Who wondrous things hath done,
In whom His world rejoices;
Who, from our mother's arms,
Hath blessed us on our way
With countless gifts of love,
And still is ours to-day.

2   Oh, may this bounteous God
Through all our life be near us,
With ever-joyful hearts
And blessed peace to cheer us;
And keep us in His grace,
And guide us when perplexed,
And free us from all ills
In this world and the next.

3   All praise and thanks to God
The Father, now be given,
The Son, and Him who reigns
With them in highest heaven;
The one eternal God,
Whom heaven and earth adore:
For thus it was, is now,
And shall be evermore.

Tr. *C. Winkworth.*

Marenza.   S.M.   German.

Alternative Tunes, DAY OF PRAISE, No. 500, and SILCHESTER, No. 105.

They sing the song of Moses, and . . . of the Lamb.—REV. xv. 3.

41

1 AWAKE, and sing the song
  Of Moses and the Lamb!
Wake every heart, and every tongue,
  To praise the Saviour's Name!

2 Sing of His dying love,
  Sing of His rising power;
Sing how He intercedes above
  For us whose sins He bore.

3 Sing on your heavenly way;
  Ye ransomed sinners, sing;
Sing on, rejoicing every day
  In Christ, the eternal King.

4 Soon shall we hear Him say,
  "Ye blessèd children, come!"
Soon will He call us hence away,
  And take His wanderers home.

5 There shall our raptured tongue,
  His endless praise proclaim;
And sweeter voices swell the song
  Of Moses and the Lamb!   *W. Hammond.*

Arizona.   L.M.   R. H. EARNSHAW.

Alternative Tune, BRESLAU, No. 552.

42   *God forbid that I should glory, save in the cross of our Lord Jesus Christ.*—GAL. vi. 14.

1 WE sing the praise of Him who died,
  Of Him who died upon the cross;
The sinner's hope let men deride,
  For this we count the world but loss.

2 Inscribed upon the cross we see
  In shining letters, "God is Love;"
He bears our sins upon the tree;
  He brings us mercy from above.

3 The cross! it takes our guilt away;
  It holds the fainting spirit up;
It cheers with hope the gloomy day,
  And sweetens every bitter cup.

4 It makes the coward spirit brave,
  And nerves the feeble arm for fight;
It takes its terror from the grave,
  And gilds the bed of death with light,

5 The balm of life, the cure of woe,
  The measure and the pledge of love,
The sinner's refuge here below,
  The angels' theme in heaven above.

6 To Christ, who won for sinners grace
  By bitter grief and anguish sore,
Be praise from all the ransomed race
  For ever and for evermore.   *T. Kelly.*

43 God is Love.   P.M.

1. Come, let us all u-nite to sing— God is love! . . God is
love! . . While heav'n and earth their prais-es bring— God is
love! . . God is love! . . Let ev-'ry soul from sin a-
wake, . . Each in his heart sweet mu-sic make, . . And . .
sweet-ly sing for Je-sus' sake— God is love! . . God is love!

We have known and believed the love that God hath to us. God is love.—1 John iv. 16.

2 Oh, tell to earth's remotest bound,
    God is love! God is love!
  In Christ is full redemption found—
    God is love! God is love!
  His blood can cleanse our sins away;
  His Spirit turns our night to day,
  And leads our souls with joy to say—
    God is love! God is love!

3 How happy is our portion here—
    God is love! God is love!
  His promises our spirits cheer—
    God is love! God is love!
  He is our Sun and Shield by day,
  By night He near our tents will stay,
  He will be with us all the way—
    God is love! God is love!

4 What though my heart and flesh shall fail—
    God is love! God is love!
  Through Christ I shall o'er death prevail—
    God is love! God is love!
  E'en Jordan's swell I will not fear,
  For Jesus will be with me there,
  My soul above the waves to bear—
    God is love! God is love!

                        H. Kingsbury. (?)

Philippi. 6.6.4.6.6.6.4. J. G. EBELING.

Alternative Tune, MOSCOW, *No.* 618.

44   *It is good to sing praises unto our God.*—PSALM cxlvii. 1.

1 PRAISE God, ye seraphs bright,
  Praise Him, ye sons of light,
      Jesus adore!
  What earthly choirs can swell,
  What mortal tongues can tell,
  Thy love, Immanuel,
      God evermore.

2 Come, saints, in God rejoice!
  Lift up a mighty voice;
      Sing to the Lamb!
  For us His blood was shed,
  For us He left the dead,
  His foes discomfited!
      Praise the I AM!

3 Soon shall we see His face,
  Wearing no mournful trace—
      Oh, what a sight!
  Soon shall we hear Him say,
  "Come, waiting child, away!
  Lo, now has dawned the day
      That knows not night!"
                        J. Marriott.

45 Praise Him! Praise Him!   P.M.

CHESTER G. ALLEN.

45

Thou, O Lord, . . . art our Redeemer.—ISA. lxiii. 16.

1 PRAISE Him! praise Him! Jesus, our blessèd Redeemer;
   Sing, O earth! His wonderful love proclaim!
Hail Him! hail Him! highest archangels in glory,
   Strength and honour give to His holy Name.
Like a shepherd, Jesus will guard His children,
   In His arms He carries them all day long;
O ye saints that dwell in the mountains of Zion!
   Praise Him! praise Him! ever in joyful song.

2 Praise Him! praise Him! Jesus, our blessèd Redeemer,
   For our sins He suffered and bled and died!
He, our Rock, our hope of eternal salvation,
   Hail Him! hail Him! Jesus the Crucified;—
Loving Saviour, meekly enduring sorrow,
   Crowned with thorns that cruelly pierced His brow;
Once for us rejected, despised, and forsaken,
   Prince of glory, ever triumphant now.

3 Praise Him! praise Him! Jesus, our blessèd Redeemer,
   Heavenly portals loud with hosannas ring!
Jesus, Saviour, reigneth for ever and ever,
   Crown Him! crown Him! Prophet and Priest and King!
Death is vanquished! Tell it with joy, ye faithful;
   Where is now thy victory, boasting grave?
Jesus lives! no longer thy portals are cheerless;
   Jesus lives, the mighty and strong to save.

Fanny J. Crosby.

St. Luke.   11.11.11.11.   Anon.

46   *Blessed be Thy glorious Name.*—NEHEMIAH ix. 5.

1 WE praise Thee, we bless Thee, our Saviour Divine,
All power and dominion for ever be Thine!
We sing of Thy mercy with joyful acclaim,
For Thou hast redeemed us: all praise to Thy Name!

2 All honour and praise to Thine excellent Name,
Thy love is unchanging—for ever the same!
We bless and adore Thee, O Saviour and King;
With joy and thanksgiving Thy praises we sing!

3 The strength of the hills and the depths of the sea,
The earth and its fulness, belong unto Thee;
And yet to the lowly Thou bendest Thine ear,
So ready their humble petitions to hear.

4 Thine infinite goodness our tongues shall employ;
Thou givest us richly all things to enjoy;
We'll follow Thy footsteps, we'll rest in Thy love,
And soon we shall praise Thee in mansions above!

Fanny J. Crosby.

Ellacombe.   7.6.7.6., D.   German

47   *I will sing of the mercies of the Lord for ever.*—PSALM lxxxix. 1.

1 COME, sing with holy gladness,
     High Alleluias sing,
  Uplift your loud hosannas
     To Jesus, Lord and King;
  Sing, boys, in joyful chorus
     Your hymn of praise to-day,
  And sing, ye gentle maidens,
     Your sweet responsive lay.

2 'Tis good for boys and maidens
     Sweet hymns to Christ to sing,
  'Tis meet that children's voices
     Should praise the children's King;
  For Jesus is salvation,
     And glory, grace and rest;
  To babe, and boy and maiden
     The one Redeemer blest.

3 Oh, boys! be strong in Jesus,
     To toil for Him is gain,
  And Jesus wrought with Joseph
     With chisel, saw and plane;
  Oh, maidens! live for Jesus,
     Who was a maiden's Son;
  Be patient, pure and gentle,
     And perfect grace begun.

4 Soon in the golden city
     The boys and girls shall play;
  And in the dazzling mansions
     Rejoice in endless day;
  O Christ, prepare Thy children
     With that triumphant throng
  To pass the burnished portals
     And sing the eternal song.

                                        J. J. Daniell

48

I will sing unto the Lord, because He hath dealt bountifully with me.—PSALM xiii. 6.

1 COME, let us sing of Jesus,
   While hearts and accents blend;
Come, let us sing of Jesus,
   The sinner's only Friend.
His holy soul rejoices,
   Amid the choirs above,
To hear our youthful voices
   Exulting in His love.

2 We love to sing of Jesus,
   Who died our souls to save;
We love to sing of Jesus,
   Triumphant o'er the grave;
And in our hour of danger
   We'll trust His love alone,
Who once slept in a manger,
   And now sits on the throne.

3 Then let us sing of Jesus,
   While yet on earth we stay,
And hope to sing of Jesus,
   Throughout the eternal day.
For those who here confess Him
   He will in heaven confess;
And faithful hearts that bless Him
   He will for ever bless.   *G. W. Bethune.*

The above may be sung to ELLACOMBE, *No.* 47, *or* LYMINGTON, *No.* 3.

Harewood.   6.6.6.6.8.8.   S. S. WESLEY.

Alternative Tune, DARWALL'S 148TH, *No.* 487.

49   *Behold, I lay in Zion for a foundation a stone, a tried stone.*—ISA. xxviii. 16.

1 CHRIST is our corner-stone,
   On Him alone we build;
With His true saints alone
   The courts of heaven are filled;
On His great love our hopes we place
Of present grace and joys above.

2 Oh, then with hymns of praise
   These hallowed courts shall ring;
Our voices we will raise
   The Three in One to sing;
And thus proc'aim in joyful song,
Both loud and long, that glorious Name.

3 Here may we gain from heaven
   The grace which we implore;
And may that grace, once given,
   Be with us evermore;
Until that day when all the blest
To endless rest are called away.   *J. Chandler.*

Kandersteg. [FIRST TUNE.] 10.10.10.4. CECIL J. ALLEN.

Austalis. [SECOND TUNE.] 10.10.10.4. F. S. TURNEY.

50

O Lord, how manifold are Thy works.—PSALM civ. 24.

1 FOR all the glories of the earth and sky,
   For night's soft voice, and morning's silent haze,
   For trees that whisper, and for winds that sigh,
         We give Thee praise.

2 For summer sunshine and for cooling showers,
   For stars that light the heavens' darkening maze,
   For dewdrops sparkling on the new-born flowers,
         Our hearts would praise.

3 For lightning's flash, and thunder's echoing roar,
   For seas that beat upon their endless ways,
   For wild waves' anthem on a rock-bound shore,
         We offer praise.

4 For mighty mountains and eternal snows,
　　Enduring changeless through the changing days,
　For moon-lit valleys and for sunset glows,
　　　　Accept our praise.

5 But for that great redeeming work of Thine,
　　Our souls their loftiest hymn of thanks would raise,
　For free salvation through a love divine,
　　　　We render praise.

6 For all the matchless wonders of Thy grace
　　Seen in that cross on which we humbly gaze,
　For peace and pardon to a fallen race,
　　　　Thy Name we praise.

Dorothy Dennison.

Nicæa.　　　　　　　11.12.12.10.　　　　　J. B. Dykes.

51　　　*Holy, holy, holy, is the Lord of hosts.*—Isa. vi. 3.

1 Holy, Holy, Holy, Lord God Almighty!
　　Early in the morning our song shall rise to Thee:
　Holy, Holy, Holy! merciful and mighty,
　　God in Three Persons, blessèd Trinity!

2 Holy, Holy, Holy! all the saints adore Thee,
　　Casting down their golden crowns around the glassy sea;
　Cherubim and seraphim falling down before Thee,
　　Who wert, and art, and evermore shalt be.

3 Holy, Holy, Holy! though the darkness hide Thee,
　　Though the eye of sinful man Thy glory may not see;
　Only Thou art holy, there is none beside Thee
　　Perfect in power, in love, and purity.

4 Holy, Holy, Holy, Lord God Almighty!
　　All Thy works shall praise Thy Name, in earth, and sky, and sea;
　Holy, Holy, Holy, merciful and mighty,
　　God in Three Persons, blessèd Trinity!

R. Heber.

Ephesus.   8.7.8.7.8.7.   J. Neander.

Alternative Tune, Dismissal, *No.* 608.

52   *Let the children of Zion be joyful in their King.*—Psalm cxlix. 2.

1 Come, ye children, praise the Saviour;
  He regards you from above;
Praise Him for His great salvation!
  Praise Him for His precious love!
Sweet hosannas, sweet hosannas,
  To the Name of Jesus sing!

2 When He left His throne in glory,
  When He lived with mortals here,
Little children sang His praises,
  And it pleased His gracious ear.
Sweet hosannas, sweet hosannas,
  To the Name of Jesus sing!

3 When the anxious mothers round Him
  With their tender infants pressed,
He with open arms received them,
  And the little ones He blessed.
Sweet hosannas, sweet hosannas,
  To the Name of Jesus sing!

4 Up in yonder heavenly regions,
  Angels sound the chorus high;
Twice ten thousand times ten thousand
  Sound His praises through the sky.
Sweet hosannas, sweet hosannas,
  To the Name of Jesus sing!

5 Come, ye children, praise the Saviour!
  Praise Him, your undying Friend;
Praise Him, till in heaven you meet Him,
  There to praise Him without end.
Sweet hosannas, sweet hosannas,
  To the Name of Jesus sing!
      "Juvenile Harmonist," 1847.

53 Antwerp.   L.M.   W. Smallwood.

53   *Thou, Lord, hast made me glad through Thy work.*—PSALM xcii. 4.

1 SWEET is the work, my God, my King,
  To praise Thy Name, give thanks, and sing,
  To show Thy love by morning light,
  And talk of all Thy truth at night.

2 Sweet is the day of sacred rest;
  No mortal cares shall seize my breast:
  Oh, may my heart in tune be found,
  Like David's harp of solemn sound!

3 My heart shall triumph in my Lord,
  And bless His works, and bless His Word;

Thy works of grace, how bright they shine!
How deep Thy counsels, how divine!

4 And I shall share a glorious part,
  When grace hath well refined my heart;
  And fresh supplies of joys are shed,
  Like holy oil, to cheer my head.

5 Then shall I see, and hear, and know
  All I desired or wished below;
  And every power find sweet employ
  In that eternal world of joy.

Isaac Watts.

54   *Then was our mouth filled with . . . singing.*—PSALM cxxvi. 2.

1 I FEEL like singing all the time,
  My tears are wiped away;
  For Jesus is a Friend of mine,
  I'll serve Him every day.

2 When on the cross my Lord I saw,
  Nailed there by sins of mine,
  Fast fell the burning tears; but now
  I'm singing all the time.

3 When fierce temptations try my heart,
  I'll sing "Jesus is mine":

And so, though tears at times may start,
I'm singing all the time.

4 The wondrous story of the Lamb,
  Tell with that voice of thine,
  Till others with the glad new song
  Go singing all the time.

5 The angels sing a glorious song,
  But not a song like mine,
  For I am washed in Jesus' blood,
  And singing all the time.

E. Payson Hammond.

The Echo.   6.6.6.6.8.8.   W. B. BRADBURY.

And send the e-cho,   send the e-cho,

REFRAIN.

send the e-cho, send the e-cho, send the e-cho, send the e-cho back a-gain?

This Hymn may be sung (without the repeats) to CHRISTCHURCH, *No.* 56.

55

Declare His glory among the heathen, His wonders among all people.—PSALM xcvi. 3.

1 SHALL hymns of grateful love
    Through heaven's high arches ring,
And all the hosts above
    Their songs of triumph sing;
And shall not we take up the strain,
And send the echo back again?
      And send the echo, etc.

2 Shall every ransomed tribe
    Of Adam's scattered race
To Christ all power ascribe,
    Who saved them by His grace;
And shall not we take up the strain,
And send the echo back again?

3 Shall they adore the Lord,
    Who bought them with His blood,
And all the love record
    That led them home to God;
And shall not we take up the strain,
And send the echo back again?

4 Oh! spread the joyful sound,
    The Saviour's love proclaim,
And publish all around
    Salvation through His Name;
Till all the world take up the strain,
And send the echo back again!

J. J. Cummins.

Christchurch.   6.6.6.6.8.8.   CHAS. STEGGALL.

56   *Publish with the voice of thanksgiving.*—PSALM XXVI. 7.

1   COME, every youthful heart
        That loves the Saviour's Name,
     Your noblest powers exert
        To celebrate His fame:
     Tell all above and all below
     The debt of love to Him you owe.

2   He left His starry crown,
        He laid His robes aside,
     On wings of love came down,
        And wept, and bled, and died:
     What He endured, oh! who can tell,
     To save our souls from death and hell?

3   From the dark grave He rose,
        The mansion of the dead;
     And thence His mighty foes
        In glorious triumph led:
     Up through the sky the Conqueror rode,
     And reigns on high the Saviour God.

4   From thence He'll quickly come,
        His chariot will not stay,
     And bear our spirits home
        To realms of endless day;
     Then shall we see His lovely face
     And ever be in His embrace.

5   Jesus, we ne'er can pay
        The debt we owe Thy love;
     Yet tell us how we may
        Our gratitude approve:
     Our hearts, our all to Thee we give,
     The gift, though small, do Thou receive.
                    S. Stennett.

Penitentia. 10.10.10.10. E. DEARLE.

57 *A better hope . . . by the which we draw nigh unto God.*—HEB. vii. 19.

1 FATHER, again in Jesus' Name we meet,
And bow in penitence beneath Thy feet:
Again to Thee our feeble voices raise,
To sue for mercy, and to sing Thy praise.

2 Lord, we would bless Thee for Thy ceaseless care,
And all Thy love from day to day declare:
Is not our life with hourly mercies crowned?
Does not Thine arm encircle us around?

3 Alas! unworthy of Thy boundless love,
Too oft with careless feet from Thee we rove:
But now, encouraged by Thy voice, we come,
Returning sinners to a Father's home.

4 Oh, by that Name, in whom all fulness dwells,
Oh, by that love, which every love excels,
Oh, by that blood, so freely shed for sin,
Open sweet mercy's gate, and let us in!

Lady Lucy E. G. Whitmore.

Derby. 6.5.6.5. F. FILITZ.

58

The precious blood of Christ.—1 PETER i. 19.

1 GLORY be to Jesus,
Who in bitter pains
Poured for me the life-blood
From His sacred veins.

2 Grace and life eternal
In that blood I find;
Blest be His compassion,
Infinitely kind!

8 Blest through endless ages
Be the precious stream,
Which from endless torments
Did the world redeem.

4 Abel's blood for vengeance
Pleaded to the skies;
But the blood of Jesus
For our pardon cries.

5 Oft as earth exulting
Wafts its praise on high,
Angel-hosts rejoicing
Make their glad reply.

6 Lift ye then your voices;
Swell the mighty flood;
Louder still and louder
Praise the precious blood.

Tr. *E. Caswall.*

Wentworth. 8.4.8.4.8.4. F. C. MAKER.

59

The living God, who giveth us richly all things to enjoy.—1 TIM. vi. 17.

1 MY God, I thank Thee who hast made
The earth so bright,
So full of splendour and of joy,
Beauty and light;
So many glorious things are here,
Noble and right.

2 I thank Thee, too, that Thou hast made
Joy to abound,
So many gentle thoughts and deeds
Circling us round,
That, in the darkest spot of earth
Some love is found.

3 I thank Thee more, that all our joy
Is touched with pain,
That shadows fall on brightest hours,
That thorns remain;
So that earth's bliss may be our guide,
And not our chain.

4 For Thou, who knowest, Lord, how soon
Our weak heart clings,
Hast given us joys, tender and true,
Yet all with wings,
So that we see, gleaming on high,
Diviner things.

5 I thank Thee, Lord, that Thou hast kept
The best in store:
We have enough, but not too much
To long for more—
A yearning for a deeper peace
Not known before.

6 I thank Thee, Lord, that here our souls,
Though amply blest,
Can never find, although they seek,
A perfect rest,
Nor ever shall, until they lean
On Jesus' breast.

Adelaide A Procter.

Mainzer.   L.M.   J. MAINZER.

60   *The loving-kindnesses of the Lord.*—ISAIAH lxiii. 7.

1 AWAKE, my soul, in joyful lays,
  And sing thy great Redeemer's praise;
  He justly claims a song from thee:
  His loving-kindness, oh, how free!

2 He saw me ruined in the Fall,
  Yet loved me, notwithstanding all:
  He saved me from my lost estate:
  His loving-kindness, oh, how great!

3 Though numerous hosts of mighty foes,
  Though earth and hell my way oppose,
  He safely leads my soul along;
  His loving-kindness, oh, how strong!

4 When trouble, like a gloomy cloud,
  Has gathered thick and thundered loud,
  He near my soul has always stood:
  His loving-kindness, oh, how good!

5 Often I feel my sinful heart
  Prone from my Saviour to depart;
  But though I have Him oft forgot,
  His loving-kindness changes not.
                     S. Medley.

61 The New Song.   11.12.   P. P. BLISS.

Allegretto.

CHORUS.

Un - to Him who hath loved us and

wash'd us from sin, Un-to Him be the glo-ry for ev-er! A-men.

61

They sung as it were a new song before the throne.—REV. xiv. 3.

1 WITH harps and with vials there stand a great throng
In the presence of Jesus, and sing this new song:
Unto Him who hath loved us, etc.

2 All these once were sinners, defiled in His sight,
Now arrayed in pure garments in praise they unite.

3 He maketh the rebel a priest and a king,
He hath bought us, and taught us this new song to sing.

4 How helpless and hopeless we sinners had been,
If He never had loved us till cleansed from our sin!

5 Aloud in His praises our voices shall ring,
So that others, believing, this new song shall sing.

A. T. Pierson.

Westminster. C.M. J. TURLE.

62 *The Lord is a great God, and a great King above all gods.—PSALM xcv. 3.*

1 MY God, how wonderful Thou art,
Thy majesty how bright!
How beautiful Thy mercy-seat,
In depths of burning light!

2 How dread are Thine eternal years,
O everlasting Lord,
By prostrate spirits day and night
Incessantly adored!

3 How wonderful, how beautiful,
The sight of Thee must be,
Thine endless wisdom, boundless power,
And awful purity!

4 Oh, how I fear Thee, Living God,
With deepest, tenderest fears,
And worship Thee with trembling hope,
And penitential tears!

5 Yet I may love Thee, too, O Lord,
Almighty as Thou art,
For Thou hast stooped to ask of me
The love of my poor heart.

6 No earthly father loves like Thee;
No mother, e'er so mild,
Bears and forbears as Thou hast done
With me, Thy sinful child.

7 Father of Jesus, love's reward,
What rapture will it be,
Prostrate before Thy throne to lie,
And gaze and gaze on Thee!

F. W. Faber.

St. Godric. 6.6.6.6.8.8. J. B. DYKES.

Alternative Tune, DARWALL'S 148TH, *No.* 487.

63 *Let the children of Zion be joyful in their King.*—PSALM cxlix. 2.

1 REJOICE, the Lord is King,
    Your Lord and King adore;
  Mortals, give thanks and sing,
    And triumph evermore:
  Lift up your heart, lift up your voice;
  Rejoice, again I say, rejoice!

2 Jesus, the Saviour, reigns,
    The God of truth and love:
  When He had purged our stains,
    He took His seat above:
  Lift up your heart, lift up your voice;
  Rejoice, again I say, rejoice!

3 His kingdom cannot fail;
    He rules o'er earth and heaven;
  The keys of death and hell
    Are to our Jesus given:
  Lift up your heart, lift up your voice;
  Rejoice, again I say, rejoice!

4 He sits at God's right hand
    Till all His foes submit,
  And bow to His command,
    And fall beneath His feet:
  Lift up your heart, lift up your voice;
  Rejoice, again I say, rejoice!
                 C. Wesley.

Section II.—Prayer.

Converse.

8.7.8.7., D.

C. C. Converse.

Alternative Tunes, Lux Eoi, *No. 542, and* Alleluia, *No. 30.*

64

His ears are open unto their prayers.—1 Pet. iii. 12.

1 What a Friend we have in Jesus
　All our sins and griefs to bear!
What a privilege to carry
　Everything to God in prayer!
Oh, what peace we often forfeit!
　Oh, what needless pain we bear!
All because we do not carry
　Everything to God in prayer.

2 Have we trials and temptations?
　Is there trouble anywhere?
We should never be discouraged;
　Take it to the Lord in prayer.
Can we find a friend so faithful
　Who will all our sorrows share?
Jesus knows our every weakness;
　Take it to the Lord in prayer.

3 Are we weak and heavy-laden,
　Cumbered with a load of care?
Precious Saviour, still our refuge—
　Take it to the Lord in prayer.
Do thy friends despise, forsake thee?
　Take it to the Lord in prayer;
In His arms He'll take and shield thee,
　Thou wilt find a solace there.

J. Scriven.

C

Tryst.

6.4.0.4.6.6.6.4.

W. H. DOANE.

Alternative Tune, ST. EDMUND, *No.* 453.

65   *Draw nigh to God, and He will draw nigh to you.*—JAMES iv. **8.**

1 HERE from the world we turn,
  Jesus to seek;
Here may His loving voice
  Tenderly speak.
Jesus, our dearest Friend,
While at Thy feet we bend,
Oh, let Thy smile descend!
  'Tis Thee we seek.

2 Come, Holy Comforter,
  Presence Divine,
Now in our longing hearts
  Graciously shine;
Oh, for Thy mighty power!
Oh, for a blessèd shower,
Filling this hallowed hour
  With joy divine!

3 Saviour, Thy work revive,
  Here may we see
Those who are dead in sin
  Quickened by Thee;
Come to our hearts' delight,
Make every burden light,
Cheer Thou our waiting sight;
  We long for Thee.

Fanny J. Crosby.

Walton. L.M. Arr. from BEETHOVEN.

Alternative Tune, EDEN, *No.* 190.

66 *Then I will command My blessing upon you.*—LEVITICUS xxv. 21.

1 COMMAND Thy blessing from above,
  O God! on all assembled here:
Behold us with a Father's love,
  While we look up with filial fear.

2 Command Thy blessing, Jesus, Lord!
  May we Thy true disciples be;
Speak to each heart the mighty word,
  Say to the weakest, "Follow Me."

3 Command Thy blessing in this hour,
  Spirit of truth! and fill the place
With wounding and with healing power,
  With quickening and confirming grace.

4 With Thee and Thine for ever found,
  May all the souls who here unite,
With harps and songs Thy throne surround,
  Rest in Thy love, and reign in light.
                                 J. Montgomery.

Sherborne. 7.7.7.7. Adapted from MENDELSSOHN.

Alternative Tune, PROVIDENCE, *No.* 348.

67 *God . . . giveth to all men liberally, and upbraideth not.*—JAMES i. 5.

1 COME, my soul, thy suit prepare,
  Jesus loves to answer prayer;
He Himself has bid thee pray,
  Therefore will not say thee nay.

2 Thou art coming to a King,
  Large petitions with thee bring;
For His grace and power are such,
  None can ever ask too much.

3 With my burden I begin;
  Lord, remove this load of sin!
Let Thy blood for sinners spilt
  Set my conscience free from guilt.

4 Lord, I come to Thee for rest,
  Take possession of my breast;
There Thy blood-bought right maintain,
  And without a rival reign.

5 While I am a pilgrim here,
  Let Thy love my spirit cheer;
As my Guide, my Guard, my Friend,
  Lead me to my journey's end.   *John Newton.*

Maryton. L.M. H. Percy Smith.

68 *I will commune with thee from above the mercy-seat.*—Exodus xxv. 22.

1 From every stormy wind that blows,
From every swelling tide of woes,
There is a calm, a safe retreat;
'Tis found beneath the mercy-seat.

2 There is a place where Jesus sheds
The oil of gladness on our heads,
A place than all beside more sweet;
It is the blood-stained mercy-seat.

3 There is a spot where spirits blend,
And friend holds fellowship with friend;
Though sundered far, by faith they meet
Around one common mercy-seat.

4 There, there on eagle-wing we soar,
And time and sense seem all no more;
And heaven comes down our souls to greet,
And glory crowns the mercy-seat.
Hugh Stowell.

St. Marguerite. C.M. E. C. Walker.

Alternative Tune, Holy Trinity, *No. 81.*

69 *The eye of the Lord is upon them that fear Him.*—Psalm xxxiii. 18.

1 There is an eye that never sleeps
Beneath the wing of night;
There is an ear that never shuts
When sink the beams of light.

2 There is an arm that never tires
When human strength gives way;
There is a love which never fails
When earthly loves decay.

3 That eye is fixed on seraph throngs;
That arm upholds the sky;
That ear is filled with angel songs;
That love is throned on high.

4 But there's a power which man can wield
When mortal aid is vain,
That eye, that arm, that love to reach.
That listening ear to gain.

5 That power is prayer, which soars on high,
Through Jesus to the throne,
And moves the hand which moves the world,
To bring salvation down.
J. A. Wallace.

Showers of Blessing.   P.M.   J. McGranahan.

CHORUS.

Show - - - ers of bless - ing, Show - ers, show-ers of bless - ing, Show-ers of bless-ing we need;

Mer - cy drops round us are fall - ing, .. But for the show-ers we plead.

Words and Music by permission of Mrs. H. C. Dixon.

70

There shall be showers of blessing.—EZEKIEL xxxiv. 26.

1 "THERE shall be showers of blessing:"
   This is the promise of love;
There shall be seasons refreshing,
   Sent from the Saviour above.
     Show- . ers of blessing, etc.

2 "There shall be showers of blessing"—
   Precious reviving again;
Over the hills and the valleys,
   Sound of abundance of rain.

3 "There shall be showers of blessing:"
   Send them upon us, O Lord!
Grant to us now a refreshing;
   Come, and now honour Thy word.

4 "There shall be showers of blessing:"
   Oh, that to-day they might fall,
Now as to God we're confessing,
   Now as on Jesus we call!
          El. Nathan.

Hamburg.   L.M.   Arr. by Dr. L. Mason

Alternative Tune, Arizona, *No. 42.*

71   *He is a rewarder of them that diligently seek Him.*—Heb. xi. 6.

1 Lord Jesus Christ, we seek Thy face;
   Within the vail we bow the knee,
Oh, let Thy glory fill the place,
   And bless us while we wait on Thee.

2 We thank Thee for the precious blood
   That purged our sins and brought us nigh,
All cleansed and sanctified to God,
   Thy holy Name to magnify.

3 Shut in with Thee far, far above
   The restless world that wars below,
We seek to learn and prove Thy love,
   Thy wisdom and Thy grace to know.

4 The brow that once with thorns was bound,
   Thy hands, Thy side, we fain would see,
Draw near, Lord Jesus, glory-crowned,
   And bless us while we wait on Thee.
                         A. Stewart.

72 Warrington.   L.M.   Ralph Harrison.

72 *There am I in the midst of them.*—MATT. xviii. 20.

1 JESUS, where'er Thy people meet,
   There they behold Thy mercy-seat:
   Where'er they seek Thee, Thou art found,
   And every place is hallowed ground.

2 For Thou, within no walls confined,
   Inhabitest the humble mind:
   Such ever bring Thee where they come,
   And going, take Thee to their home.

3 Great Shepherd of Thy chosen few,
   Thy former mercies here renew;
   Here to our waiting hearts proclaim
   The sweetness of Thy saving Name.

4 Here may we prove the power of prayer,
   To strengthen faith, and sweeten care;
   To teach our faint desires to rise,
   And bring all heaven before our eyes.

5 Lord, we are few, but Thou art near,
   Nor short Thine arm, nor deaf Thine ear;
   Oh, rend the heavens, come quickly down,
   And make a thousand hearts Thine own!

W. Cowper.

Cairnbrook.   8.5.8.3.   E. PROUT.

73 *The Lord watch between me and thee, when we are absent one from another.*—GEN. xxxi. 49.

1 HOLY Father, in Thy mercy
   Hear our anxious prayer,
   Keep our loved ones, now far distant,
   'Neath Thy care.

2 Jesus, Saviour, let Thy presence
   Be their light and guide;
   Keep, oh, keep them, in their weakness,
   At Thy side.

3 When in sorrow, when in danger,
   When in loneliness,
   In Thy love look down and comfort
   Their distress.

4 May the joy of Thy salvation
   Be their strength and stay;
   May they love and may they praise Thee
   Day by day.

5 Holy Spirit, let Thy teaching
   Sanctify their life;
   Send Thy grace, that they may conquer
   In the strife.

6 Father, Son, and Holy Spirit,
   God the One in Three,   [them
   Bless them, guide them, save them, keep
   Near to Thee.

Isabella S. Stevenson.

In the Secret of His Presence.   P.M.

GEO. C. STEBBINS.

to the se-cret place I go.

74   *Thou shalt hide them in the secret of Thy presence.*—PSALM xxxi. 20.

1 IN the secret of His presence how my soul delights to hide!
Oh, how precious are the lessons which I learn at Jesus' side!
Earthly cares can never vex me, neither trials lay me low;
For when Satan comes to tempt me, to the secret place I go.

2 When my soul is faint and thirsty, 'neath the shadow of His wing
There is cool and pleasant shelter, and a fresh and crystal spring;
And my Saviour rests beside me, as we hold communion sweet;
If I tried, I could not utter what He says when thus we meet.

3 Only this I know: I tell Him all my doubts and griefs and fears;
Oh, how patiently He listens! and my drooping soul He cheers:
Do you think He ne'er reproves me? what a false friend He would be,
If He never, never told me of the sins which He must see!

4 Would you like to know the sweetness of the secret of the Lord?
Go and hide beneath His shadow; this shall then be your reward;
And whene'er you leave the silence of that happy meeting place,
You will bear the shining image of the Master in your face.

Ellen Lakshmi Goreh.

Bedford. C.M. W. WHEALL.

75 *Let us therefore come boldly unto the throne of grace.*—HEB. iv. 16.

1 APPROACH, my soul, the mercy-seat,
   Where Jesus answers prayer;
   There humbly fall before His feet,
   For none can perish there.

2 Thy promise is my only plea;
   With this I venture nigh;
   Thou callest burdened souls to Thee,
   And such, O Lord, am I.

3 Bowed down beneath a load of sin,
   By Satan sorely pressed,
   By wars without, and fears within,
   I come to Thee for rest.

4 Be Thou my Shield and Hiding-place,
   That, sheltered near Thy side,
   I may my fierce accuser face,
   And tell Him Thou hast died.

5 Oh, wondrous love! to bleed and die,
   To bear the cross and shame,
   That guilty sinners, such as I,
   Might plead Thy gracious Name!

John Newton.

Windsor. C.M. G. KIRBYE in ESTE'S *Psalter.*

Alternative Tune, ST. FLAVIAN, *No.* 356.

76 *Let us lift up our heart with our hands unto God in the heavens.*—LAM. iii. 41.

1 LORD, when we bend before Thy throne,
   And our confessions pour,
   Teach us to feel the sins we own,
   And hate what we deplore.

2 Our broken spirits pitying see,
   True penitence impart;
   Then let a kindling glance from Thee
   Beam hope upon the heart.

3 When we disclose our wants in prayer,
   May we our wills resign;
   And not a thought our bosoms share,
   Which is not wholly Thine.

4 May faith each weak petition fill,
   And waft it to the skies,
   And teach our hearts 'tis goodness still
   That grants it or denies.

J. D. Carlyle.

C*

Dennis.   S.M.   H. G. Nägeli.

77   *The multitude of them that believed were of one heart and of one soul.*—Acts iv. 32.

1 Blest be the tie that binds
  Our hearts in Christian love:
The fellowship of kindred minds
  Is like to that above.

2 Before our Father's throne
  We pour our ardent prayers:
Our fears, our hopes, our aims are one,
  Our comfort and our cares.

3 We share our mutual woes,
  Our mutual burdens bear,
And often for each other flows
  The sympathising tear.

4 When we asunder part,
  It gives us inward pain;
But we shall still be joined in heart,
  And hope to meet again.

5 This glorious hope revives
  Our courage by the way,
While each in expectation lives,
  And longs to see the day.

6 From sorrow, toil and pain,
  And sin we shall be free;
And perfect love and friendship reign
  Through all eternity.

J. Fawcett.

Consecration.   7.7.7.7.   Charles Vincent.

78   *Where two or three are gathered together in My Name, there am I in the midst of them.*—Matt. xviii. 20.

1 Jesus, we Thy promise claim,
We are gathered in Thy Name
In the midst do Thou appear;
Manifest Thy presence here.

2 Sanctify us, Lord, and bless:
Breathe Thy Spirit, give Thy peace:
Come and dwell within each heart,
Light and life and joy impart.

3 Make us all in Thee complete,
Make us all for glory meet—
Meet t' appear before Thy sight,
Partners with the saints in light.   *C. Wesley.*

Crüger.   7.6.7.6., D.   J. CRÜGER.

79   *Pray without ceasing.*—1 THESS. v. 17.

1 Go, when the morning shineth;
   Go, when the noon is bright;
Go, when the eve declineth;
   Go, in the hush of night;
Go, with pure mind and feeling,
   Fling earthly cares away,
And, in thy chamber kneeling,
   Do thou in secret pray.

2 Remember all who love thee,
   All who are loved by thee;
Pray, too, for those who hate thee,
   If any such there be:
Then, for thyself, in meekness,
   A blessing humbly claim,
And link with each petition
   Thy great Redeemer's Name.

3 Or, if 'tis here denied thee
   In solitude to pray,
Should holy thoughts come o'er thee
   When friends are round thy way,
E'en then in silent pleading
   The spirit, raised above,
Will reach the throne of glory,
   Of mercy, truth, and love.

4 Oh, not a joy or blessing
   With this can we compare,
The power that He has given
   To pour our souls in prayer!
Whene'er thou art in sadness,
   Before His footstool fall;
Remember, in thy gladness,
   His grace who gives thee all.

                Jane C. Simpson.

St. Cecilia. 6.6.6.6. L. G. Hayne.

Alternative Tune, Quam Dilecta, *No. 576.*

80 *Lord, I have loved the habitation of Thy house.*—Psalm xxvi. 8.

1 We love Thy house, O God,
 Wherein Thy children meet:
For Thou, O Lord, art here,
 Thy little flock to greet.

2 We love the hour of prayer,
 No hour on earth so sweet;
For then we cast our care
 At our Redeemer's feet.

3 We love the Word of life,
 The Word that tells of peace,
Of comfort in the strife,
 And joys that never cease.

4 We love to sing below
 Of mercies freely given;
But oh! we long to know
 The triumph-song of heaven.

5 Lord Jesus, give us grace
 On earth to love Thee more,
In heaven to see Thy face,
 And with Thy saints adore.

W. Bullock.

Holy Trinity. C.M. Sir Joseph Barnby.

81 *Praying always with all prayer and supplication in the Spirit.*—Eph. vi. 18.

1 Prayer is the soul's sincere desire,
 Uttered or unexpressed,
The motion of a hidden fire
 That trembles in the breast.

2 Prayer is the burden of a sigh,
 The falling of a tear,
The upward glancing of an eye
 When none but God is near.

3 Prayer is the simplest form of speech,
 That infant lips can try;
Prayer, the sublimest strains that reach
 The Majesty on high.

4 Prayer is the Christian's vital breath,
 The Christian's native air,
His watchword at the gate of death;
 He enters heaven with prayer.

5 Prayer is the contrite sinner's voice,
 Returning from his ways;
While angels in their songs rejoice,
 And cry, "Behold, he prays!"

6 O Thou by whom we come to God,
 The Life, the Truth, the Way!
The path of prayer Thyself hast trod;
 Lord, teach us how to pray!

J. Montgomery.

Croft's 148th.   6.6.6.6.8.8.   W. Croft.

Alternative Tune, St. John, *No. 696.*

82   *In whom we have boldness and access with confidence.*—Eph. iii. 12.

1   FATHER, to seek Thy face
    Thy children now draw near;
  Before the throne of grace
    With boldness we appear:
  We plead His Name, His precious blood,
  Who loved, and made us priests to God.

2   No more we shun the light,
    No more Thy presence fear;
  In robes of spotless white
    Before Thee we appear;
  Our great High Priest for us is there,
  And He presents our praise and prayer.

3   No power have we to praise
    Thy Name, O God of Love,
  Unless Thy Spirit raise
    Our thoughts and hearts above;
  His grace avails in all our need,
  May He our priestly worship lead.

4   Lord, give us faith to plead
    Thy true and faithful Word—
  Grace for each time of need,
    And help to us afford:
  Thy promises in Christ are yea,
  In Him Amen! to endless day.
                  J. G. Deck.

Arch Street.　　　　　8.7.8.7., with Chorus.　　　　　JNO. R. SWENEY.

CHORUS.
Let it come,　　　　　　　　Let the show'r

Let it come, O Lord, we pray Thee,　　Let the show'r of bless-ing fall;

We are wait - ing, we are wait-ing—Oh, re-vive the hearts of all.
We are waiting, we are wait - ing—　Oh, re-vive the hearts of all.

83　　　　　*Revive us again.*—PSALM lxxxv. 6.

1 GOD is here, and that to bless us
　　With the Spirit's quickening power!
　See the cloud, already bending,
　　Waits to drop the grateful shower.
　　　　Let it come, etc.

2 God is here! we feel His presence
　　In this consecrated place;
　But we need the soul-refreshing
　　Of His free, unbounded grace.

3 God is here! oh, then, believing,
　　Bring to Him our one desire,
　That His love may now be kindled,
　　Till its flame each heart inspire.

4 Saviour, grant the prayer we offer,
　　While in simple faith we bow;
　From the windows of Thy mercy
　　Pour us out a blessing now.

J. L. Black.

Southport.　　　　　8.8.8.4.　　　　GEORGE LOMAS.

The hour of prayer.—ACTS iii. 1.

84

1 MY God, is any hour so sweet,
From blush of morn to evening star,
As that which calls me to Thy feet—
The hour of prayer?

2 Then is my strength by Thee renewed;
Then are my sins by Thee forgiven;
Then dost Thou cheer my solitude
With hopes of heaven.

3 No words can tell what sweet relief
Here for my every want I find:
What strength for warfare, balm for grief,
What peace of mind!

4 Hushed is each doubt, gone every fear;
My spirit seems in heaven to stay;
And e'en the penitential tear
Is wiped away.

5 Lord, till I reach yon blissful shore,
No privilege so dear shall be
As thus my inmost soul to pour
In prayer to Thee.

C. Elliott.

Rhodes.　　　　　S.M.　　　　C. WARWICK JORDAN

There I will meet with the children of Israel.—EXODUS xxix. 43.

85

1 JESUS, in Thy blest Name,
With joyful hearts we meet,
In fellowship with saints above,
Around the mercy-seat.

2 Lord, animate our hearts
With fervent love to Thee,
And nerve each fainting warrior here
With holy energy.

3 With joyfulness we wait
To see our Master's face;
Come, Jesus, to Thy waiting ones,
And fill this lowly place!

4 Fill it with light and love,
Fill it with power divine,
And may Thy children hence depart,
Fresh sealed and signed as Thine!

W. Pennefather.

Section III.—God in Creation, Providence, and Grace.

Studland.   S.M.D.   E. A. Burroughs.

Alternative Tunes, Diademata, *No. 2, and* St. Ishmael, *No. 297.*

86

Thou hast granted me life and favour.—Job x. 12.

1 Lord God, from whom all life,
  And all true gladness springs,
Whose love and care shine everywhere
  Among earth's common things;
Be present while we lift
  Our song to Thee, and pay
Heart-gratitude for all things good
  About our path to-day.

2 We praise Thee for the light
  That floats on sea and hill,
The unstinted wealth of joy and health
  With which our pulses thrill;
Oh, may the light of heaven
  In us enkindled be,
Heaven's glory "roll from soul to soul"
  And make us strong for Thee!

3 We thank Thee for the grace
  In friend and brother found;
For human love that points above
  To where all love is crowned;
Oh, may such friendship here
  To us Thy sons be given,
As shall endure, deep, fair, and pure,
  Till all be one in heaven!

4 But most we bless Thee, Lord,
  That here Thy Spirit's breath
Blows clear and strong to baffle wrong
  And win our lives from death;
Oh, may each heart accept
  The entrance of Thy power,
And take Thee hence for sure defence
  And help in evil hour!

5 So, when the lives, to-day
  Within one circle brought,
Are sundered wide along the tide
  Of human work and thought,
One song shall yet be ours,
  One life, one family,
One pathway still, by vale or hill,
  Shall lead us home to Thee.

E. A. Burroughs.

All Things Bright and Beautiful. 7.6.7.6., with Refrain.   W. H. Monk.

Verse 1, and the Refrain after Verses 2, 3, 4, 5.

Verses 2, 3, 4, 5.

Thou hast created all things.—Rev. iv. 11.

87

1 ALL things bright and beautiful,
   All creatures great and small,
   All things wise and wonderful,
   The Lord God made them all.

2 Each little flower that opens,
   Each little bird that sings,
   He made their glowing colours,
   He made their tiny wings.
          All things bright, etc.

3 The purple-headed mountain,
   The river running by,
   The sunset, and the morning
   That brightens up the sky.
          All things bright, etc.

4 The cold wind in the winter,
   The pleasant summer sun,
   The ripe fruits in the garden,
   He made them every one.
          All things bright, etc.

5 He gave us eyes to see them,
   And lips that we might tell
   How great is God Almighty,
   Who hath done all things well.
          All things bright, etc.
                    Mrs. C. F. Alexander.

Armstrong. [FIRST TUNE.] 7.7.5.7.7.5. G. W. CHADWICK.

Used by permission. Copyright by A. S. Barnes & Co.

Lee. [SECOND TUNE.] 7.7.5.7.7.5. LOUISE DUGDALE.

Copyright. By permission of the composer.

88 *He took a child, and set him in the midst.*—MARK ix. 36.

1 LORD, who by Thy word of power
 Did'st, in nature's earliest hour,
  Fashion sun and star:
 Dear are these great worlds to Thee;
 Yet more dear than they can be
  Souls of children are.

2 Earth has treasures strange and rare,
 Skies are set with jewels fair,
  Clear they shine and far.
 Thou didst make those worlds of light;
 Yet more precious in Thy sight
  Hearts of children are.

3 Ever near Thy great white throne
 Dwell our angels with Thine own,
  There no sin can mar:
 'Tis Thy will that we should stand,
 Sinless in the deathless land,
  Where Thy children are.

4 Thou who still dost guard and save,
 Keep us faithful, make us brave
  In Thy holy war;
 Till Thy fuller life we find,
 And in lowly heart and mind
  Thy true children are.

F. Goldsmith French.

Almsgiving. 8.8.8.4. J. B. DYKES.

89 *Freely ye have received, freely give.*—MATT. X. 8.

1 O LORD of Heaven, and earth, and sea,
  To Thee all praise and glory be;
  How shall we show our love to Thee;
    Who givest all?

2 The golden sunshine, vernal air,
  Sweet flowers and fruits, Thy love declare;
  Where harvests ripen, Thou art there,
    Who givest all.

3 For peaceful homes and healthful days,
  For all the blessings earth displays,
  We owe Thee thankfulness and praise,
    Who givest all.

4 Thou didst not spare Thine only Son,
  But gav'st Him for a world undone;
  And freely with the blessèd One
    Thou givest all.

5 Thou giv'st the Spirit's blessèd dower,
  Spirit of life and love and power,
  And dost His sevenfold graces shower
    Upon us all.

6 For souls redeemed, for sins forgiven,
  For means of grace and hopes of heaven,
  Father, what can to Thee be given,
    Who givest all?

7 We lose what on ourselves we spend,
  We have as treasure without end
  Whatever, Lord, to Thee we lend,
    Who givest all.

8 To Thee, from whom we all derive
  Our life, our gifts, our power to give!
  Oh, may we ever with Thee live,
    Who givest all!
      C. Wordsworth.

Behold, what Love!   C.M.   J. McGRANAHAN.

Words and Music by permission of Mrs. H. C. Dixon.
Alternative Tune (without Chorus), ABRIDGE, *No.* 472.

90   *Behold, what manner of love the Father hath bestowed upon us, that we
should be called the sons of God!*—1 JOHN iii. 1.

1 BEHOLD, what love, what boundless love,
   The Father hath bestowed
On sinners lost, that we should be
   Now called "the sons of God."

2 No longer far from Him, but now
   By "precious blood" made nigh!
Accepted in the Well-beloved,
   Near to God's heart we lie.

3 What we in glory soon shall be
   "It doth not yet appear";
But when our precious Lord we see,
   We shall His image bear.

4 With such a blessèd hope in view,
   We would more holy be,
More like our risen, glorious Lord,
   Whose face we soon shall see.

                               M. S. Sullivan.

Munich.   7.6.7.6., D.   German.

Alternative Tunes, AURELIA, *No. 503, and* LANCASHIRE, *No. 248.*

91   *Thou art the same, and Thy years shall have no end.*—PSALM cii. 27.

1 O GOD, the Rock of Ages,
   Who evermore hast been,
What time the tempest rages,
   Our dwelling-place serene:
Before Thy first creations,
   O Lord, the same as now,
To endless generations
   The Everlasting Thou!

2 Our years are like the shadows
   On sunny hills that lie,
Or grasses in the meadows
   That blossom but to die:
A sleep, a dream, a story
   By strangers quickly told,
An unremaining glory
   Of things that soon are old.

3 O Thou, who canst not slumber,
   Whose light grows never pale,
Teach us aright to number
   Our years before they fail.
On us Thy mercy lighten,
   On us Thy goodness rest,
And let Thy Spirit brighten,
   The hearts Thyself hast blest.

4 Lord, crown our faith's endeavour
   With beauty and with grace,
Till, clothed in light for ever,
   We see Thee face to face:
A joy no language measures;
   A fountain brimming o'er;
An endless flow of pleasures;
   An ocean without shore.

E. H. Bickersteth.

Lilies. P.M. W. B. BRADBURY.

92 *Consider the lilies of the field.*—MATT. vi. 28.

1 How fair are the lilies, what fragrance they yield,
   Unwatched and untended by man!
For the Lord gives them beauty to brighten the field,
   And the flowers are a part of His plan.
        Let me never despair
        Of His love and His care,
If He thinks of the flowers, if on fields He has smiled,
   He will care so much more for a child.

2 There is not a sparrow that cleaves the blue air
   Unnoticed by God in its fall;
For He made them, He knows them, they all have His care,
   And He loves them, although they're so small.
     Let us bless His dear Name
     For the lesson so plain;
For He wants us to know that we're thought of above,
   And that each little child has His love.

3 The moss grows unseen in the niche of the wall,
   But could not be there without God;
And the dew-drops, that find it where rain cannot fall,
   He has purposely scattered abroad.
     So in my lowly place,
     I may still feel His grace,
For the dew of His love can e'en fall on me there,
   And His blessing in answer to prayer.

4 As we in His beautiful image were made,
   He loves us beyond all beside;
But it grieved Him when sin caused that image to fade,
   And then to redeem us He died.
     And He now from His throne
     In His beautiful home
Still is saying with love that is boundless and free,
   "Let the little ones come unto Me."

          E. H. Jackson (altd.).

Waltham.   L.M.   J. BAPTISTE CALKIN.

By permission of Novello and Company, Limited.

93   *The Lord is good to all.*—PSALM cxlv. 9.

1 YES, God is good; in earth and sky,
   From ocean depths and spreading wood,
Ten thousand voices seem to cry—
   God made us all, and God is good.

2 The sun that keeps his trackless way,
   And downward pours his golden flood,
Night's sparkling host, all seem to say,
   In accents clear, that God is good.

3 The merry birds prolong the strain,
   Their song with every spring renewed;
And balmy air, and falling rain,
   Each softly whisper—God is good.

4 I hear it in the rushing breeze;
   The hills that have for ages stood,
The echoing sky and roaring seas,
   All swell the chorus—God is good.

5 Yes, God is good, all nature says,
   By God's own hand with speech endued;
And man, in louder notes of praise,
   Should sing for joy that God is good.

6 For all Thy gifts we bless Thee, Lord;
   But most for Thy redeeming blood,
Thy pardoning grace, Thy quickening word,
   These prompt our song that God is good.

         E. L. Follen and J. H. Gurney.

Cross of Jesus. 8.7.8.7. Sir JOHN STAINER.
From "The Crucifixion."

By permission of Novello and Company, Limited.

94 *They were scattered abroad, as sheep having no shepherd.*—MATT. ix. 36.

1 Souls of men, why will ye scatter
  Like a crowd of frightened sheep?
Foolish hearts, why will ye wander
  From a love so true and deep?

2 Was there ever kindest shepherd
  Half so gentle, half so sweet,
As the Saviour who would have us
  Come and gather round His feet?

3 There's a wideness in God's mercy,
  Like the wideness of the sea;
There's a kindness in His justice,
  Which is more than liberty.

4 There is plentiful redemption
  In the blood that has been shed;
There is joy for all the members
  In the sorrows of the Head.

5 For the love of God is broader
  Than the measures of man's mind;
And the heart of the Eternal
  Is most wonderfully kind.

6 If our love were but more simple,
  We should take Him at His word,
And our lives would be all sunshine
  In the sweetness of our Lord.

F. W. Faber.

Tudor. C.M. J. P. JEWSON.

95 *Goodness and mercy shall follow me all the days of my life.*—PSALM xxiii. 6.

1 LORD, I would own Thy tender care,
  And all Thy love to me;
The food I eat, the clothes I wear,
  Are all bestowed by Thee.

2 'Tis Thou preservest me from death
  And dangers every hour;
I cannot draw another breath
  Unless Thou give me power.

3 My health, and friends, and parents dear
  To me by God are given;
I have not any blessing here
  But what is sent from heaven.

4 Such goodness, Lord. and constant care
  A child can ne'er repay;
But may it be my daily prayer
  To love Thee and obey.

Ann Taylor.

Ellacombe.   7.6.7.6., D.   German.

96   *Bless the Lord, all His works in all places of His dominion.*—PSALM ciii. 22.

1 'TWAS God that made the ocean,
   And laid its sandy bed;
He gave the stars their motion,
   And built the mountain's head;
He made the rolling thunder,
   The lightning's flashing flame;
His works are full of wonder,
   All-glorious is His Name.

2 And must it not surprise us
   That One so high and great
Should see and not despise us,
   Poor sinners, at His feet?
Yet day by day He gives us
   Our raiment and our food;
In sickness He relieves us,
   And is in all things good.

3 But things that are far greater
   His mighty hand hath done,
And sent us blessings sweeter
   Through Christ, His only Son;
Who, when He saw us dying
   In sin and sorrow's night,
On wings of mercy flying,
   Came down with life and light.

4 He gives His Word to teach us
   Our danger and our wants,
And kindly doth beseech us
   To take the life He grants.
His Holy Spirit frees us
   From Satan's deadly powers,
Leads us by faith to Jesus,
   And makes His glory ours.

Anon.

Pilgrims of the Night.   6.5.6.5. D., with Chorus.

Oh! these flowers of sum-mer, An-gel-like are they; Lis-ten to the mes-sage Which they bring to - day,

Lis-ten to the mes - sage Which they bring to - day.

Alternative Tune, HERMAS, No. 174.

97   *Solomon in all his glory was not arrayed like one of these.*—MATT. vi. 29.

1 PANSIES, lilies, roses,
    Flowers of every hue,
  Take each one as coming
    Straight from God to you;
  Telling wondrous secrets
    Of His power and love,
  Wearing still the brightness
    Of the home above.
      Oh! these flowers of summer, etc.

2 Just as earth's creation
    Showed the might of God,
  So does every floweret
    Springing from the sod.
  He who guides the star-worlds,
    Curbs the ocean's power,
  With the same hand painteth
    Every leaf and flower.

3 Touch these sweet flowers gently,
    So divinely dressed,
  They are, in earth's language,
    Thoughts of God expressed.
  Thoughts of heavenly glory—
    Sweetness, purity—
  Must not He who framed them
    Wholly lovely be?

4 Praise Him then with singing,
    Tell His love abroad;
  Be the whole earth ringing
    With the Name of God.
  Lakes and hills be telling,
    Sunset skies, and flowers,
  Something of the beauty
    Of this God of ours.

C. Griffiths.

Copyright. Words by permission of the National Sunday School Union.

Ruth.   6.5., 8 lines.   S. Smith.

By permission of Novello and Company, Limited.

98   *Thou hast prepared the light and the sun.*—Psalm lxxiv. 16.

1 Summer suns are glowing
    Over land and sea;
  Happy light is flowing,
    Bountiful and free.
  Every thing rejoices
    In the mellow rays;
  All earth's thousand voices
    Swell the psalm of praise.

2 God's free mercy streameth
    Over all the world,
  And His banner gleameth,
    Everywhere unfurled.
  Broad and deep and glorious
    As the heaven above,
  Shines in might victorious
    His eternal love.

3 Lord, upon our blindness
    Thy pure radiance pour;
  For Thy loving-kindness
    Make us love Thee more;
  And, when clouds are drifting
    Dark across our sky,
  Then, the veil uplifting,
    Father, be Thou nigh.

4 We will never doubt Thee,
    Though Thou veil Thy light;
  Life is dark without Thee;
    Death with Thee is bright.
  Light of Light! shine o'er us
    On our pilgrim way;
  Go Thou still before us
    To the endless day.

W. W. How.

Ashburton. 7.7.7.7.7.7. R. Jackson.

99 *All things were made by Him.*—John i. 3.

1 For the beauty of the earth,
    For the beauty of the skies,
For the love which from our birth
    Over and around us lies,
Christ, our God, to Thee we raise
This our sacrifice of praise.

2 For the beauty of each hour
    Of the day and of the night,
Hill and vale, and tree and flower,
    Sun and moon and stars of light,
Christ, our God, to Thee we raise
This our sacrifice of praise.

3 For the joy of ear and eye,
    For the heart and mind's delight,
For the mystic harmony
    Linking sense to sound and sight
Christ, our God, to Thee we raise
This our sacrifice of praise.

4 For the joy of human love,
    Brother, sister, parent, child,
Friends on earth and friends above,
    For all gentle thoughts and mild,
Christ, our God, to Thee we raise
This our sacrifice of praise.

5 For each perfect gift of Thine
    To our race so freely given,
Graces human and divine,
    Flowers of earth and buds of heaven,
Christ, our God, to Thee we raise
This our sacrifice of praise.

        F. S. Pierpoint.

100 Sommerlied. 5.6.6.4. Hermann von Müller.

1. God, who made the earth, The air, the sky, the sea, Who

gave the light its birth, .. Car - eth for me.

*He careth for you.—*1 PET. v. 7.

100

2 God, who made the grass,
The flower, the fruit, the tree,
The day and night to pass,
   Careth for me.

3 God, who made the sun,
The moon, the stars, is He
Who when life's clouds come on,
   Careth for me.

4 God, who sent His Son
To die on Calvary,
He, if I lean on Him,
   Will care for me.

5 When in heaven's bright land
I all His loved ones see,
I'll sing with that blest band,
   God cared for me.

Sarah B. Rhodes.

Greenland.   7.6.7.6., D.   Lausanne Psalter.

Alternative Tunes, ANGELS' STORY, *No.* 627, *and* MUNICH, *No.* 91.

101   *We have known and believed the love that God hath to us.—*1 JOHN iv. 16.

1 How dearly God must love us,
   And this poor world of ours,
To spread blue skies above us,
   And deck the earth with flowers!
There's not a weed so lowly,
   Nor bird that cleaves the air,
But tells, in accents holy,
   His kindness and His care.

2 He bids the sun to warm us,
   And light the path we tread;
At night, lest aught should harm us,
   He guards our welcome bed;

He gives us needful clothing,
   And sends our daily food;
His loves denies us nothing
   His wisdom deemeth good.

3 The Bible too He sends us,
   That tells how Jesus came,
Whose blood can cleanse and save us
   From guilt and sin and shame.
Oh, may God's mercies move us
   To serve Him with our powers;
For, oh, how He must love us,
   And this poor world of ours!

S. W. Partridge.

London New.   C.M.   *Psalmes of David,* 1635.

Alternative Tunes, IRISH, No. 593, and DUNDEE, No. 284.

102   *The Lord hath His way in the whirlwind and in the storm.*—NAHUM i. 3.

1 GOD moves in a mysterious way
    His wonders to perform ;
He plants His footsteps in the sea,
    And rides upon the storm.

2 Deep in unfathomable mines
    Of never-failing skill,
He treasures up His bright designs,
    And works His sovereign will.

3 Ye fearful saints, fresh courage take !
    The clouds ye so much dread
Are big with mercy, and shall break
    In blessings on your head.

4 Judge not the Lord by feeble sense,
    But trust Him for His grace ;
Behind a frowning providence
    He hides a smiling face.

5 His purposes will ripen fast,
    Unfolding every hour ;
The bud may have a bitter taste,
    But sweet will be the flower.

6 Blind unbelief is sure to err,
    And scan His work in vain ;
God is His own interpreter,
    And He will make it plain.

W. Cowper.

103 Wharmby.   7.6.7.6. D.   LUTHER T. WHARMBY.

1. I know who makes the dai-sies, And paints them star-ry bright;
I know who clothes the lil-ies So sweet and soft and white; ..
And sure-ly need-ful rai-ment He will for me pro-vide, ..

Who know Him as my Je - sus, And in His love con - fide. . .

Alternative Tune, LANCASHIRE, No. 248.

103 *The flower fadeth: but the Word of our God shall stand for ever.—ISA. xl. 8.*

2 I know who feeds the sparrow,
  And robin, red and gay;
I know who makes the skylark
  Soar up to greet the day:
And me much more He cares for,
  And feeds with daily bread,
Whom He has taught to love Him,
  And trust what He has said.

3 The daisy and the lily
  Obey Him all they can;
The robin and the skylark
  Fulfil His perfect plan:

And I, to whom are given
  A heart and mind and will,
Must try to serve Him better,
  And all His laws fulfil.

4 The daisies, they must perish,
  The lark and robin die;
But I shall live for ever,
  Above the bright blue sky:
Dear Saviour, Thou wilt help me
  To love Thee more and more,
Until in heaven I see Thee,
  Am like Thee, and adore.

Newman Hall.

Melcombe. L.M. SAMUEL WEBBE.

Alternative Tune, ANTWERP, No. 53.

104 *I will sing . . . of Thy mercy in the morning.—PSA. lix. 16.*

1 OH, timely happy, timely wise,
  Hearts that with rising morn arise;
Eyes that the beam celestial view
Which evermore makes all things new.

2 New every morning is the love
  Our wakening and uprising prove;
Through sleep and darkness safely brought,
Restored to life, and power, and thought.

3 New mercies, each returning day,
  Hover around us while we pray;
New perils past, new sins forgiven,
New thoughts of God, new hopes of heaven.

4 If, on our daily course, our mind
  Be set to hallow all we find,
New treasures still of countless price
God will provide for sacrifice.

5 Old friends, old scenes will lovelier be,
  As more of heaven in each we see;
Some softening gleam of love and prayer
Shall dawn on every cross and care.

6 The trivial round, the common task,
  Will furnish all we ought to ask:
Room to deny ourselves; a road
To bring us daily nearer God.

7 Only, O Lord, in Thy dear love
  Fit us for perfect rest above,
And help us, this and every day,
To live more nearly as we pray.

J. Keble.

Silchester. S.M. C. MALAN.

Alternative Tune, ST. GEORGE, *No.* 220.

105 *By grace ye are saved.*—EPH. ii. 5.

1 GRACE! 'tis a charming sound,
　Harmonious to the ear:
　Heaven with the echo shall resound,
　And all the earth shall hear.

2 'Twas grace that wrote my name
　In life's eternal book:
　'Twas grace that gave me to the Lamb,
　Who all my sorrows took.

3 Grace taught my wandering feet
　To tread the heavenly road;
　And new supplies each hour I meet
　While pressing on to God.

4 Grace taught my soul to pray,
　And made my eyes o'erflow;
　'Tis grace has kept me to this day,
　And will not let me go.

5 Grace all the work shall crown
　Through everlasting days;
　It lays in heaven the topmost stone,
　And well deserves the praise.

6 Oh, let that grace inspire
　My soul with strength divine!
　May all my powers to Thee aspire,
　And all my days be Thine.

P. Doddridge.

Brockley. P.M., with Refrain. E. H. GLADSTONE SARGENT.

Chorus.

We will praise Thee, O our Fa - ther, We will praise Thee in our song:

While the grateful thoughts of our lov - ing hearts True prais - es shall pro - long.

106 *Be thankful unto Him, and bless His Name.*—PSALM c. 1.

1 FOR the sunshine of the summer
   That makes all nature bright;
For the gladness which it brings us,
   With its joyous warmth and light:

2 For the beauteous flowers and blossoms,
   Which speak Thy skill and love;
For the music of the song-birds
   All around us and above:

3 For the golden fruits of harvest,
   Which ripen o'er the plain,
Giving bread to all Thy children,
   And the seed to sow again:

4 For the message of the Gospel,
   For the Saviour's life and death,
For the blessings which He gives us,
   We will praise Thee with each breath.

E. G. Sargent.

Ceres.   **S.M.**   PAISIELLO.

107 *In the day of the first fruits . . . bring a new meat-offering unto the Lord.*—NUM. xxviii. 26.

1   FAIR waved the golden corn
      In Canaan's pleasant land,
   When full of joy, some shining morn,
      Went forth the reaper-band.

2   To God so good and great,
      Their cheerful thanks they pour,
   Then carry to His temple gate
      The choicest of their store.

3   For thus the holy word,
      Spoken by Moses, ran—
   "The first ripe ears are for the Lord,
      The rest He gives to man."

4   Like Israel, Lord, we give
      Our earliest fruits to Thee,
   And pray that, long as we shall live,
      We may Thy children be.

5   Thine is our youthful prime,
      And life and all its powers;
   Be with us in our morning time,
      And bless our evening hours.

6   In wisdom let us grow,
      As years and strength are given,
   That we may serve Thy church below
      And join Thy saints in heaven.

J. Hampden Gurney.

D

Watermouth.   7.6.7.6, D.   R. JACKSON.

Slower.

108   *Suffer little children . . . to come unto Me.*—MATT. xix. 14.

1 GOD who hath made the daisies
  And every lovely thing,
  He will accept our praises,
  And hearken while we sing.
  He says (though we be simple,
    Though ignorant we be)—
  "Suffer the little children,
    And let them come to Me!"

2 Though we are young and simple,
  In praise we may be bold;
  The children in the Temple,
  He heard in days of old.
  And if our hearts are humble,
    He says to you and me—
  "Suffer the little children,
    And let them come to Me!"

3 He sees the bird that wingeth
  Its way o'er earth and sky,
  He hears the lark that singeth
  Up in the heaven so high;
  He sees the heart's low breathing,
    And says (well pleased to see)—
  "Suffer the little children,
    And let them come to Me!"

4 Therefore we will come near Him,
  And joyfully we'll sing,
  No cause to shrink or fear Him,
  We'll make our voices ring;
  For in our temple speaking,
    He says to you and me—
  "Suffer the little children,
    And let them come to Me!"

E. Paxton Hood.

SECTION IV.—The Lord Jesus Christ.

(I.) His Birth and Childhood.

Holy Child.   P.M.   JAMES S. TYLER.

109

Thy holy Child Jesus.—ACTS iv. 27.

1 THERE came a little Child to earth
        Long ago;
    And the angels of God proclaimed His birth,
        High and low.

2 Out on the night, so calm and still,
        Their song was heard;
    For they knew that the Child on Bethlehem's hill
        Was Christ the Lord.

3 Far away in a goodly land,
        Fair and bright,
    Children with crowns of glory stand
        Robed in white;

4 In white more pure than the spotless snow;
        And their tongues unite
    In the psalm which the angels sang long ago,
        On Christmas night.

5 They sing how the Lord of that world so fair,
        A Child was born;
    And that they might a crown of glory wear,
        Wore a crown of thorn.

6 And in mortal weakness, in want, and pain,
        Came forth to die;
    That the children of earth might for ever reign
        With Him on high.

7 And for evermore, in their robes most fair
        And undefiled,
    Those ransomed children His praise declare,
        Who was once a Child.
                            E. E. Steele Elliott.

Care must be taken to adapt the music to variations in the verses.

Kensington New.   8.7.8.7.8.7.   J. TILLEARD.

Alternative Tune, TRIUMPH, *No. 32.*

110   *We are come to worship Him.*—MATT. ii. 2.

1 ANGELS from the realms of glory,
    Wing your flight o'er all the earth;
  Ye who sang creation's story
    Now proclaim Messiah's birth:
      Come and worship!
  Worship Christ, the new-born King!

2 Shepherds in the fields abiding,
    Watching o'er their flocks by night;
  God with man is now residing,
    Yonder shines the Infant light:
      Come and worship!
  Worship Christ, the new-born King!

3 Sages, leave your contemplations;
    Brighter visions beam afar!
  Seek the great "Desire of nations,"
    Ye have seen His natal star:
      Come and worship!
  Worship Christ, the new-born King!

4 Saints before the altar bending,
    Watching long in hope and fear,
  Suddenly the Lord, descending,
    In His temple shall appear:
      Come and worship!
  Worship Christ, the new-born King!

J. Montgomery.

111 Pox Præcessit. [FIRST TUNE.]   C.M.   J. B. CALKIN.

By permission of John F. Shaw & Co.

St. Saviour. [SECOND TUNE.]   C.M.   F. G. BAKER.

111   *The Lord hath anointed Me to preach good tidings.*—ISA. lxi. 1.

1 HARK, the glad sound! the Saviour comes,
  The Saviour promised long;
  Let every heart prepare a throne,
  And every voice a song.

2 He comes, the prisoners to release
  In Satan's bondage held;
  The gates of brass before Him burst,
  The iron fetters yield.

3 He comes from thickest films of vice
  To clear the mental ray,

And on the eye-balls of the blind
  To pour celestial day.

4 He comes the broken heart to bind,
  The bleeding soul to cure;
  And with the treasures of His grace
  To enrich the humble poor.

5 Our glad hosannas, Prince of Peace,
  Thy welcome shall proclaim;
  And heaven's eternal arches ring
  With Thy belovèd Name.

P. Doddridge.

Raynolds.   11.10.11.10.   MENDELSSOHN (*arr.*)

112   *The government shall be upon His shoulder.*—ISA. ix. 6.

1 WE praise Thee, Lord, for this Thy great provision
    For our great need—Thy Strong Deliverer sent.
  Lo, unto us this day is born a Saviour,
    And on His shoulder is the government.

2 Thy ways, O Lord, are past our understanding,
    Yet now, our Father, are we well content,
  Since Thou hast told us in Thy word of promise,
    That on His shoulder is the government.

3 Great are my needs and many my temptations,
    Thy loving wisdom knows their full extent:
  I feel their burden, yet, my God, Thou bidd'st me
    Lay on His shoulder all the government.

4 So, then, O Father, I would claim Thy promise,
    Resting on Jesus, for my strength is spent;
  And thus will I, on Thy blest word relying,
    Leave on His shoulder all the government.

J. W. Lloyd.

113 Thou didst leave.

P.M.

IRA D. SANKEY.

Slowly.

1. Thou didst leave Thy throne and Thy king - ly .. crown, When Thou cam - est to earth for .. me; But in Beth - lehem's home there was found no .. room For Thy ho - ly na - tiv - i - ty.

Oh, come to my heart, Lord Je - sus! There is room in my heart for Thee,

Oh, come to my heart, Lord Je-sus, come! There is room in my heart for Thee.

Music by permission. From Sankey's *Sacred Songs and Solos.*

113 *Though He was rich, yet for your sakes He became poor.*—2 COR. viii. **9**

2 Heaven's arches rang when the angels sang,
    Proclaiming Thy royal degree;
But of lowly birth cam'st Thou, Lord, on earth,
    And in great humility.
Oh, come to my heart, Lord Jesus!
    There is room in my heart for Thee.

3 The foxes found rest, and the birds had their nest,
    In the shade of the cedar tree;
But Thy couch was the sod, O Thou Son of God,
    In the deserts of Galilee.
Oh, come to my heart, Lord Jesus!
    There is room in my heart for Thee.

4 Thou camest, O Lord, with the living word
    That should set Thy children free;
But with mocking scorn, and with crown of thorn,
    They bore Thee to Calvary.
Oh, come to my heart, Lord Jesus!
    Thy cross is my only plea.

5 When heaven's arches shall ring, and her choirs shall sing,
    At Thy coming to victory,
Let Thy voice call me home, saying, "Yet there is room,
    There is room at My side for thee."
And my heart shall rejoice, Lord Jesus,
    When Thou comest and callest for me.

E. E. Steele Elliott.

Winchester Old.   **C.M.**   ESTE's Psalter.

114   *Unto you is born this day . . . a Saviour, which is Christ the Lord.*—LUKE ii. 11.

1 WHILE shepherds watched their flocks by night,
    All seated on the ground,
The angel of the Lord came down,
    And glory shone around.

2 "Fear not," said he, for mighty dread
    Had seized their troubled mind;
"Glad tidings of great joy I bring
    To you and all mankind.

3 "To you, in David's town, this day,
    Is born, of David's line,
A Saviour, who is Christ the Lord;
    And this shall be the sign

4 "The heavenly Babe you there shall find
    To human view displayed,
All meanly wrapped in swathing bands,
    And in a manger laid."

5 Thus spake the seraph; and forthwith
    Appeared a shining throng
Of angels, praising God, who thus
    Addressed their joyful song:

6 "All glory be to God on high,
    And on the earth be peace;
Good-will henceforth from heaven to men,
    Begin and never cease."

N. Tate.

Yorkshire.   10.10.10.10.10.10.   J. WAINWRIGHT.

115   *The angel said . . . I bring you good tidings of great joy.*—LUKE ii. 10.

1 CHRISTIANS, awake, salute the happy morn,
  Whereon the Saviour of mankind was born;
  Rise to adore the mystery of love,
  Which hosts of angels chanted from above;
  With them the joyful tidings first begun
  Of God Incarnate and the Virgin's Son.

2 Then to the watchful shepherds it was told,
  Who heard the angelic herald's voice: "Behold,
  I bring good tidings of a Saviour's birth
  To you and all the nations upon earth:
  This day hath God fulfilled His promised word
  This day is born a Saviour, Christ the Lord."

3 He spake: and straightway the celestial choir
  In hymns of joy, unknown before, conspire;
  The praises of redeeming love they sang,
  And heaven's whole orb with alleluias rang;
  God's highest glory was their anthem still,
  Peace upon earth, and unto men good will.

4 To Bethlehem straight the enlightened shepherds ran,
To see the wonder God had wrought for man;
And found, with Joseph and the blessèd Maid,
Her Son, the Saviour, in a manger laid;
Then to their flocks, still praising God, return,
And their glad hearts with holy rapture burn.

5 Oh! may we keep and ponder in our mind,
God's wondrous love in saving lost mankind;
Trace we the Babe, who hath retrieved our loss,
From His poor manger, to His bitter cross;
Tread in His steps, assisted by His grace,
Till man's first heavenly state again takes place.

6 Then may we hope, the angelic hosts among,
To sing, redeemed, a glad triumphal song;
He that was born upon this joyful day
Around us all His glory shall display;
Saved by His love, incessant we shall sing
Eternal praise to heaven's Almighty King.   *John Byrom.*

Dix.   7.7.7.7.7.7.   C. KOCHER.

116   *When they saw the star, they rejoiced with exceeding great joy.*—MATT. ii. 10.

1 As with gladness men of old
Did the guiding star behold,
As with joy they hailed its light,
Leading onward, beaming bright:
So, most gracious Lord, may we
Evermore be led to Thee.

2 As with joyful steps they sped,
Saviour, to Thy lowly bed,
There to bend the knee before
Thee whom heaven and earth adore:
So may we with willing feet
Ever seek the mercy-seat.

3 As they offered gifts most rare
At Thy cradle rude and bare;
So may we with holy joy,
Pure, and free from sin's alloy,
All our costliest treasures bring,
Christ, to Thee, our heavenly King.

4 Holy Jesus, every day
Keep us in the narrow way;
And, when earthly things are past,
Bring our ransomed souls at last
Where they need no star to guide,
Where no clouds Thy glory hide.

W. C. Dix.

D*

Adeste Fideles.   P.M.   J. F. WADE's "Cantus Diversi."

117   *Let us now go even unto Bethlehem.*—LUKE ii. 15.

1   OH, come, all ye faithful,
    Joyful and triumphant;
Oh, come ye! oh, come ye to Bethlehem;
    Come and behold Him,
    Born the King of angels;
Oh, come, let us adore Him,
    Christ the Lord!

2   God of God
    Light of light,
Lo! He abhors not the Virgin's womb;
    Very God,
    Begotten, not created;
Oh, come, let us adore Him,
    Christ the Lord!

3   Sing, choirs of Angels,
    Sing in exultation,
Sing, all ye powers of heaven above:
    " Glory to God
    In the highest : "
Oh, come, let us adore Him,
    Christ the Lord!

4   Yea, Lord, we greet Thee,
    Born this happy morning;
Jesus, to Thee be glory given;
    Word of the Father,
    In our flesh appearing:
Oh, come, let us adore Him,
    Christ the Lord!

Tr. from the Latin by F. Oakeley.

Noel. **D.C.M.** Arranged by Sir ARTHUR S. SULLIVAN.

118 *And suddenly there was with the angel a multitude of the heavenly host praising God.*—LUKE ii. 13.

1 IT came upon the midnight clear,
 That glorious song of old,
From angels bending near the earth
 To touch their harps of gold:
Peace on the earth, goodwill to men
 From heaven's all-gracious King—
The world in solemn stillness lay
 To hear the angels sing.

2 Still through the cloven skies they come
 With peaceful wings unfurled:
And still their heavenly music floats
 O'er all the weary world:
Above its sad and lowly plains
 They bend on hovering wing,
And ever, o'er its Babel-sounds,
 The blessèd angels sing.

3 O ye, beneath life's crushing load
 Whose forms are bending low,
Who toil along the climbing way
 With painful steps and slow;
Look up! for glad and golden hours
 Come swiftly on the wing;
Oh, rest beside the weary road,
 And hear the angels sing!

4 For lo! the days are hastening on,
 By prophet-bards foretold,
When, with the ever-circling years,
 Comes round the age of gold;
When peace shall over all the earth
 Its ancient splendours fling,
And the whole world send back the song
 Which now the angels sing!

E. H. Sears.

By permission of Novello and Company, Limited.

119   *Unto you is born this day, in the city of David, a Saviour, which is Christ the Lord.*—LUKE ii. 11.

1 HARK! the herald angels sing,
"Glory to the new-born King!
 Peace on earth and mercy mild,
 God and sinners reconciled."
 Joyful, all ye nations rise,
 Join the triumph of the skies;
 With the angelic host proclaim,
"Christ is born in Bethlehem!"
 Hark! the herald angels sing,
 "Glory to the new-born King!"

2 Hail, the heaven-born Prince of Peace !
Hail, the Sun of Righteousness !
Light and life to all He brings,
Risen with healing in His wings.
Mild He lays His glory by,
Born that man no more may die ;
Born to raise the sons of earth,
Born to give them second birth.

3 Come, Desire of nations, come,
Fix in us Thy humble home :
Rise, the woman's conquering Seed,
Bruise in us the serpent's head :
Sing we then, with angels sing,
" Glory to the new-born King !
Glory in the highest heaven,
Peace on earth, and sins forgiven."
C. Wesley.

Irby.   8.7.8.7.7.7.   H. J. GAUNTLETT.

120   The Word was made flesh, and dwelt among us.—JOHN i. 14.

1 ONCE, in royal David's city,
Stood a lowly cattle-shed,
Where a mother laid her Baby,
In a manger for His bed.
Mary was that mother mild,
Jesus Christ her little child.

2 He came down to earth from heaven,
Who is God and Lord of all,
And His shelter was a stable,
And His cradle was a stall :
With the poor and mean and lowly
Lived on earth our Saviour holy.

3 And through all His wondrous childhood
He would honour and obey,
Love and watch the lowly mother,
In whose gentle arms He lay.
Christian children all must be
Mild, obedient, good as He.

4 For He is our childhood's pattern :
Day by day like us He grew ;
He was little, weak, and helpless ;
Tears and smiles like us He knew :
And He feeleth for our sadness,
And He shareth in our gladness.

5 And our eyes at last shall see Him,
Through His own redeeming love ;
For that Child, so dear and gentle,
Is our Lord in heaven above ;
And He leads His children on
To the place where He is gone.

6 Not in that poor, lowly stable,
With the oxen standing by,
We shall see Him ; but in heaven,
Set at God's right hand on high ;
When like stars His children crowned,
All in white shall wait around.
Mrs. C. F. Alexander.

Epiphany Hymn. 11.10.11.10. (dactylic). J. F. THRUPP.

121 *We have seen His star in the east, and are come to worship Him.*—MATT. ii. 2.

1 BRIGHTEST and best of the sons of the morning,
   Dawn on our darkness, and lend us thine aid!
Star of the east, the horizon adorning,
   Guide where our infant Redeemer is laid!

2 Cold on His cradle the dewdrops are shining,
   Low lies His head with the beasts of the stall;
Angels adore Him in slumber reclining—
   Maker, and Monarch, and Saviour of all!

3 Say, shall we yield Him, in costly devotion,
   Odours of Edom and offerings divine;
Gems of the mountain, and pearls of the ocean,
   Myrrh from the forest, and gold from the mine?

4 Vainly we offer each ample oblation,
   Vainly with gifts would His favour secure:
Richer by far is the heart's adoration;
   Dearer to God are the prayers of the poor.

5 Brightest and best of the sons of the morning,
   Dawn on our darkness, and lend us thine aid!
Star of the east, the horizon adorning,
   Guide where our infant Redeemer is laid!
                                        R. Heber.

Section IV.—The Lord Jesus Christ.
(2.) His Life and Work.

Scopas.

8.7.8.7., D.

C. Hancock.

Bold.

122   *In all things it behoved Him to be made like unto His brethren.*—Heb. ii. 17.

1 Who is this so weak and helpless,
  Child of lowly Hebrew maid,
Rudely in a stable sheltered,
  Coldly in a manger laid?
'Tis the Lord of all creation,
  Who this wondrous path hath trod;
He is God from everlasting,
  And to everlasting God.

2 Who is this—a Man of Sorrows,
  Walking sadly life's hard way,
Homeless, weary, sighing, weeping
  Over sin and Satan's sway?
'Tis our God, our glorious Saviour,
  Who above the starry sky
Now for us a place prepareth,
  Where no tear can dim the eye.

3 Who is this—behold Him shedding
  Drops of blood upon the ground?
Who is this—despised, rejected,
  Mocked, insulted, beaten, bound?
'Tis our God, who gifts and graces
  On His Church now poureth down;
Who shall smite in righteous judgment
  All His foes beneath His throne.

4 Who is this that hangeth dying,
  While the rude world scoffs and scorns;
Numbered with the malefactors,
  Torn with nails, and crowned with thorns?
'Tis the God who ever liveth
  'Mid the shining ones on high,
In the glorious golden city
  Reigning everlastingly.   *W. W. How.*

The Sweetest Story. 8.7.8.7., D., with Refrain. JNO. R. SWENEY.

Tell me the sto-ry of Je - sus, Write on my heart ev - 'ry word,

Tell me the sto - ry most pre - cious, Sweet - est that ev - er was heard.

123 *These are written, that ye might believe that Jesus is the Christ, the Son of God.*—JOHN xx. 31.

1 TELL me the story of Jesus,
　Write on my heart every word !
Tell me the story most precious,
　Sweetest that ever was heard.
Tell how the angels in chorus
　Sang, as they welcomed His birth,
" Glory to God in the highest,
　Peace and good tidings to earth."

2 Fasting alone in the desert,
　Tell of the days that He passed ;
How He was tried and was tempted,
　Yet was triumphant at last.

Tell of the years of His labours,
　Tell of the sorrows He bore ;
He was despised and afflicted,
　Homeless, rejected, and poor.

3 Tell of the cross where they nailed Him,
　Hanging in anguish and pain ;
Tell of the grave where they laid Him ;
　Tell how He liveth again.
Love, in that story so tender,
　Clearer than ever I see ;
Stay, let me weep while you whisper
　Love paid the ransom for me.

Fanny J. Crosby.

Credo.   8.8.8.8.8.8.   Sir J. Stainer.

A little slower.

f

Org.

Alternative Tune, STELLA, *No.* 380.

124   *Blessed are they that have not seen, and yet have believed.*—JOHN xx. 29.

1 WE saw Thee not when Thou didst come
　　To this poor world of sin and death,
　Nor e'er beheld Thy cottage-home
　　In that despisèd Nazareth;
　But we believe Thy footsteps trod
　Its streets and plains, Thou Son of God.

2 We did not see Thee lifted high
　　Amid that wild and savage crew,
　Nor heard Thy meek imploring cry,
　　"Forgive; they know not what they do":
　Yet we believe the deed was done,
　Which shook the earth and veiled the sun.

3 We stood not by the empty tomb
　　Where late Thy sacred body lay,
　Nor sat within that upper room,
　　Nor met Thee in the open way;
　But we believe that angels said,
　"Why seek the living with the dead?"

4 We did not mark the chosen few,
　　When Thou didst through the clouds ascend,
　First lift to heaven their wondering view,
　　Then to the earth all prostrate bend;
　Yet we believe that mortal eyes
　Beheld that journey to the skies.

5 And now that Thou dost reign on high,
　　And thence Thy waiting people bless,
　No ray of glory from the sky
　　Doth shine upon our wilderness;
　But we believe Thy faithful Word,
　And trust in our redeeming Lord.　*J. H. Gurney.*

Seeking for Me!

P.M.

E. E. Hasty (arr.)

REFRAIN. For me!..... For me!....

1. Seek-ing for me! Seek-ing for me! Seek-ing for me! Seek-ing for me!
2. Dy-ing for me! Dy-ing for me! Dy-ing for me! Dy-ing for me!
3. Call-ing for me! Call-ing for me! Call-ing for me! Call-ing for me!
4. Com-ing for me! Com-ing for me! Com-ing for me! Com-ing for me!

1. Oh, it was won-der-ful—blest be His name! Seek-ing for me, for me!...
2. Oh, it was won-der-ful—how could it be? Dy-ing for me, for me!...
3. Gent-ly and long did He plead with my soul, Call-ing for me, for me!...
4. Oh, I shall see Him de-scending the sky, Com-ing for me, for me!...

125 *I will both search My sheep, and seek them out.*—Ezek. xxxiv. 11.

1.
Jesus, my Saviour, to Bethlehem came,
Born in a manger to sorrow and shame;
Oh, it was wonderful—blest be His Name!
    Seeking for me, for me!
      Seeking for me, for me! etc.

2.
Jesus, my Saviour, on Calvary's tree,
Paid the great debt, and my soul He set free;
Oh, it was wonderful—how could it be?
    Dying for me, for me!
      Dying for me, for me! etc.

3.
Jesus, my Saviour, the same as of old,
While I was wandering afar from the fold,
Gently and long did He plead with my soul,
    Calling for me, for me!
      Calling for me, for me! etc.

4.
Jesus, my Saviour, shall come from on high—
Sweet is the promise as passing years fly;
Oh, I shall see Him descending the sky,
    Coming for me, for me!
      Coming for me, for me! etc. *A. N.*

Glenorme.   7.6.7.6., D.   KATHLEEN ROBSON.

Alternative Tune, ANGELS' STORY, *No.* 627.

126   *He took them up in His arms, put His hands upon them, and blessed*
               them.—MARK x. 16.

1 THE Saviour loves all children,
    For He was once a child—
So joyous and so happy,
    So gentle, meek, and mild.
He loves the young in heaven,
    He loves the young on earth;
For every child that liveth
    Reminds Him of His birth.

2 Oh, happy were those children—
    We wish we had been there—
Who gained the Saviour's blessing,
    And heard His loving prayer.
We wish His hands had rested
    Upon our heads as well,
And we had heard the lessons
    Which from the Master fell.

3 And yet we know that Jesus
    Is with us every day;
He stands within our chamber,
    When we kneel down to pray.
He speaks when we are reading,
    Although no voice is heard;
And whispers many blessings
    To children in His Word.

4 And if we seek Him early
    He'll lead us by the hand,
Until some day in glory
    We at His side shall stand:
And then with those same children,
    Our harps of gold we'll bring,
And sit down at His footstool,
    And endless praises sing.

                               E. Hodder.

Waiting at the Well.   P.M.   Anon.

Hear, oh, hear the won-drous sto-ry! Let the winds and wa-ters tell—

'Tis the Christ, the King of glo-ry, Wait-ing at the well.

127

Give me this water, that I thirst not.—JOHN iv. 15.

1 LITTLE thought Samaria's daughter,
    On that ne'er-forgotten day,
That the tender Shepherd sought her,
    As a sheep astray;
That from sin He longed to win her—
    Knowing more than she could tell
Of the wretchedness within her,
    Waiting at the well.

        Hear, oh, hear the wondrous story! etc.

2 'Neath the stately palm-tree swaying,
   Listened she to words of truth:
   While each thought was backward straying
   O'er her wasted youth.
   Hastening homeward, with desire
   All His wondrous speech to tell,
   Asked she, "Is not this Messiah
   Waiting at the well?"

3 Living waters still are flowing,
   Full and free for all mankind,
   Blessings sweet on all bestowing;
   All a welcome find.
   All the world may come and prove Him;
   Every doubt will Christ dispel,
   When each heart shall truly love Him,
   Waiting at the well

Anon.

Wondrous Story. P.M. B. R. HANBY.

Tenderly.

CHORUS. *Joyful.*

'Tis the Lord! oh, wondrous sto - ry! 'Tis the Lord, the King of glo - ry! At His

feet we hum-bly fall— Crown Him! crown Him, Lord of all!

128 *We see Jesus . . . crowned with glory and honour.*—HEB. ii. 9.

1 WHO is He in yonder stall,
   At whose feet the shepherds fall?
   'Tis the Lord! oh, wondrous story! etc.

2 Who is He in deep distress
   Fasting in the wilderness?

3 Who is He the people bless
   For His words of gentleness?

4 Who is He to whom they bring
   All the sick and sorrowing?

5 Who is He that stands and weeps
   At the grave where Lazarus sleeps?

6 Who is He the gathering throng
   Greet with loud triumphant song?

7 Lo! at midnight, who is He
   Prays in dark Gethsemane?

8 Who is He on yonder tree
   Dies in grief and agony?

9 Who is He who from the grave
   Comes to succour, help, and save

10 Who is He who from His throne
    Rules through all the worlds alone?

B. R. Hanby

One Day.　　　11.10.11.10., with Chorus.　　　CHAS. H. MARSH.

Liv-ing, He loved me; dy-ing, He saved me; Bur-ied, He car-ried my sins far a-way; .. Ris-ing, He jus-ti-fied free-ly for ev-er: One day He's com-ing— Oh, glo-ri-ous day! ..

Words and Music by permission of Mrs. H. C. Dixon.

129

The day of Christ.—PHILIPPIANS i. 6.

1 ONE day when heaven was filled with His praises,
One day when sin was as black as could be,
Jesus came forth to be born of a virgin—
Dwelt amongst men, my example is He!

Living, He loved me; dying, He saved me, etc.

2 One day they led Him up Calvary's mountain,
   One day they nailed Him to die on the tree;
Suffering anguish, despised and rejected;
   Bearing our sins, my Redeemer is He!

3 One day they left Him alone in the garden,
   One day He rested, from suffering free;
Angels came down o'er His tomb to keep vigil;
   Hope of the hopeless, my Saviour is He!

4 One day the grave could conceal Him no longer,
   One day the stone rolled away from the door;
Then He arose, over death He had conquered;
   Now is ascended, my Lord evermore!

5 One day the trumpet will sound for His coming,
   One day the skies with His glory will shine;
Wonderful day, my belovèd ones bringing;
   Glorious Saviour, this Jesus is mine!

J. Wilbur Chapman.

Moravia.   S.M.   L. R. WEST.

Alternative Tunes, TRENTHAM, *No. 151, and* ST. BRIDE, *No. 157.*

130   *He said "It is finished."*—JOHN xix. 30.

1   O PERFECT life of love!
    All, all is finished now;
All that He left His throne above
    To do for us below.

2   No work is left undone
    Of all the Father willed;
His toil, His sorrows, one by one
    The Scriptures have fulfilled.

3   No pain that we can share
    But He has felt its smart;
All forms of human grief and care
    Have pierced that tender heart.

4   And on His thorn-crowned head,
    And on His sinless soul,
Our sins in all their guilt were laid,
    That He might make us whole.

5   In perfect love He dies—
    For me He dies, for me;
O all-atoning Sacrifice,
    I cling by faith to Thee.

6   In every time of need,
    Before the judgment-throne,
Thy work, O Lamb of God, I'll plea
    Thy merits, not my own.

7   Yet work, O Lord, in me
    As Thou for me hast wrought;
And let my love the answer be
    To grace Thy love has brought.

Sir H. W. Baker.

Park Langley.　　　　　9.8.9.8., D.　　　　　E. H. G. SARGENT.

131　　*The Lord whom ye seek shall suddenly come to His temple.*—MALACHI iii. 1.

1.

A CROWD fills the court of the temple,
　A sound as of praise fills the air,
Jerusalem thrills with emotion,
　The Lord of the temple is there!
In vain is the priestly displeasure,
　To silence the anthems that ring,
Hosanna! Hosanna! Hosanna!
　The children all joyfully sing.

2.

And if in this temple of worship,
　Where now we are met in His Name,
The Lord should appear in His beauty,
　Himself His own Gospel proclaim,
What anthems of grateful devotion
　Around Him would echo and ring,
Hosanna! Hosanna! Hosanna!
　The children would joyfully sing.

3.

Lord, make each young heart Thine own temple,
　Reveal Thy sweet presence within,
Illumine our minds by Thy coming,
　Expel every longing for sin;
For when in our souls we adore Thee,
　How pure the glad praise we shall bring;
Hosanna! Hosanna! Hosanna!
　The children will joyfully sing.

4.

And when in that temple of glory,
　Where falls never shadow of night,
Where sorrow and sin never sadden,
　And Thou shalt Thyself be the Light!
When round Thee the ransomed are thronging,
　High heaven with their praises will ring,
Hosanna! Hosanna! Hosanna!
　Thy children for ever will sing.

F. W. Goadby

132 A Little Ship.

C.M.

J. T. LIGHTWOOD.

Even the wind and the sea obey Him.—MARK iv. 41.

mf 1. A lit - tle ship was on the sea, It was a pret - ty sight:
3. And all but One were sore a - fraid Of sink - ing in the deep;
p 5. He to the storm says, "Peace; be still!" The ra - ging bil - lows cease;

It sailed a - long so plea - sant - ly, And all was calm and bright.
dim. His head was on a pil - low laid, And He was fast a - sleep.
The might - y winds o - bey His will, And all are hush'd to peace.

Verses 2, 4 and 6.

f 2. When, lo! a storm be - gan to rise, The wind grew loud and strong;
f 4. "Mas - ter, we per - ish: Mas - ter, save!" They cried. Their Mas - ter heard:
f 6. Oh! well we know it was the Lord, Our Sa - viour and our Friend,

D.C.

It blew the clouds a - cross the skies, It blew the waves a - long. . .
He rose, re - buked the wind and wave, And stilled them with a word. . .
Whose care of those who trust His word Will nev - er, nev - er end. . .

D. A. Thrupp.

Music Copyright. By permission of the National Sunday School Union.
Alternative Tune, BELMONT, *No.* 148.

Petition. 7.6.7.6., D. *From* HAYDN.

Alternative Tunes, MUNICH, *No.* 91, *and* DAY OF REST, *No.* 363.

To whom be glory for ever and ever.—HEB. xiii. 21.

133

1 WE sing a loving Jesus,
   Who left His throne above,
And came on earth to ransom
   The children of His love;
It is an oft-told story,
   And yet we love to tell
How Christ, the King of glory,
   Once deigned with man to dwell.

2 We sing a holy Jesus,
   No taint of sin defiled,
The Babe of David's city,
   The pure and stainless Child.
O teach us, blessèd Saviour,
   Thy heavenly grace to seek;
And let our whole behaviour,
   Like Thine, be mild and meek.

3 We sing a lowly Jesus:
   No kingly crown He had;
His heart was bowed with anguish;
   His face was marred and sad;

In deep humiliation
   He came, His work to do:
O Lord of our salvation,
   Let us be humble too.

4 We sing a mighty Jesus,
   Whose voice could raise the dead;
The sightless eyes He opened,
   The famished souls He fed.
Thou camest to deliver
   Mankind from sin and shame;
Redeemer and Life-giver,
   We praise Thy holy Name!

5 We sing a coming Jesus:
   The time is drawing near
When Christ with all His angels
   In glory shall appear.
Lord, save us, we entreat Thee,
   In this Thy day of grace,
That we may gladly meet Thee,
   And see Thee face to face.

Sarah Dowdney.

St. Agnes.   C.M.   J. B. Dykes.

My meditation of Him shall be sweet.—Psalm civ. 34.

134

1 Jesus, the very thought of Thee
  With sweetness fills my breast;
But sweeter far Thy face to see,
  And in Thy presence rest.

2 Nor voice can sing, nor heart can frame,
  Nor can the memory find
A sweeter sound than Thy blest Name,
  O Saviour of mankind!

3 Oh, hope of every contrite heart,
  Oh, joy of all the meek;
To those who fall, how kind Thou art!
  How good to those who seek!

4 But what to those who find? Ah! this
  Nor tongue nor pen can show;
The love of Jesus, what it is
  None but His loved ones know.

5 Jesus, our only joy be Thou,
  As Thou our prize wilt be;
Jesus, be Thou our glory now,
  And through eternity.

Bernard of Clairvaux, tr. E. Caswall.

Dublin.   C.M.   Sir J. Stevenson.

Our Lord Jesus, that great Shepherd of the sheep.—Heb. xiii. 20.

135

1 See Israel's gentle Shepherd stands,
  With all engaging charms:
Hark! how He calls the tender lambs
  And folds them in His arms.

2 "Permit them to approach," He cries,
  "Nor scorn their humble name"
For 'twas to bless such souls as these
  The Lord of angel's came.

3 The feeblest lamb amidst the flock
  Shall be its Shepherd's care;
While folded in the Saviour's arms,
  We're safe from every snare.

4 Ye little flock, with pleasure hear;
  Ye children, seek His face:
And fly with transport to receive
  The blessings of His grace.

P. Doddridge.

Harts.   7.7.7.7.   B. Milgrove.

136   *Though He was rich, yet for your sakes He became poor, that ye through*
His poverty might be rich.—2 Cor. viii. 9.

1 Christ is merciful and mild;
   He was once a little child;
   He whom heavenly hosts adore
   Lived on earth among the poor.

2 Thus He laid His glory by
   When for us He stooped to die;
   How I wonder when I see
   His unbounded love to me!

3 He the sick to health restored,
   To the poor He preached the word;

   Even children had a share
   Of His love and tender care.

4 Every bird can build its nest,
   Foxes have their place of rest;
   He by whom the world was made
   Had not where to lay His head.

5 He who is the Lord most high
   Then was poorer far than I,
   That I might hereafter be
   Rich to all eternity.
               J. Buckworth.

St. Drostane.   L.M.   J. B. Dykes.

Alternative Tune, Winchester New, *No.* 288.

137   *Behold, thy King cometh unto thee.*—Matt. xxi. 5.

1 Ride on! ride on in majesty!
   Hark! all the tribes "Hosanna!" cry;
   O Saviour meek, pursue Thy road,
   With palms and scattered garments strowed.

2 Ride on! ride on in majesty!
   In lowly pomp ride on to die:
   O Christ, Thy triumphs now begin
   O'er captive death and conquered sin.

3 Ride on! ride on in majesty!
   The angel armies of the sky

   Look down with sad and wondering eyes
   To see the approaching sacrifice.

4 Ride on! ride on in majesty!
   Thy last and fiercest strife is nigh:
   The Father on His sapphire throne;
   Awaits His own anointed Son.

5 Ride on! ride on in majesty!
   In lowly pomp ride on to die;
   Bow Thy meek head to mortal pain,
   Then take, O God, Thy power, and reign.
              H. H. Milman

SECTION IV.—The Lord Jesus Christ.
(8.) His Redeeming Love.

Ebenezer.   8.7.8.7., D.   T. J. WILLIAMS.

By permission of W. Gwenlyn Evans & Son, Carnarvon.
Alternative Tune, HYFRYDOL, *No.* 158.

He loved them unto the end.—JOHN xiii. 1.

138

1 Oh, the deep, deep love of Jesus!
  Vast, unmeasured, boundless, free;
Rolling as a mighty ocean
  In its fulness over me.
Underneath me, all around me,
  Is the current of Thy love;
Leading onward, leading homeward,
  To my glorious rest above.

2 Oh, the deep, deep love of Jesus!
  Spread His praise from shore to shore;
How He loveth, ever loveth,
  Changeth never, nevermore;
How He watches o'er His loved ones,
  Died to call them all His own;
How for them He intercedeth,
  Watcheth o'er them from the throne.

3 Oh, the deep, deep love of Jesus!
  Love of every love the best:
'Tis an ocean vast of blessing,
  'Tis a haven sweet of rest.
Oh, the deep, deep love of Jesus!
  'Tis a heaven of heavens to me;
And it lifts me up to glory,
  For it lifts me up to Thee.

S. Trevor Francis.

139 Jesus Died.   P.M.   B. R. PARKINSON.

1. There is a word I fain would speak—Je-sus died, Je-sus died... Eyes that weep and hearts that break; Jesus died, Jesus died. No music from the quivering string Could such sweet sounds of rapture bring; Oh! may I al ways love to sing— Je-sus died, Je-sus died.

Christ died for the ungodly.—ROM. v. 6.

2 Satan seeks my soul to have:
     Jesus died.
   Jesus died my soul to save:
     Jesus died.
   The holy Lord, the bleeding Lamb,
   The Crucified, the great I AM;
   There's life in every lovely Name:
     Jesus died.

2 And now I need not fear to pray:
     Jesus died.
   He washes all my sins away:
     Jesus died.
   He washes all my sins away,
   He is the Life, the Truth, the Way,
   And now to all men I can say—
     Jesus died.

4 'Twill soothe my heart with death in view:
     Jesus died.
   And bear me that cold river through:
     Jesus died.   [unclose,
   That word will heaven's bright gates
   Release me from my mortal woes,
   And bear me where His glory glows;
     Jesus died.

5 There is a word I fain would speak—
     Jesus lives.
   Eyes that weep and hearts that break;
     Jesus lives.
   No music from the quivering string
   Could such sweet sounds of rapture bring;
   Oh! may I always love to sing—
     Jesus lives.   *E. Paxton Hood.*

140 St. Austell.   5.5.6.5.   E. H. GLADSTONE SARGENT.

140

While we were yet sinners, Christ died for us.—ROM. v. 8.

1 GOD commends His love—
　Greater could not be:
While I was a sinner,
　Jesus died for me.

2 Justified by faith,
　I have peace with God:
In my heart the Spirit
　Sheds His love abroad.

3 Thus, where sin abounded,
　Grace did more abound:
And where death was reigning,
　Life in Christ I found.

4 Jesus, Son of God,
　Now Thy grace I see:
Thou who loved'st the sinner
　Gav'st Thyself for me.

G. Goodman.

Spohr.　　　　　8.6.8.6.8.6.　　　　L. SPOHR.

Alternative Tune, ST. SILAS, *No.* 368.

141 *The chastisement of our peace was upon Him; and with His stripes we are healed.*—ISA. liii. 5.

1 O CHRIST, what burdens bowed Thy head!
　Our load was laid on Thee;
Thou stoodest in the sinner's stead,
　Didst bear all ill for me.
A Victim led, Thy blood was shed!
　Now there's no load for me.

2 Death and the curse were in our cup:
　O Christ, 'twas full for Thee!
But Thou hast drained the last dark drop,
　'Tis empty now for me:
That bitter cup, love drank it up,
　Now blessing's draught for me.

3 Jehovah lifted up His rod:
　O Christ, it fell on Thee!
Thou wast sore stricken of Thy God;
　There's not one stroke for me.
Thy tears, Thy blood, beneath it flowed;
　Thy bruising healeth me.

4 The tempest's awful voice was heard;
　O Christ, it broke on Thee!
Thy open bosom was my ward,
　It braved the storm for me.
Thy form was scarred, Thy visage marred
　Now cloudless peace for me.

5 Jehovah bade His sword awake:
　O Christ, it woke 'gainst Thee;
Thy blood the flaming blade must slake,
　Thy heart its sheath must be.
All for my sake, my peace to make:
　Now sleeps that sword for me.

6 For me, Lord Jesus, Thou hast died,
　And I have died in Thee:
Thou'rt risen—my bands are all untied:
　And now Thou liv'st in me;
When purified, made white, and **tried**,
　Thy glory then for me.

Mrs. A. R. Cousin.

Can It be True?

P.M.

BOYTON SMITH.

Softly and slowly.

CHORUS. Solemnly.

For - give me, Lord, for it is true On Thee my guilt was laid;

My pun - ish-ment Thy bo - dy bore, By Thee my debt was paid.

142

Christ also hath once suffered . . . the just for the unjust, that He might bring us to God.—1 PETER iii. 18.

1 CAN it be true that Thou didst leave,
  For this cold, barren wild,
Thy heaven, that I might become
  God's own belovèd child?
  Forgive me, Lord, etc.

2 Can it be true that Thou didst bear,
  Upon the accursèd tree,
My load of sin, its curse, its sting,
  Its stripes, instead of me?

3 Can it be true that I have scorned
  The offer mercy made,
And vainly hoped myself to pay
  The debt Thy death has paid?

4 Can it be true that I still cling
  To earth and all my sin;
That I have closely barred the door,
  Lest Thou shouldst enter in?

5 Lord, enter now, possession take,
  And cleanse me from my sin;
Thy kingdom come, Thy will be done;
  Lord, reign Thyself within.

6 Oh, make me Thine! and give me grace
  To live for Thee alone.
Shine in my heart, till it becomes
  A mirror of Thine own.

J. Stephens.

Gideon. L.M. T. B. Southgate.

143 *We love Him, because He first loved us.*—1 John iv. 19.

1 It is a thing most wonderful,
Almost too wonderful to be, [heaven
That God's own Son should come from
And die to save a child like me.

2 And yet I know that it is true:
He came to this poor world below,
And wept and toiled and mourned and died,
Only because He loved us so.

3 I cannot tell how He could love
A child so weak and full of sin;
His love must be most wonderful,
If He could die my love to win.

4 I sometimes think about His cross,
And shut my eyes, and try to see

The cruel nails, and crown of thorns,
And Jesus crucified for me.

5 But even could I see Him die,
I could but see a little part
Of that great love, which, like a fire,
Is always burning in His heart.

6 It is most wonderful to know
His love for me so free and sure;
But 'tis more wonderful to see
My love for Him so faint and poor.

7 And yet I want to love Thee, Lord:
Oh, light the flame within my heart,
And I will love Thee more and more
Until I see Thee as Thou art!
W. W. How.

Hallelujah! What a Saviour! P.M.

Moderato. P. P. Bliss.

144 *A Man of Sorrows, and acquainted with grief.*—Isa. liii. 3.

1 "Man of Sorrows!" what a name
For the Son of God, who came
Ruined sinners to reclaim!
Hallelujah! what a Saviour!

2 Bearing shame and scoffing rude,
In my place condemned He stood;
Sealed my pardon with His blood:
Hallelujah! what a Saviour!

3 Guilty, vile, and helpless, we;
Spotless Lamb of God was He:

"Full atonement,"—can it be?
Hallelujah! what a Saviour!

4 "Lifted up" was He to die,
"It is finished!" was His cry:
Now in heaven exalted high:
Hallelujah! what a Saviour!

5 When He comes, our glorious King,
All His ransomed home to bring,
Then anew this song we'll sing:
"Hallelujah! what a Saviour!"
P. P. Bliss.

E

The Wonderful Story. 9.8 9 8., and Chorus. CHAS. H. GABRIEL.

CHORUS.

Oh, won - derful, wonderful sto - ry, The dear - est that ever was
Oh, wonder-ful sto - ry, oh, wonderful story, The dearest that ev - er, that

told, . . . I'll re - peat it in glo - ry The won - der - ful
ev - er was told, I'll re - peat it in glo - ry The

sto - ry, Where I . . . shall His beau-ty be - hold. . . .
won-der-ful sto - ry, Where I shall His beau - ty, His beauty be-hold.

145

*God forbid that I should glory, save in the cross of our Lord
Jesus Christ.—Gal. vi. 14.*

1 Oh, sweet is the story of Jesus,
   The wonderful Saviour of men,
Who suffered and died for the sinner—
   I'll tell it again and again!
     Oh, wonderful, wonderful story, etc.

2 He came from the mansions of glory;
   His blood as a ransom He gave,

To purchase eternal redemption,
   And oh. He is mighty to save!

3 His mercy flows on like a river,
   His love is unmeasured and free ;
His grace is for ever sufficient,
   It reaches and purifies me.
          Chas. H. Gabriel.

Nothing but the Blood of Jesus. P.M.   GEORGE F. KNOWLES.

CHORUS.

Oh, pre - cious is the flow, That makes me white as snow!

No oth - er fount I know, Nothing but the blood of Je - sus!

146   *Without shedding of blood is no remission.*—HEB. ix. 22.

1.

WHAT can wash away my stain?
Nothing but the blood of Jesus!
What can make me whole again?
Nothing but the blood of Jesus!
Oh, precious is the flow, etc.

2.

For my cleansing this I see—
Nothing but the blood of Jesus!
For my pardon this my plea—
Nothing but the blood of Jesus!

3.

Nothing can for sin atone—
Nothing but the blood of Jesus!
Naught of good that I have done—
Nothing but the blood of Jesus!

4.

This is all my hope and peace—
Nothing but the blood of Jesus!
This is all my righteousness—
Nothing but the blood of Jesus!
R. Lowry.

8.5.8.3., with Refrain.

Precious, Precious Blood of Jesus

J. MOUNTAIN.

Tenderly.

Pre-cious, precious blood of Je - sus, Shed on Cal - va - ry, . .

Oh, be - lieve it; oh, re - ceive it, 'Tis . . for . . thee.

147 *Christ was once offered to bear the sins of many.*—HEB. ix. 28.

1 PRECIOUS, precious blood of Jesus,
  Shed on Calvary;
  Shed for rebels, shed for sinners,
  Shed for thee!

    Precious, precious blood of Jesus,
    Shed on Calvary,
    Oh, believe it; oh, receive it,
    'Tis for thee!

2 Precious, precious blood of Jesus,
  Let it make thee whole;
  Let it flow in mighty cleansing,
  O'er thy soul.

3 Though thy sins are red like crimson,
  Deep in scarlet glow,
  Jesus' precious blood shall wash thee
  White as snow.

4 Precious blood that hath redeemed us!
  All the price is paid!
  Perfect pardon now is offered,
  Peace is made.

5 Now the holiest with boldness
  We may enter in;
  For the open fountain cleanseth
  From all sin.

6 Precious blood, by this we conquer
  In the fiercest fight,
  Sin and Satan overcoming
  By its might.

7 Precious blood whose full atonement
  Makes us nigh to God!
  Precious blood, our way of glory,
  Praise and laud.

Frances R. Havergal.

Belmont. C.M. Arr. from W. Gardiner's "Sacred Melodies."

1. There is a foun-tain filled with blood Drawn from Im-man-uel's veins;

D.C. I do be-lieve, I will be-lieve, That Je - sus died for me,

D.C. for Chorus.

And sin-ners plung'd be-neath that flood, Lose all their guilt - y stains.

That on the cross He shed His blood, From sin to set me free.

Alternative Tune, Evan, *No.* 587.

148 *A Fountain opened . . . for sin.*—Zech. xiii. 1.

2 The dying thief rejoiced to see
That fountain in his day ;
And there may I, though vile as he,
Wash all my sins away.

3 Dear dying Lamb, Thy precious blood
Shall never lose its power,
Till all the ransomed church of God
Be saved, to sin no more.

4 E'er since, by faith, I saw the stream
Thy flowing wounds supply,
Redeeming love has been my theme,
And shall be till I die.

5 Then in a nobler, sweeter song
I'll sing Thy power to save,
When this poor lisping, stammering tongue
Lies silent in the grave. *W. Cowper.*

Abney. C.M. Asa Hull.

1. A - las! and did my Sa-viour bleed? And did my Sovereign die?

D.C. Help me, dear Sa - viour, Thee to own, And ev - er faith-ful be;

D.C. for Chorus.

Would He de-vote that sa-cred head For such a worm as I?

And when Thou sit - test on Thy Throne, O Lord, re-mem-ber me!

Alternative Tune, Belmont, *No.* 148.

149 *Lord, remember me when Thou comest into Thy kingdom.*—Luke xxiii. 42.

2 Was it for sins that I had done
He groaned upon the tree?
Amazing pity! grace unknown!
And love beyond degree!

3 Well might the sun in darkness hide,
And shut his glories in,
When Christ, the mighty Maker, died
For man, the creature's sin.

4 Thus might I hide my blushing face
While His dear cross appears,
Dissolve my heart in thankfulness,
And melt mine eyes to tears.

5 But drops of grief can ne'er repay
The debt of love I owe:
Here, Lord, I give myself away:
'Tis all that I can do. *Isaac Watts.*

150 Kelso. [FIRST TUNE.]   6.6.8.6.10.12.   Anon.

Seamill. [SECOND TUNE.]   6.6.8.6.10.12.   R. HUDSON POPE.

150

One sacrifice for sins for ever.—HEB. X. 12.

No blood, no altar now:
　The sacrifice is o'er;
No flame, no smoke ascends on high,
　The lamb is slain no more:
But richer blood has flowed from nobler veins
To purge the soul from guilt, and cleanse the reddest stains.

2　We thank Thee for the blood,
　　The blood of Christ, Thy Son:
　The blood by which our peace is made,
　　Our victory is won;
Great victory o'er hell, and sin, and woe,
That needs no second fight, and leaves no second foe.

3　We thank Thee for the grace,
　　Descending from above,
　That overflows our widest guilt—
　　The Eternal Father's love:
Love of the Father's everlasting Son,
Love of the Holy Ghost—Jehovah, Three in One.

4　We thank Thee for the hope,
　　So glad, and sure, and clear,
　It holds the drooping spirit up
　　Till the long dawn appear:
Fair hope! with what a sunshine does it cheer
Our roughest path on earth, our dreariest desert here.　*H. Bonar.*

Trentham.　　　　　　　　S.M.　　　　　　　R. JACKSON.

Alternative Tune, ST. MICHAEL, *No. 275.*

151
*This Man receiveth sinners, and eateth with them.—*LUKE xv. 2.

1　Jesus, the sinner's Friend!
　　We hide ourselves in Thee:
　God looks upon Thy sprinkled blood,—
　　It is our only plea.

2　He hears Thy precious Name,
　　We claim it as our own:
　The Father must accept and bless
　　His well-beloved Son.

3　He sees Thy spotless robe,
　　It covers all our sin;
　The golden gates have welcomed Thee,
　　And we may enter in.

4　Thou hast fulfilled the law,
　　And we are justified:
　Ours is the blessing, Thine the curse;
　　We live, for Thou hast died!

5　Jesus, the sinner's Friend!
　　We cannot speak Thy praise!
　No mortal voice can sing the song
　　That ransomed hearts would raise.

6　But when before the throne,
　　Upon the glassy sea,
　Clothed in our blood-bought robes of white,
　　We stand complete in Thee:

7　Jesus, we'll give Thee then
　　Such praises as are meet,
　And cast ten thousand golden crowns,
　　Adoring, at Thy feet!　*Mrs. C. Pennefather.*

3 Stand all Amazed.　　　P.M., and Chorus.　　　CHAS. H. GABRIEL.

Oh, it is won-der-ful that He should

care for me Enough to die for me! Oh, it is won-der-ful, won-derful to me!
wonderful!　　　wonderful!

152　　　*The love of Christ which passeth knowledge.—*EPH. iii. 19.

1 I STAND all amazed at the love Jesus offers me,
　Confused at the grace that so fully He proffers me;
　I tremble to know that for me He was crucified—
　That for me, a sinner, He suffered, He bled, He died.
　　Oh, it is wonderful, etc.

2 I marvel that He should descend from His throne divine
　To rescue a soul so rebellious and proud as mine;
　That He should extend His great love unto such as I;
　Sufficient to own, to redeem, and to justify.

3 I think of His hands pierced and bleeding to pay the debt!
　Such mercy, such love and devotion can I forget?
　No, no! I will praise and adore at the mercy-seat,
　Until at the glorified throne I kneel at His feet.

C. H. Gabriel.

More than Tongue can Tell! 8.8.8.6., and Chorus.   J. E. HALL.

CHORUS.

His love is more than tongue can tell! His
tell! than tongue can tell!

love is more than tongue can tell! The love that Je-sus had for
tell! than tongue can tell!

me . . . Is more than tongue can tell!

Alternative Tune (without Chorus), SILVERSTONE, *No.* 411.
Greater love hath no man than this.—JOHN xv. 13.

153

1 THE love that Jesus had for me,
To suffer on the cruel tree,
That I a ransomed soul might be,
Is more than tongue can tell!
His love is more, etc.

2 The bitter sorrow that He bore,
And, oh, the crown of thorns He wore,
That I might live for evermore,
Is more that tongue can tell!

3 The peace I have in Him, my Lord,
Who pleads before the throne of God
The merit of His precious blood,
Is more than tongue can tell!

4 The joy that comes when He is near,
The rest He gives, so free from fear,
The hope in Him, so bright and clear,
Is more than tongue can tell!

J. E. Hall.

E*

Rutherford.　　　　7.6.7.6., D.　　　　D'Urhan.

154　　*While we were yet sinners Christ died for us.*—Rom. v. 8.

1 Oh, teach me what it meaneth—
　That cross uplifted high,
With One—the Man of Sorrows—
　Condemned to bleed and die!
Oh, teach me what it cost Thee
　To make a sinner whole;
And teach me, Saviour, teach me
　The value of a soul!

2 Oh, teach me what it meaneth—
　That sacred crimson tide—
The blood and water flowing
　From Thine own wounded side.
Teach me that if none other
　Had sinned, but I alone,
Yet still, Thy blood, Lord Jesus,
　Thine only, must atone.

3 Oh, teach me what it meaneth—
　Thy love beyond compare,
The love that reacheth deeper
　Than depths of self-despair!
Yea, teach me, till there gloweth
　In this cold heart of mine
Some feeble, pale reflection
　Of that pure love of Thine.

4 Oh, teach me what it meaneth,
　For I am full of sin;
And grace alone can reach me,
　And love alone can win.
Oh, teach me, for I need Thee—
　I have no hope beside,—
The chief of all the sinners
　For whom the Saviour died!

Verse 5 on next page.

5 O Infinite Redeemer!
I bring no other plea,
Because Thou dost invite me
I cast myself on Thee.
Because Thou dost accept me
I love and I adore;
Because Thy love constraineth,
I'll praise Thee evermore!

Lucy A. Bennett.

Old, Yet Ever New.   C.M., with Chorus.   W. A. Williams.

Alternative Tune (*without Chorus*), St. Agnes, No. 134.

They sang as it were a new song before the throne.—Rev. xiv. 3.

155

1 There is a story sweet to hear,
I love to tell it too:
It fills my heart with hope and cheer,
'Tis old, yet ever new.
'Tis old, yet ever new! etc.

2 They tell me God the Son came down
From His bright throne to die,
That I might wear a starry crown,
And dwell with Him on high.

3 They say He bore the cross for me,
And suffered in my place,
That I might always happy be,
And ransomed by His grace.

4 Oh, wondrous love, so great, so vast,
So boundless, and so free!
Low at Thy feet my all I cast;
I covet only Thee.

W. A. Williams.

Horsley. [FIRST TUNE.]   C.M.   W. HORSLEY.

Alternative Tune (third line in each verse repeated), REST, *No.* 402.

156

There they crucified Him.—LUKE xxiii. 33.

1 THERE is a green hill far away,
   Without a city wall,
Where the dear Lord was crucified,
   Who died to save us all.

2 We may not know, we cannot tell,
   What pains He had to bear ;
But we believe it was for us
   He hung and suffered there.

3 He died that we might be forgiven,
   He died to make us good,
That we might go at last to heaven,
   Saved by His precious blood.

4 There was no other good enough
   To pay the price of sin,
He only could unlock the gate
   Of heaven, and let us in.

5 Oh, dearly, dearly has He loved !
   And we must love Him too,
And trust in His redeeming blood,
   And try His works to do.

Mrs. C. F. Alexander.

Lambourne. [SECOND TUNE.]*   C.M.D.   R. S. WILLIS.

* NOTE.—When the Second Tune (C.M.D.) is used, verse 5 forms second half of first double verse.

157 St. Bride. S.M. S. HOWARD.

Alternative Tune, AUGUSTINE, *No.* 418.

157   *The Lord hath laid on Him the iniquity of us all.*—ISA. liii. 6.

1 BEHOLD the amazing sight!
  The Saviour lifted high;
The Son of God, His soul's delight,
  Expires in agony.

2 For whom, for whom, my heart,
  Were all those sorrows borne?
Why did He feel that piercing smart,
  And wear that crown of thorn?

3 For us in love He bled,
  For us in anguish died;
'Twas love that bowed His sacred head,
  And pierced His precious side.

4 We see, and we adore,
  We trust that dying love;
We feel its strong attractive power
  To lift our souls above.

5 Behold the amazing sight!
  Nor trace His griefs alone,
But from the cross pursue our flight
  To His triumphant throne.
              P. Doddridge.

Hyfrydol. 8.7.8.7. D. R. H. Pritchard.

CHORUS.

Yes, I'll sing the won-drous sto-ry Of the Christ who died for me;

Sing it with the saints in glo-ry, Gathered by the crys-tal sea.

158 *The Son of God, who loved me, and gave Himself for me.*—GAL. ii. 20.

1 I WILL sing the wondrous story
  Of the Christ who died for me;
  How He left His home in glory,
  For the cross on Calvary.
    Yes, I'll sing, etc.

2 I was lost: but Jesus found me—
  Found the sheep that went astray;
  Threw His loving arms around me,
  Drew me back into His way.

3 I was bruised: but Jesus healed me—
  Faint was I from many a fall;
  Sight was gone, and fears possessed me:
  But He freed me from them all.

4 Days of darkness still come o'er me;
  Sorrow's paths I often tread:
  But the Saviour still is with me,
  By His hand I'm safely led.

5 He will keep me till the river
    Rolls its waters at my feet:
  Then He'll bear me safely over,
    Where the loved ones I shall meet.
        F. H. Rawley.

I will Pass Over You. C.M., and Chorus. J. McGRANAHAN.

It is His word, God's pre-cious word, It stands for ev-er true;
It is His word, God's pre-cious word,

"When I the Lord shall see the blood, I will pass o-ver you."
When I the Lord shall see the blood,

Words and Music by permission of Mrs. H. C. Dixon.
Alternative Tune (without Chorus), WESTMINSTER, *No.* 62.

159 *When I see the blood, I will pass over you.*—EXODUS xii. 13.

1 WHEN God of old the way of life
  Would teach to all His own,
  He placed them safe beyond the reach
  Of death, by blood alone.
    It is His word, etc.

2 By Christ, the sinless Lamb of God,
  The precious blood was shed,
  When He fulfilled God's holy word,
  And suffered in our stead.

3 O soul, for thee salvation thus
  By God is freely given;
  The blood of Christ atones for sin,
  And makes us meet for heaven.

4 The wrath of God that was our due,
  Upon the Lamb was laid;
  And by the shedding of His blood
  The debt for us was paid.

5 How calm the judgment hour shall pass
  To all who do obey
  The word of God, and trust the blood,
  And make that word their stay!
    El Nathan.

Bass View.

6.5.6.5., D.

R. HUDSON POPE.

160

All we like sheep have gone astray.—ISA. liii. 6.

1 SHEEP without a shepherd
    We have gone astray,
Turning in our blindness
    Each to his own way;
But upon His Servant
    God in grace has laid
All our guilt and trespass
    Who the debt has paid.

2 Yet when we beheld Him,
    Beauty was there none,
That we should desire Him
    Or His title own;
We esteemed Him stricken,
    Smitten of His God,
Man of grief and sorrows
    Bruised beneath the rod.

3 'Twas for our transgressions
    He was wounded sore,
And for our iniquities
    He the bruising bore;
By the bitter scourging
    He secured our peace,
By His stripes so many
    Brought us sweet release.

4 Of the generation
    Living in His day
Who could tell the mystery,
    Or believing say:
" For His people's trespass
    He has suffered thus,
And His bitter portion
    Was to ransom us."

5 As a lamb He suffered,
    To the slaughter brought,
" Sheep before her shearers,'
    Dumb, He answered not;
Of His soul's deep travail
    He the fruit shall see,
And in many thousands
    Satisfied shall be.

George Goodman.

Oh, Make me Understand it.   P.M.   K. A. M. KELLY.

CHORUS. *A trifle slower.*

Oh, make me un - der-stand it, Help me to take it in, . . .

What it meant to Thee, the Ho - ly One, To bear a - way my sin. . . .

161   *That thou mightest know the certainty of those things.*—LUKE i. 4.

1 GIVE me a sight, O Saviour,
   Of Thy wondrous love to me,
   Of the love that brought Thee down to
   To die on Calvary.   [earth,
      Oh, make me understand it, etc.

2 Was it the nails, O Saviour,
   That bound Thee to the tree?
   Nay, 'twas Thine everlasting love,
   Thy love for me, for me.

3 Oh, wonder of all wonders,
   That through Thy death for me,
   My open sins, my secret sins,
   Can all forgiven be!

4 Then melt my heart, O Saviour,
   Bend me, yes, break me down,
   Until I own Thee Conqueror,
   And Lord and Sovereign crown.

                        K. A. M. Kelly

The Loving Shepherd.

DUET.   P.M.   WM. J. KIRKPATRICK.

CHORUS.   poco rit.

Out in the des-ert they wan-der, Hungry and helpless and cold; . .

f a tempo.

Oft to the res-cue He hast - ens, Bringing them back to the fold. . .
4th verse. we'll hast - en,

162   *I am the good Shepherd, and know My sheep.*—JOHN x. 14.

1 DEAR to the heart of the Shepherd,
   Dear are the sheep of His fold;
  Dear is the love that He gives them;
   Dearer than silver or gold.
  Dear to the heart of the Shepherd,
   Dear are His "other" lost sheep;
  Over the mountains He follows,
   Over the waters so deep.
    Out in the desert, etc.

2 Dear to the heart of the Shepherd,
   Dear are the lambs of His fold;
  Some from the pastures are straying,
   Hungry and helpless and cold.
  See, the Good Shepherd is seeking,
   Seeking the lambs that are lost;
  Bringing them in with rejoicing,
   Saved at such infinite cost.
    Out in the desert, etc.

3 Dear to the heart of the Shepherd,
  Dear are the "ninety and nine,"
Dear are the sheep that have wandered
  Out in the desert to pine.
Hark! He is earnestly calling,
  Tenderly pleading to-day;
"Will you not seek for My lost ones,
  Far from my shelter astray?"
    Out in the desert, etc.

4 Green are the pastures inviting,
  Sweet are the waters and still;

Lord, we will answer Thee gladly,
  "Yes, blessèd Master, we will!
Make us Thy true under-shepherds,
  Give us a love that is deep,
Send us out into the desert,
  Seeking Thy wandering sheep."
Out in the desert they wander,
  Hungry and helpless and cold;
Oft to the rescue we'll hasten,
  Bringing them back to the fold.

Mrs. Mary B. Wingate.

Wondrous Love! C.M., and Chorus. W. G. FISCHER.

CHORUS.

Oh, 'twas love, 'twas won-drous love! The love of God to me;
It brought my Sa-viour from a-bove, To die on Cal-va-ry.

163 *God so loved the world.*—JOHN iii. 16.

1 GOD loved the world of sinners lost
  And ruined by the Fall.
Salvation full, at highest cost,
  He offers free to all.
    Oh, 'twas love, etc.

2 E'en now by faith I claim Him mine,
  The risen Son of God.
Redemption by His death I find,
  And cleansing through the blood.

3 Believing ones, rejoicing go;
  There shall to you be given
A glorious foretaste, here below,
  Of endless life in heaven.

4 Of victory now o'er Satan's power
  Let all the ransomed sing,
And triumph, in the dying hour,
  Through Christ the Lord, our King.

Mrs. M. M. Stockton.

St. Christian. 8.7.8 7.8.7. P. G. LARBALESTIER.

Alternative Tune, DISMISSAL, *No.* 608.

164 *It is finished!*—JOHN xix. 30.

1.

HARK! the voice of love and mercy
　　Sounds aloud from Calvary;
See! it rends the rocks asunder,
　　Shakes the earth, and veils the sky:
　　　" It is finished! "
　　Hear the dying Saviour cry.

2.

" It is finished! " Oh, what pleasure
　　Do the wondrous words afford!
Heavenly blessings without measure
　　Flow to us through Christ the Lord:
　　　" It is finished! "
　　Saints the dying words record!

3.

Finished all the types and shadows
　　Of the ceremonial law,
Finished what our God had promised;
　　Death and hell no more shall awe.
　　　" It is finished! "
　　Saints, from hence your comfort draw.

4.

Saints and angels shout His praises!
　　Children, join to sing the same!
All on earth and all in heaven
　　Join to praise Immanuel's Name!
　　　Hallelujah!
　　Endless glory to the Lamb!

J. Evans.

SECTION IV.—The Lord Jesus Christ.
(4.) His Resurrection and Ascension.

Victory. 8.8.8.4. C. P. DA PALESTRINA.

Al - le - lu - ia! Al - le - lu - ia! Al - le - lu - ia!

Org.

165

O sing unto the Lord a new song; for He hath done marvellous things.—PSALM xcviii. 1, 2.

1 ALLELUIA! Alleluia! Alleluia!
The strife is o'er, the battle done;
The victory of life is won;
The song of triumph has begun.
    Alleluia!

2 The powers of death have done their worst,
But Christ their legions hath dispersed;
Let shouts of holy joy outburst.
    Alleluia!

3 The three sad days have quickly sped:
He rises glorious from the dead;
All glory to our risen Head!
    Alleluia!

4 He brake the bonds of death and hell;
The bars from heaven's high portals fell;
Let hymns of praise His triumph tell.
    Alleluia!

5 Lord, by the stripes which wounded Thee,
From death's dread sting Thy servants free,
That we may live, and sing to Thee;
    Alleluia!

Tr. from the Latin by Rev. F. Pott.

Christ Arose! P.M. R. LOWRY.

CHORUS. *Faster.*

Up from the grave He a - rose, With a might -y triumph o'er His foes ;
He a-rose! He a-rose!

He a - rose a Vic-tor from the dark do - main, And He lives for ev - er with His

saints to reign ! He a - rose ! He a - rose ! Hal-le - lu - jah ! Christ a - rose !
He a-rose ! He a-rose!

166 *This Jesus hath God raised up, whereof we all are witnesses.*—ACTS ii. **32.**

1 Low in the grave He lay—
   Jesus, my Saviour !
   Waiting the coming day—
   Jesus, my Lord !
      Up from the grave He arose, etc.

2 Vainly they watch His bed—
   Jesus, my Saviour !
   Vainly they seal the dead—
   Jesus, my Lord !

3 Death cannot keep his prey—
   Jesus, my Saviour !
   He tore the bars away—
   Jesus, my Lord !
                    R. Lowry

St. Albinus. 7.8.7.8.4. H. J. GAUNTLETT.

167 *Behold, I am alive for evermore.*—REV. i. 18.

1 JESUS lives! Thy terrors now
   Can, O Death, no more appal us;
   Jesus lives! by this we know
   Thou, O Grave, canst not enthral us.
       Alleluia!

2 Jesus lives! henceforth is death
   But the gate of life immortal;
   This shall calm our trembling breath
   When we pass its gloomy portal.
       Alleluia!

3 Jesus lives! for us He died;
   Then, alone to Jesus living,
   Pure in heart may we abide,
   Glory to our Saviour giving.
       Alleluia!

4 Jesus lives! our hearts know well
   Naught from us His love shall sever;
   Life, nor death, nor powers of hell
   Tear us from His keeping ever.
       Alleluia!

5 Jesus lives! to Him the throne
   Over all the world is given;
   May we go where He is gone,
   Rest and reign with Him in heaven.
       Alleluia!
       F. E. Cox. (tr.)

Church Triumphant. L.M. J. W. ELLIOTT.

By permission of Novello and Company, Limited.
Alternative Tune, MAINZER, *No.* 60.

168 *I am He that liveth, and was dead.*—REV. i. 18.

1 I KNOW that my Redeemer lives:
   What comfort this sweet sentence gives!
   He lives, He lives, who once was dead;
   He lives, my everlasting Head.

2 He lives, triumphant from the grave;
   He lives, eternally to save;
   He lives, all glorious in the sky;
   He lives, exalted there on high.

3 He lives, to bless me with His love,
   And still He pleads for me above;

He lives to raise me from the grave,
And me eternally to save.

4 He lives, my kind, wise, constant Friend;
   Who still will keep me to the end;
   He lives, and while He lives I'll sing,
   Jesus, my Prophet, Priest, and King.

5 He lives my mansion to prepare;
   And He will bring me safely there;
   He lives, all glory to His Name!
   Jesus, unchangeably the same!
       S. Medley.

Easter Hymn. 7.7.7.7., with Hallelujah. H. CAREY.

1. Christ, the Lord, is ris'n to - day: Hal - le - lu - jah!

Sons of men and an - gels say, Hal - le - lu - jah!

Raise your joys and tri-umphs high; Hal - le - lu - jah!

Sing, ye heav'ns; thou earth, re - ply, Hal - le - lu - jah!

169 *The Lord is risen indeed.*—LUKE xxiv. 34.

2 Love's redeeming work is done;
Fought the fight, the battle won:
Lo! our Sun's eclipse is o'er;
Lo! He sets in blood no more.

3 Vain, the stone, the watch, the seal,
Christ hath burst the gates of hell:
Death in vain forbids Him rise!
Christ hath opened paradise.

4 Lives again our glorious King!
Where, O death, is now thy sting?
Once He died our souls to save;
Where thy victory, O grave?

5 Soar we now where Christ hath led,
Following our exalted Head:
Made like Him, like Him we rise,
Ours the cross, the grave, the skies.

6 Hail the Lord of earth and heaven,
Praise to Thee by both be given;
Thee we greet triumphant now,
Hail, the Resurrection Thou!

C. Wesley.

Now is Christ risen from the dead.—1 Cor. xv. 20.

170

(To Tune on opposite page.)

1 Jesus Christ is risen to-day,
  Hallelujah !
 Our triumphant holy day,
  Hallelujah !
 Who did once, upon the cross,
  Hallelujah !
 Suffer to redeem our loss.
  Hallelujah !

2 Hymns of praise then let us sing,
  Hallelujah !
 Unto Christ, our heavenly King,
  Hallelujah !
 Who endured the cross and grave,
  Hallelujah !
 Sinners to redeem and save.
  Hallelujah !

3 But the pains which He endured,
  Hallelujah !
 Our salvation have procured ;
  Hallelujah !
 Now above the sky He's King,
  Hallelujah !
 Where the angels ever sing
  "Hallelujah !"

Anon.

Würtemberg. 7.7.7.7.4. J. Rosenmuller.

171 *The Prince of life, whom God hath raised from the dead.*—Acts iii. 15.

1 Christ the Lord is risen again ;
 Christ hath broken every chain ;
 Hark ! angelic voices cry,
 Singing evermore on high,
  Alleluia !

2 He, who gave for us His life,
 Who for us endured the strife,
 Is our Paschal Lamb to-day ;
 We too sing for joy, and say
  Alleluia !

3 He, who bore the pain and loss
 Comfortless upon the cross,
 Lives in glory now on high,
 Pleads for us, and hears our cry ;
  Alleluia !

4 He, who slumbered in the grave,
 Is exalted now to save ;
 Now through Christendom it rings
 That the Lamb is King of kings.
  Alleluia !

5 Now He bids us tell abroad
 How the lost may be restored,
 How the penitent forgiven,
 How we too may enter heaven.
  Alleluia !

6 Thou, our Paschal Lamb indeed,
 Christ, Thy ransomed people feed ;
 Take our sins and guilt away,
 That we all may sing for aye
  Alleluia !

Tr from M. Weisse by C. Winkworth.

Fortunatus.   11s., five lines.   Sir ARTHUR S. SULLIVAN.

By permission of Novello and Company, Limited.

172   *Very early in the morning, the first day of the week.*—MARK xvi. 2.

1 " WELCOME, happy morning!" age to age shall say;
Hell to-day is vanquished; Heaven is won to-day!
Lo! the Dead is living, God for evermore!
Him, their true Creator, all His works adore.
    " Welcome, happy morning!" age to age shall say.

2 Earth with joy confesses, clothing her for spring,
All good gifts returned with her returning King:
Bloom in every meadow, leaves on every bough,
Speak His sorrows ended, hail His triumph now.
    Hell to-day is vanquished; Heaven is won to-day!

3 Months in due succession, days of lengthening light,
Hours and passing moments praise Thee in their flight;
Brightness of the morning, sky and fields and sea,
Vanquisher of darkness, bring their praise to Thee.
    " Welcome, happy morning!" age to age shall say.

4 Maker and Redeemer, Life and Health of all,
   Thou from heaven beholding human nature's fall,
   Of the Father's Godhead true and only Son,
   Manhood to deliver, manhood didst put on.
     Hell to-day is vanquished; Heaven is won to-day!

5 Thou, of Life the Author, death didst undergo,
   Tread the path of darkness, saving strength to show :
   Come, then, True and Faithful, now fulfil Thy word;
   'Tis Thine own third morning! Rise, O buried Lord!
     " Welcome, happy morning!" age to age shall say.

6 Loose the souls long prisoned, bound with Satan's chain;
   All that now is fallen raise to life again,
   Show Thy face in brightness, bid the nations see ;
   Bring again our daylight: day returns with Thee!
     Hell to-day is vanquished ; Heaven is won to-day !
                          Tr. by *J. Ellerton.*

St. Magnus.   **C.M.**   J. CLARK.

173   *We see Jesus . . . . . crowned with glory and honour.*—HEB. ii. 9.

1 THE head that once was crowned with
   Is crowned with glory now;   [thorns
   A royal diadem adorns
   The mighty Victor's brow.

2 The highest place that heaven affords
   Is His by sovereign right,
   The King of kings, the Lord of lords,
   And heaven's eternal Light.

3 The joy of all who dwell above,
   The joy of all below,
   To whom He manifests His love,
   And grants His Name to know.

4 To them the cross, with all its shame,
   With all its grace, is given ;
   Their name an everlasting name,
   Their joy the joy of heaven.

5 They suffer with their Lord below,
   They reign with Him above ;
   Their profit and their joy to know
   The mystery of His love.

6 The cross He bore is life and health,
   Though shame and death to Him :
   His people's hope, His people's wealth,
   Their everlasting theme.
                       T. Kelly.

Hermas.

6.5.6.5. D., and Chorus.

Frances R. Havergal.

CHORUS.

All His work is end - ed;

Joy - ful-ly we sing— Je-sus hath as-cend - ed! Glo-ry to our King!

174 *Him hath God exalted . . . to be a Prince and a Saviour.*—Acts v. 31.

1 GOLDEN harps are sounding,
   Angel voices sing,
Pearly gates are opened,
   Opened for the King;
Christ, the King of glory,
   Jesus, King of love,
Is gone up in triumph
   To His throne above.

     All His work is ended, etc.

2 He, who came to save us,
  He, who bled and died,
  Now is crowned with glory
  At His Father's side;
  Never more to suffer,
  Never more to die,
  Jesus, King of Glory,
  Has gone up on high!

3 Praying for His children,
  In that blessèd place;
  Calling them to glory,
  Sending them His grace;
  His bright home preparing,
  Faithful ones, for you;
  Jesus ever liveth,
  Ever loveth too.

  Frances R. Havergal.

Regent Square.   8.7.8.7.8.7.   H. SMART.

175   *And He hath on His vesture and on His thigh a Name written, King of kings and Lord of lords.*—REV. xix. 16.

1 LOOK, ye saints, the sight is glorious,
    See the "Man of Sorrows" now
  From the fight return victorious:
    Every knee to Him shall bow!
    Crown Him! crown Him!
  Crowns become the Victor's brow.

2 Crown the Saviour! angels, crown Him!
    Rich the trophies Jesus brings;
  In the seat of power enthrone Him,
    While the vault of heaven rings!
    Crown Him! crown Him!
  Crown the Saviour "King of kings."

3 Sinners in derision crowned Him,
    Mocking thus the Saviour's claim;
  Saints and angels crowd around Him,
    Own His title, praise His Name.
    Crown Him! crown Him!
  Spread abroad the Victor's fame.

4 Hark, the bursts of acclamation!
    Hark, those loud triumphant chords.
  Jesus takes the highest station,
    Oh, what joy the sight affords!
    Crown Him! crown Him,
  "King of kings, and Lord of lords!"

  T. Kelly.

SECTION IV.—The Lord Jesus Christ.
(5.) His Second Coming.

Beverley. *In quick time.*   P.M.   W. H. MONK.

176   *He . . . saith, Surely I come quickly. Amen. Even so, come, Lord Jesus.—*REV. xxii. 20.

1 THOU art coming, O my Saviour,
    Thou art coming, O my King,
  In Thy beauty all-resplendent,
  In Thy glory all-transcendent ;
    Well may we rejoice and sing :
  Coming ! In the opening east
  Herald brightness slowly swells ;
  Coming ! O my glorious Priest,
    Hear we not Thy golden bells ?

2 Thou art coming, Thou art coming :
    We shall meet Thee on Thy way,
  We shall see Thee, we shall know Thee,
  We shall bless Thee, we shall show Thee
    All our hearts could ever say :
  What an anthem that will be,
    Ringing out our love to Thee,
  Pouring out our rapture sweet
    At Thine own all-glorious feet !

3 Thou art coming ; we are waiting
    With a hope that cannot fail
  Asking not the day or hour,
  Resting on Thy word of power,
    Anchored safe within the veil.
  Time appointed may be long,
    But the vision must be sure ;
  Certainty shall make us strong,
    Joyful patience can endure.

4 Oh, the joy to see Thee reigning,
    Thee, my own belovèd Lord !
  Every tongue Thy Name confessing,
  Worship, honour, glory, blessing,
    Brought to Thee with one accord ;
  Thee, my Master, and my Friend
    Vindicated and enthroned,
  Unto earth's remotest end
    Glorified, adored, and owned !

Frances R. Havergal.

Christ Returneth.   P.M.   J. McGranahan.

O Lord Je - sus, how long? How long ere we shout the glad song?—Christ re - turn-eth, Hal-le - lu-jah! Hal-le - lu-jah! A - men, Hal-le - lu-jah! A - men.

177   *I will come again, and receive you unto Myself.*—John xiv. 3.

1 It may be at morn, when the day is awaking,
   When sunlight through darkness and shadow is breaking
   That Jesus will come in the fulness of glory,
      To receive from the world "His own."
         Oh, Lord Jesus, how long? etc.

2 It may be at midday, it may be at twilight,
   It may be, perchance, that the blackness of midnight
   Will burst into light in the blaze of His glory,
      When Jesus receives "His own."

3 While hosts cry "Hosanna!" from heaven descending,
   With glorified saints and the angels attending,
   With grace on His brow, like a halo of glory,
      Will Jesus receive "His own."

4 Oh, joy! Oh, delight! should we go without dying;
   No sickness, no sadness, no dread, and no crying;
   Caught up through the clouds with our Lord into glory,
      When Jesus receives "His own."
                              H. L. Turner.

178 When the King Comes.   P.M.

E. E. Steele Elliott.

1. They come and go, the sea-sons fair, And bring their spoil to vale and hills; But

oh, there is wait-ing in the air, And a passion-ate hope the spi-rit fills.

Why doth He tar-ry, the ab-sent Lord? When shall the Kingdom be re-stored, And

earth and heaven with one ac-cord, Ring out the cry that the King comes!

Refrain.

What will it be when the King comes! What will it be when the King comes!

accel.   when He comes! . .   *Slower.*

What will it be when He comes, when He comes! What will it be when the King comes!

When   He   comes!

The notes must be divided to suit the accent of the words.

178 *And He that sitteth on the throne said, Behold I make all things new.—*
REV. xxi. 5 (R.V.)

2 The floods have lifted up their voice:
   The King hath come to His own, His
The little hills and vales rejoice,   [own!
   His right it is to take the crown.
Sleepers awake, and meet Him first!
Now let the marriage-hymn outburst!
And powers of darkness flee, disperst;
   What will it be when the King comes!
   What will it be, etc.

3 A ransomed earth breaks forth in song,
   Her sin-stained ages overpast,
Her yearning "Lord, how long, how long?"
   Exchanged for joy, at last, at last!

Angels carry the royal commands;
Peace beams forth throughout all the lands;
The trees of the field shall clap their hands;
   What will it be when the King comes!

4 O brothers, stand as men that wait,
   The dawn is purpling in the east,
And banners wave from heaven's high gate;
   The conflict now, but soon the feast!
Mercy and truth shall meet again;
Worthy the Lamb that once was slain!
We can suffer now, He will know us then;
   What will it be when the King comes!
                          E. E. Steele Elliott.

Helmsley.   8.7.8.7.4.4.4.7.   M. MADAN.

1. { Lo! He comes with clouds des-cend-ing, Once for fa-vour'd
     Thou-sand thou-sand saints at-tend-ing Swell the tri-umph

sin-ners slain; }
of .. His train. } Hal - le - lu - jah! Hal - le - lu - jah!

Hal - le - lu - jah! Christ ap - pears on earth to .. reign.

179   *Behold, He cometh with clouds.*—REV. i. 7.

2 Every eye shall now behold Him
   Robed in dreadful majesty;
Those who set at naught and sold Him,
   Pierced and nailed Him to the tree,
      Deeply wailing,
   Shall the true Messiah see.

3 Now redemption, long expected,
   See in solemn pomp appear!
All His saints, by man rejected,
   Now shall meet Him in the air.
      Hallelujah!
   See the day of God appear.

4 Yea, Amen, let all adore Thee,
   High on Thine eternal throne;
Saviour, take the power and glory,
   Claim the kingdoms for Thine own.
      Hallelujah!
   Hallelujah! Come, Lord, come!
                          C. Wesley and J. Cennick.

180 The Crowning Day. P.M. J. McGranahan

Oh, the crown-ing day is coming! Is coming by-and-by! When our

Lord shall come in pow-er And glo-ry from on high! Oh, the glorious sight will gladden Each

waiting, watch-ful eye, In the crown-ing day that's coming By-and-by.

Words and Music by permission of Mrs. H. C. Dixon.

180

They shall see the Son of man coming in the clouds of heaven with power and great glory.—MATT. xxiv. 30.

1 OUR Lord is now rejected,
  And by the world disowned,
By the many still neglected,
  And by the few enthroned;
But soon He'll come in glory!
  The hour is drawing nigh,
For the crowning day is coming
    By-and-by.
    Oh, the crowning day is coming! etc.

2 The heavens shall glow with splendour;
  But brighter far than they,
The saints shall shine in glory,
  As Christ shall them array:
The beauty of the Saviour
  Shall dazzle every eye,
In the crowning day that's coming
    By-and-by.

3 Our pain shall then be over,
  We'll sin and sigh no more,
Behind us all of sorrow,
  And naught but joy before:
A joy in our Redeemer,
  As we to Him are nigh,
In the crowning day that's coming
    By-and-by.

4 Let all that look for hasten
  The coming joyful day,
By earnest consecration,
  To walk the narrow way:
By gathering in the lost ones,
  For whom our Lord did die,
For the crowning day that's coming
    By-and-by.
    El Nathan.

Wells.   7.7.7.7.7.7.   D. BORTNIANSKI.

181   *Ye do shew forth the Lord's death till He come.—1 COR. xi. 26.*

1 "Till He come!" Oh, let the words
  Linger on the trembling chords;
Let the little while between
  In their golden light be seen;
Let us think how heaven and home
Lie beyond that "Till He come!"

2 When the weary ones we love
  Enter on their rest above,
Seems the world so poor and vast?
  All our life-joy overcast?
Hush! be every murmur dumb,
It is only till He come!

3 Clouds and darkness round us press!
  Would we have one sorrow less?
All the sharpness of the cross,
  All that tells the world is loss,
Death, and darkness, and the tomb,
Only whisper, "Till He come."

4 See, the feast of love is spread,
  Drink the wine and break the bread:
Sweet memorials—till the Lord
  Call us round His heavenly board;
Some from earth, from glory some,
Severed only till He come!

E. H. Bickersteth.

Jesus is Coming!

P.M.

J. McGranahan

CHORUS.

Je-sus is coming, is coming a-gain! Je-sus is coming a - gain! . . . Oh,
Yes, Je-sus is coming!

shout the glad ti-dings o'er mountain and plain! Je - sus is com-ing a - gain!

Words and Music by permission of Mrs. H. C. Dixon.

182

The Lord Himself shall descend from heaven.—1 THESS. iv. 16.

1 JESUS is coming! sing the glad word!
Coming for those He redeemed by His blood,
Coming to reign as the glorified Lord!
    Jesus is coming again!
    Jesus is coming, is coming again! etc.

2 Jesus is coming! the dead shall arise,
Loved ones shall meet in a joyful surprise,
Caught up together to Him in the skies;
    Jesus is coming again!

3 Jesus is coming! His saints to release;
Coming to give the warring earth peace!
Sinning and sighing and sorrow shall cease:
    Jesus is coming again!

4 Jesus is coming! the promise is true:
Who are the chosen, the faithful, the few,
Waiting and watching, prepared for review?
    Jesus is coming again!   *El Nathan.*

SECTION V.—The Work of the Holy Spirit.

St. Stephen.   C.M.   W. JONES.

183   *The Comforter, which is the Holy Ghost.*—JOHN xiv. 26.

1 COME, Holy Ghost, our hearts inspire;
  Let us Thine influence prove,
  Source of the old prophetic fire,
  Fountain of light and love.

2 Come, Holy Ghost, for moved by Thee
  Thy prophets wrote and spoke;
  Unlock the truth, Thyself the key,
  Unseal the sacred Book.

3 Expand Thy wings, celestial Dove,
  Brood o'er our nature's night;
  On our disordered spirits move,
  And let there now be light.

4 God, through Himself, we then shall know
  If Thou within us shine;
  And sound, with all Thy saints below,
  The depths of love divine. *C. Wesley.*

Ernstein.   6.5.6.5.   J. F. SWIFT.

184   *For as many as are led by the Spirit of God, they are the sons of God.*—ROM. viii. 14.

1 HOLY Spirit, hear us;
  Help us while we sing;
  Breathe into the music
  Of the praise we bring.

2 Holy Spirit, prompt us
  When we kneel to pray;
  Nearer come and teach us
  What we ought to say.

3 Holy Spirit, shine Thou
  On the Book we read;
  Gild its holy pages
  With the light we need.

4 Holy Spirit, give us
  Each a lowly mind;
  Make us more like Jesus,
  Gentle, pure, and kind.

5 Holy Spirit, help us
  Daily by Thy might,
  What is wrong to conquer,
  And to choose the right. *W. H. Parker.*

Maidstone. 7.7.7.7.7.7. W. B. GILBERT.

By permission of Novello and Company, Limited.
Alternative Tune, WELLS, *No.* 181.

185 *He dwelleth with you, and shall be in you.*—JOHN xiv. 17.

1 GRACIOUS Spirit, dwell with me!
I myself would gracious be,
And with words that help and heal
Would Thy life in mine reveal;
And with actions bold and meek
Would for Christ, my Saviour, speak.

2 Truthful Spirit, dwell with me!
I myself would truthful be,
And with wisdom kind and clear
Let Thy life in mine appear;
And with actions brotherly
Speak my Lord's sincerity.

3 Tender Spirit, dwell with me!
I myself would tender be;
Shut my heart up like a flower
In temptation's darksome hour;
Open it when shines the sun,
And His love by fragrance own.

4 Mighty Spirit, dwell with me!
I myself would mighty be,
Mighty so as to prevail
Where unaided man must fail,
Ever by a mighty hope
Pressing on and bearing up.

5 Holy Spirit, dwell with me!
I myself would holy be,
Separate from sin, I would
Choose and cherish all things good,
And whatever I can be
Give to Him who gave me Thee. *T. T. Lynch.*

186 Swabia. S.M. German.

Alternative Tune, RHODES, *No. 85.*

186

I will pour out My Spirit unto you.—PROVERBS i. 23.

1 O HOLY Spirit, come,
And Jesus' love declare;
Oh, tell us of our heavenly home
And guide us safely there!

2 Our unbelief remove
By Thine almighty breath;
Oh, work the wondrous work of love,
The mighty work of faith!

3 Come, with resistless power;
Come, with almighty grace;
Come, with the long-expected shower,
And fall upon this place!

O. Allen.

St. Cutbbert.

8.6.8.4.

J. B. DYKES.

187

The Comforter, which is the Holy Ghost, shall teach you all things.—JOHN xiv. 26.

1 OUR blest Redeemer ere He breathed
His tender last farewell,
A Guide, a Comforter, bequeathed,
With us to dwell.

2 He came in semblance of a dove,
With sheltering wings outspread,
The holy balm of peace and love
On earth to shed.

3 He came in tongues of living flame
To teach, convince, subdue;
All-powerful as the wind He came—
As viewless too.

4 He comes sweet influence to impart,
A gracious, willing Guest,
Where He can find one humble heart
Wherein to rest.

5 And His that gentle voice we hear,
Soft as the breath of even,
That checks each fault, that calms each
And speaks of heaven.   [fear,

6 For every virtue we possess,
And every victory won,
And every thought of holiness,
Are His alone.

7 Spirit of purity and grace,
Our weakness, pitying, see;
O make our hearts Thy dwelling-place,
And worthier Thee.

Harriet Auber.

THE WORK OF THE HOLY SPIRIT.

Woolwich.　　　　　　　　　　S.M.　　　　　　　　　　C. E. KETILE.

By permission of the Proprietors of the *Bristol Tune Book.*
Alternative Tune, TRENTHAM, *No.* 151.

188　　　*The breath of the Almighty hath given me life.*—JOB xxxiii. 4.

1 BREATHE on me, Breath of God,
　Fill me with life anew,
That I may love what Thou dost love,
And do what Thou wouldst do.

2 Breathe on me, Breath of God,
　Until my heart is pure;
Until my will is one with Thine
To do and to endure.

3 Breathe on me, Breath of God,
　Till I am wholly Thine;
Until this earthly part of me
Glows with Thy fire divine.

4 Breathe on me, Breath of God,
　So shall I never die,
But live with Thee the perfect life
Of Thine eternity.　*E. Hatch.*

Wareham.　　　　　　　　　　L.M.　　　　　　　　　　W. KNAPP.

Alternative Tune, HOLLEY, *No.* 378.

189　　　*Thy Spirit is good; lead me.*—PSALM cxliii. 10.

1 COME, gracious Spirit, heavenly Dove,
With light and comfort from above;
Be Thou our Guardian, Thou our Guide,
O'er every thought and step preside.

2 Conduct us safe, conduct us far
From every sin and hurtful snare;
Lead to Thy Word, which rules must give,
And teach us lessons how to live.

3 The light of truth to us display,
And make us know and choose Thy way;
Plant holy fear in every heart,
That we from God may ne'er depart.

4 Lead us to holiness, the road
That we must take to dwell with God;
Lead us to Christ, the living Way,
Nor let us from His pastures stray.

5 Lead us to God, our final rest,
　To be with Him for ever blest:
Lead us to heaven, that we may share
Fulness of joy for ever there.

S. Browne (alt.).

Eden.   L.M.   T. B. MASON.

Alternative Tunes, ARIZONA, *No.* 42, *and* MARYTON, *No.* 68.

190   *The Spirit of God descending like a dove.*—MATT. iii. 16.

1 O HOLY Dove, on wings divine,
 In all Thy tender might descend:
 In these dark hearts irradiant shine,
 With saving light our path attend.

2 Into all truth and wisdom's ways
 Guide Thou, and every fear dispel :
 Spirit Divine, throughout the days
 Direct our steps, and with us dwell.

3 From all the weight of sin's alloy
 Now set us free, blest Paraclete :

Fill every heart with purest joy,
 For Christ's employ may we be meet.

4 In trouble's hour as sorrows come,
 Blest Comforter, Thy voice be heard,
 And when in sorest grief we're dumb,
 Breathe Thou within the healing word.

5 Oh, take our faulty lives so frail,
 And 'neath the glow of Thy pure sway
 May we in faith's stern fight prevail,
 And to the world Thy power display.
 Anon.

Kelvinside.   C.M.   LISTER R. PEACE.

Alternative Tunes, WILTSHIRE, *No.* 332, *and* BEATITUDO, *No.* 571.

191   *The glory of the Lord filled the house of God.*—2 CHRON. v. 14.

1 SPIRIT Divine, attend our prayers
 And make this house Thy home ;
 Descend with all Thy gracious powers,
 Oh, come, Great Spirit, come !

2 Come as the Light : to us reveal
 Our emptiness and woe ;
 And lead us in those paths of life
 Where all the righteous go.

3 Come as the Fire, and purge our hearts
 Like sacrificial flame ;
 Let our whole soul an offering be
 To our Redeemer's Name.

4 Come as the Dew, and sweetly bless
 This consecrated hour ;
 May barrenness rejoice to own
 Thy fertilizing power.

5 Come as the Dove, and spread Thy wings,
 The wings of perfect love ;
 And let Thy church on earth become
 Blest as the church above.

6 Spirit Divine, attend our prayers ;
 Make a lost world Thy home ;
 Descend with all Thy gracious powers,
 Oh, come, Great Spirit, come !
 A. Reed.

F *

Section VI.—Gospel Hymns.

Christ Receiveth Sinful Men.   7.7.7.7.

JAMES McGRANAHAN.

Sing it o'er . . . and o'er a-gain; . . . Christ re-
Sing it o'er a-gain, *Sing it o'er a-gain,*

-ceiv - - eth sin-ful men; . . . Make the mes - - sage
-ceiv-eth sin-ful men, Christ re-ceiv-eth sin-ful men; *Make the mes-sage plain,*

clean and plain : . . . Christ re-ceiv-' eth sin-ful . . men. . .
Make the mes-sage plain :

Words and Music by permission of Mrs. H. C. Dixon.

192 *They that be whole need not a physician, but they that are sick.*—MATT. ix. 12.

1 SINNERS Jesus will receive;
  Sound this word of grace to all
  Who the heavenly pathway leave,
  All who linger, all who fall!
    Sing it o'er and o'er again, etc.

2 Come: and He will give you rest;
  Trust Him: for His word is plain;
  He will take the sinfulest:
    Christ receiveth sinful men.

3 Now my heart condemns me not,
  Pure before the law I stand;
  He who cleansed me from all spot,
  Satisfied its last demand.

4 Christ receiveth sinful men,
  Even me with all my sin;
  Purged from every spot and stain,
  Heaven with Him I enter in.
    Neumaster, arr. *D. W. Whittle.*

Lowry. P.M. R. Lowry.

1. Down from the splen-dour of His ev-erlasting throne Came the Lord of glo-ry, for our

guilt to a - tone; Son of God e-ter-nal, He the sinner's surety stood, Paid the sinner's

REFRAIN.

ran-som in His pre-cious blood. Glo - ry, glo - ry, glo-ry un-to Je - sus!

An - y - one, ev - 'ry - one He can ful-ly save. Glo - ry, glo - ry,

glo-ry un-to Je - sus! Hal-le-lu-jah! All who trust Him He will save.

193

He humbled Himself, and became obedient unto death.—PHIL. ii. 8.

2 Over death triumphant He is risen from the grave,
   Back to heaven ascended, Jesus now lives to save.
   Nothing else remaineth but salvation to receive,
   When with true repentance you on Him believe.

3 Come to-day to Jesus, do not longer stay away;
   Come and take salvation, come to Christ, while you may,
   Heavenly voices call you, and the Saviour waits to bless,
   Come to Him believing, and His Name confess.

J. Walker.

Come unto Me.　　　　　7.6.7.6., D.　　　　　J. B. DYKES.

194

I will give you rest.—MATT. xi. 28.

1 "COME unto Me, ye weary,
　　And I will give you rest:"
Oh, blessèd voice of Jesus,
　　Which comes to hearts oppressed!
It tells of benediction,
　　Of pardon, grace, and peace,
Of joy that hath no ending,
　　Of love which cannot cease.

2 "Come unto Me, ye wanderers,
　　And I will give you light:"
Oh, loving voice of Jesus,
　　Which comes to cheer the night!
Our hearts were filled with sadness,
　　And we had lost our way;
But morning brings us gladness,
　　And songs the break of day.

3 "And whosoever cometh,
　　I will not cast him out:"
Oh, welcome voice of Jesus,
　　Which drives away our doubt,
Which calls us very sinners,
　　Unworthy though we be
Of love so free and boundless,
　　To come, dear Lord, to Thee!
　　　　　　　　　W. C. Dix.

God is now Willing. P.M. James McGranahan.

CHORUS.

God is now willing : are you? are you? Will you not trust Him, so faith-ful, so true?

If you re-fuse Him, oh, what will you do? God is now willing : are you? . .

Words and Music by permission of Mrs. H. C. Dixon.

195 *Who hath reconciled us to Himself by Jesus Christ.—2 Cor. v. 18.*

1 God is now willing, in Christ reconciled,
  Willing to pardon and cleanse the defiled,
  Willing to take you and make you His child;
    God is now willing : are you?
    God is now willing, etc.

2 God is now willing to give you His peace,
  Willing from bondage of sin to release,
  Willing the conflict within you should cease;
    God is now willing : are you?

3 God is now willing to answer your prayer,
  Perfectly willing your burden to bear,
  Ready and waiting to take all your care;
    God is now willing : are you?

4 God is now willing within you to dwell,
  Willing with blessing your spirit to fill;
  Yield to His pleading and give up your will;
    God is now willing : are you?

                              El Nathan

St. Albans. [FIRST TUNE.] 6.5., 8 lines and Refrain. From Haydn.

REFRAIN.

Je-sus, I will trust Thee,

Trust Thee with my soul: Guil-ty, lost, and help-less, Thou canst make me whole.

196 *In whom ye also trusted, after that ye heard the word of truth.—EPH. i. 13.*

1 JESUS, I *will* trust Thee,
　Trust Thee with my soul,
Guilty, lost, and helpless,
　Thou canst make me whole:
There is none in heaven
　Or on earth like Thee:
Thou hast died for sinners—
　Therefore, Lord, for me.
　　Jesus, I will trust Thee, etc.

2 Jesus, I *must* trust Thee,
　Pondering Thy ways,
Full of love and mercy
　All Thine earthly days:
Sinners gathered round Thee,
　Lepers sought Thy face:
None too vile or loathsome
　For a Saviour's grace.

3 Jesus, I *can* trust Thee,
　Trust Thy written Word,
Though Thy voice of pity
　I have never heard:
When Thy Spirit teacheth,
　To my taste how sweet !
Only may I hearken,
　Sitting at Thy feet.

4 Jesus, I *do* trust Thee,
　Trust without a doubt ;
Whosoever cometh,
　Thou wilt not cast out:
Faithful is Thy promise,
　Precious is Thy blood:
These my soul's salvation,
　Thou my Saviour God !

Mary J. Walker.

6.5., 8 lines, without Refrain.

196 Decision. [SECOND TUNE.] E. H. G. SARGENT.

197 Only Trust Him. C.M., and Chorus. J. H. STOCKTON.

CHORUS.

On - ly trust Him, on - ly trust Him,

On -ly trust Him now! He will save you, He will save you, He will save you now!

197

I will trust, and not be afraid.—ISAIAH xii. 2.

1 COME, every soul by sin oppressed,
There's mercy with the Lord;
And He will surely give you rest
By trusting in His Word.
Only trust Him, etc.

2 For Jesus shed His precious blood,
Rich blessings to bestow;
Plunge now into the crimson flood,
That washes white as snow.

3 Yes, Jesus is the Truth the Way
That leads you into rest;
Believe in Him without delay,
And you are fully blest.

4 Come then and join this holy band,
And on to glory go,
To dwell in that celestial land
Where joys immortal flow.

J. H. Stockton.

198 Blessèd be the Fountain. P.M.   H. S. Perkins (arr.).

Moderato.

Whi - - - ter than the snow! . . . .
Whi - ter than   the snow!   Whi - ter than   the snow!

Whi - - - ter than the snow! . . . .   Wash me in the
Whi - ter than   the snow!   Whi - ter than   the snow!

blood of the Lamb! . . And I shall be whi - ter than snow! . .
Lamb, of the Lamb, snow, than snow!

198   *Wash me, and I shall be whiter than snow.*—PSALM li. 7.

1 BLESSÈD be the fountain of blood,
  To a world of sinners revealed ;
Blessèd be the dear Son of God :
  Only by His stripes we are healed.
Though I've wandered far from His fold,
  Bringing to my heart pain and woe,
Wash me in the blood of the Lamb,
  And I shall be whiter than snow ;
    Whiter than the snow ! etc.

2 Thorny was the crown that He wore
  On the cross, with the scoffing and shame ;
Grievous were the sorrows He bore,
  My eternal salvation to gain.
May I to that fountain be led,
  Opened for my sins here below ;
Wash me in the blood that He shed,
  And I shall be whiter than snow !

3 Father, I have wandered from Thee,
  Often has my heart gone astray ;
Crimson do my sins seem to me—
  Water cannot wash them away.
Jesus to that fountain of Thine,
  Leaning on Thy promise, I go !
Cleanse me by Thy washing divine,
  And I shall be whiter than snow !

E. R. Latta.

Weber.   7.7.7.7.   C. M. VON WEBER.

199   *Stood at His feet . . . weeping.*—LUKE vii. 38.

1 DEPTH of mercy ! can there be
Mercy still reserved for me ?
Can my God His wrath forbear ?
Me, the chief of sinners, spare ?

2 I have long withstood His grace,
Long provoked Him to His face ;
Would not hearken to His calls,
Grieved Him by a thousand falls.

3 Whence to me this waste of love ?
Ask my Advocate above !
See the cause in Jesus' face,
Now before the throne of grace.

4 There for me the Saviour stands,
Shows His wounds, and spreads His hands ;
God is love, I know, I feel ;
Jesus weeps, and loves me still.

5 Jesus, answer from above ;
Is not all Thy nature love ?
Wilt Thou not the wrong forget ?
Suffer me to kiss Thy feet ?

6 If I rightly read Thy heart,
If Thou all compassion art,
Bow Thine ear, in mercy bow,
Pardon and accept me now !   *C. Wesley.*

200 The Gospel Bells.   P.M.   S. Wesley Martin.

Gos-pel bells! how they ring, O-ver land, from sea to sea; Gos-pel
Gos-pel bells! *how they ring,*

bells free - ly bring Bless-èd news to you and me.
Gos - pel bells *free - ly bring*

200 *God so loved the world, that He gave His only begotten Son.—JOHN iii. 16.*

1 THE Gospel bells are ringing,
  Over land, from sea to sea ;
Blessèd news of free salvation
  Do they offer you and me.
"For God so loved the world,
  That His only Son He gave !
Whosoe'er believeth in Him
  Everlasting life shall have."
    Gospel bells ! how they ring, etc.

2 The Gospel bells invite us
  To a feast prepared for all :
Do not slight the invitation,
  Nor reject the gracious call.
" I am the Bread of life ;
  Eat of Me, thou hungry soul ;
Though your sins be red as crimson,
  They shall be as white as wool."

3 The Gospel bells give warning,
  As they sound from day to day,
Of the fate which doth await them
  Who for ever will delay.
"Escape thou for thy life !
  Tarry not in all the plain ;
Nor behind thee look, oh, never,
  Lest thou be consumed in pain."

4 The Gospel bells are joyful
  As they echo far and wide,
Bearing notes of perfect pardon,
  Through a Saviour crucified :
"Good tidings of great joy
  To all people do I bring ;
Unto you is born a Saviour,
  Which is Christ, the Lord and King."
    S. Wesley Martin.

Tetelestai. P.M.

E. H. G. SARGENT.

CHORUS.

"It is finished!" yes, in-deed, Fin-ished, ev-'ry jot: Sin-ner, this is all you need— Tell me, is . . it not?

201 *It is finished.—JOHN xix. 30.*

1 NOTHING either great or small—
  Nothing, sinner, no ;
Jesus did it, did it all,
  Long, long ago.
  "It is finished!" yes, indeed, etc.

2 When He, from His lofty throne,
  Stooped to do and die,
Everything was fully done :
  Hearken to His cry.

3 Weary, working, burdened one,
  Wherefore toil you so?

Cease your doing ; all was done
  Long, long ago.

4 Till to Jesus' work you cling
  By a simple faith,
"Doing" is a deadly thing—
  "Doing" ends in death.

5 Cast your deadly "doing" down—
  Down at Jesus' feet ;
Stand in Him, in Him alone,
  Gloriously complete.
    J. Proctor.

Throw out the Life=Line.

P.M.

E. S. UFFORD.
Arr. by GEO. C. STEBBINS.

Throw out the Life-line! Throw out the Life-line! Someone is drift-ing a - way! . .

Throw out the Life-line! Throw out the Life-line! Someone is sinking to - day. . .

202

That I might by all means save some.—1 COR. ix. 22.

1 THROW out the Life-line across the dark wave,
   There is a brother whom someone should save;
   Somebody's brother! oh, who then will dare
   To throw out the Life-line, his peril to share?
      Throw out the Life-line! etc.

2 Throw out the Life-line with hand quick and strong:
   Why do you tarry, my brother, so long?
   See—he is sinking; oh, hasten to-day—
   And out with the Life-boat! away then, away!

3 Throw out the Life-line to danger-fraught men,
   Sinking in anguish where you've never been:
   Winds of temptation and billows of woe
   Will soon hurl them out where the dark waters flow.

4 Soon will the season of rescue be o'er
   Soon will they drift to eternity's shore,
   Haste then, my brother! no time for delay,
   But throw out the Life-line, and save them to-day.
                              E. S. Ufford.

Munich.   7.6.7.6., D.   German.

Alternative Tunes, MISSIONARY, *No.* 622, *and* ST. GEORGE'S, BOLTON, *No.* 374.

203   *The blood of Jesus Christ His Son cleanseth us from all sin.*—1 JOHN i. 7.

1 I LAY my sins on Jesus,
    The spotless Lamb of God;
He bears them all, and frees us
    From the accursèd load.
I bring my guilt to Jesus,
    To wash my crimson stains
White in His blood most precious,
    Till not a spot remains.

2 I bring my wants to Jesus,
    All fulness dwells in Him;
He heals all my diseases,
    He doth my soul redeem.
I lay my griefs on Jesus,
    My burdens and my cares;
He from them all releases,
    He all my sorrows shares.

3 I long to be like Jesus,
    Meek, loving, lowly, mild;
I long to be like Jesus,
    The Father's holy Child.
I long to be with Jesus,
    Amid the heavenly throng;
To sing with saints His praises,
    To learn the angels' song.

H. Bonar.

7.6.7.6., D. and Refrain.

204 Tell Me the Old, Old Story. [FIRST TUNE.]

W. H. DOANE.

REFRAIN.

Tell me the old, old sto - ry, Tell me the old, old sto - ry,

Tell me the old, old sto - ry, Of Je - sus and His love.

204   *The love of Christ, which passeth knowledge.*—EPH. iii. 19.

1 TELL me the old, old story
  Of unseen things above,
Of Jesus and His glory,
  Of Jesus and His love :
Tell me the story simply,
  As to a little child,
For I am weak and weary,
  And helpless and defiled.
    Tell me the old, old story, etc.

2 Tell me the story slowly,
  That I may take it in—
That wonderful redemption,
  God's remedy for sin.
Tell me the story often,
  For I forget so soon ;
The early dew of morning
  Has passed away at noon.

3 Tell me the story softly,
  With earnest tones and grave :
Remember ! I'm the sinner
  Whom Jesus came to save.
Tell me that story always,
  If you would really be,
In any time of trouble,
  A comforter to me.

4 Tell me the same old story
  When you have cause to fear
That this world's empty glory
  Is costing me too dear.
Yes, and when *that* world's glory
  Is dawning on my soul,
Tell me the old, old story—
  " Christ Jesus makes thee whole."
           K. Hankey.

Remembrance. [SECOND TUNE.]   7.6.7.6.   J. BOOTH.

204   *We would see Jesus.*—JOHN xii. 21.

1 TELL me the old, old story
  Of unseen things above,
Of Jesus and His glory,
  Of Jesus and His love :

2 Tell me the story simply,
  As to a little child,
For I am weak and weary,
  And helpless and defiled.

3 Tell me the story slowly,
  That I may take it in—
That wonderful redemption,
  God's remedy for sin.

4 Tell me the story often,
  For I forget so soon ;
The early dew of morning
  Has passed away at noon.

5 Tell me the story softly,
  With earnest tones and grave :
Remember ! I'm the sinner
  Whom Jesus came to save.

6 Tell me that story always,
  If you would really be,
In any time of trouble,
  A comforter to me.

7 Tell me the same old story
  When you have cause to fear
That this world's empty glory
  Is costing me too dear.

8 Yes, and when *that* world's glory
  Is dawning on my soul,
Tell me the old, old story—
  "Christ Jesus makes thee whole.'
           K. Hankey.

The Light of the World. P.M. P. P. BLISS.

CHORUS.

Come to the Light, 'tis shin-ing for thee; Sweetly the Light has dawn'd up-on me, ..

Once I was blind, but now I can see; The Light of the world is Je - sus.

205 *I am come a Light into the world.*—JOHN xii. 46.

1 THE whole world was lost in the darkness of sin,
　　The Light of the world is Jesus;
　Like sunshine at noonday His glory shone in,
　　The Light of the world is Jesus.
　　　Come to the Light, 'tis shining for thee, etc.

2 No darkness have we who in Jesus abide,
　　The Light of the world is Jesus,
　We walk in the light when we follow our Guide,
　　The Light of the world is Jesus.

3 Ye dwellers in darkness, with sin-blinded eyes,
　　The Light of the world is Jesus,
　Go, wash at His bidding, and light will arise,
　　The Light of the world is Jesus.

4 No need of the sunlight in heaven, we're told;
　　The Light of that world is Jesus;
　The Lamb is the Light in the City of Gold,
　　The Light of that world is Jesus.
　　　　　　　　　　　P. P. Bliss.

Bromley.　　　　　　　P.M.　　　　　　　　　ADA ROSE.

Alternative Tune, ST. CHRISTOPHER, *No.* 448.

206　　*Unto you therefore which believe, He is precious.*—1 PETER ii. 7.

1 I COULD not do without Him,
　Jesus is more to me
Than all the richest, fairest gifts
　Of earth could ever be.
But the more I find Him precious—
And the more I find Him true—
The more I long for you to find
What He can be to you.

2 You need not do without Him,
　For He is passing by,
He is waiting to be gracious,
　Only waiting for your cry;
He is waiting to receive you—
To make you all His own,
Why will you do without Him,
And wander on alone?

3 Why will you do without Him?
　Is He not kind indeed?
Did He not die to save you "
　Is He not all you need?

Do you not want a Saviour?
Do you not want a Friend,
One who will love you faithfully,
And love you to the end?

4 You cannot do without Him,
　There is no other name
By which you ever can be saved,
　No way, no hope, no claim.
But with Him—all the empty hearts
Filled with His perfect love;
With Jesus—perfect peace below,
And perfect bliss above.

5 He would not do without you,
　He calls and calls again—
"Come unto Me! Come unto Me!"
　Oh, shall He call in vain?
He wants to have you with Him;
Do you not want Him too?
You cannot do without Him,
And He wants—even you.
　　　　　　　　F. R. Havergal.

Have You Been to Jesus?   P.M.   E. A. HOFFMAN.

Are you washed in the blood, In the soul-cleansing blood of the Lamb? Are your garments spotless? Are they white as snow? Are you washed in the blood of the Lamb?

207   *Blessed are they that wash their robes.*—REV. xxii. 14 (R.V.).

1 HAVE you been to Jesus for the cleansing power?
  Are you washed in the blood of the Lamb?
  Are you fully trusting in His grace this hour?
  Are you washed in the blood of the Lamb?
  Are you washed . . . in the blood, etc.

2 Are you walking daily by the Saviour's side?
  Are you washed in the blood of the Lamb?
  Do you rest each moment in the Crucified?
  Are you washed in the blood of the Lamb?

3 When the Bridegroom cometh, will your robes be white—
  Pure and white in the blood of the Lamb?
  Will your soul be ready for the mansions bright,
  And be washed in the blood of the Lamb?

4 Lay aside the garments that are stained with sin,
  And be washed in the blood of the Lamb!
  There's a fountain flowing for the soul unclean—
  Oh, be washed in the blood of the Lamb!

                                    E. A. Hoffman.

Regeneration.   P.M.   Geo. C. Stebbins.

CHORUS.

"Ye must be born a-gain!"... "Ye must be born a-gain!"...
"a-gain!"   "a-gain!"

I ver-i-ly, ver-i-ly say un-to thee, "Ye must be born a-gain!"...
"a-gain!"

208   *Ye must be born again.*—John iii. 7.

1 A ruler once came to Jesus by night,
    To ask Him the way of salvation and light:
    The Master made answer in words true and plain,
      "Ye must be born again!"
        "Ye must be born again!" etc.

2 Ye children of men, attend to the word,
    So solemnly uttered by Jesus the Lord;
    And let not this message to you be in vain;
      "Ye must be born again!"

3 O ye who would enter this glorious rest,
    And sing with the ransomed the song of the blest;
    The life everlasting if ye would obtain,
      "Ye must be born again!"

4 A dear one in heaven thy heart yearns to see,
    At the beautiful gate may be watching for thee;
    Then list to the note of this solemn refrain:
      "Ye must be born again!"

                                    W. T. Sleeper.

Wbat will you Do with Jesus?   P.M.

GEO. C. STEBBINS.

REFRAIN.

What shall the an-swer be? .. What shall the an-swer be? ..

What will you do with Je - sus? Oh, what shall the an - swer be? ..

By permission. From Sankey's *Sacred Songs and Solos.*

209

What shall I do with Jesus which is called Christ?—MATT. xxvii. 22.

1 Oh, what will you do with Jesus?
  The call comes low and sweet;
And tenderly He bids you
  Your burdens lay at His feet;
O soul, so sad and weary,
  That sweet voice speaks to thee :
Then what will you do with Jesus?
  Oh, what shall the answer be?
    What shall the answer be? etc.

2 Oh, what will you do with Jesus?
  The call comes loud and clear;
The solemn words are sounding
  In every listening ear;

Eternal life's in the question,
  And joy through eternity;
Then what will you do with Jesus?
  Oh, what shall the answer be?

3 Oh, think of the King of glory,
  From heaven to earth come down;
His life so pure and holy;
  His death, His cross, His crown;
Of His divine compassion,
  His sacrifice for thee;
Then what will you do with Jesus?
  Oh, what shall the answer be?
                    Nath. Norton.

Grace Divine. P.M. W. H. DOANE.

Come and wel - come, who- so- ev- er will, 'Tis the Sa-viour's gra-cious wel- come, wel-come, call, He is a - ble, will-ing, waiting now to save, Sim-ply trust Him, that is all.

210

Ye will not come to Me that ye might have life.—JOHN v. 40.

1 JESUS lingers still: 'tis for you He waits,
　　And He's waited for you long;
　He waits that Heaven, with its fadeless joys,
　　May yet to you belong.
　　　Come and welcome, etc.

2 Though your wayward feet may have wandered far,
　　And you're deeply sunk in sin;
　Yet the Saviour waits, with His patient grace,
　　Your stony heart to win.

3 Though His gracious call you have oft refused,
　　And He's sought your trust in vain;
　Yet, with love unchanged by your cold neglect,
　　He is seeking you again.

4 Oh, surrender now! yield to love divine;
　　Jesus lingers for you still:
　While in grace He says, "Oh, come to Me,"
　　Let your answer be, "I will."

　　　　　　　　　　J. Walker.

211 "Come!"

7.6.7.6. D., with Refrain.

DUET FOR SOPRANO AND ALTO.

J. McGRANAHAN.

Alternative Tune (without Refrain), GREENLAND, No. 213.

211 Come unto Me, all ye that labour and are heavy-laden, and I will give
you rest.—MATT. xi. 28.

1 O WORD, of words the sweetest,
O word, in which there lie
All promise, all fulfilment,
And end of mystery!
Lamenting, or rejoicing,
With doubt or terror nigh,
I hear the "Come!" of Jesus,
And to His cross I fly.
"Come! oh, come to Me!" etc.

2 O soul! why shouldst thou wander
From such a loving Friend?
Cling closer, closer to Him,
Stay with Him to the end:
Alas! I am so helpless,
So very full of sin,
For I am ever wandering,
And coming back again.

3 Oh, each time draw me nearer,
That soon the "Come" may be,
Naught but a gentle whisper,
To one so close to Thee;
Then, over sea and mountain,
Far from, or near my home,
I'll take Thy hand and follow,
At that sweet whisper, "Come!" *Mrs. J. G. Johnson.*

So Near to the Kingdom! 11.11.11.11., with Refrain. R. LOWRY.

REFRAIN. *rall.*

Plead - ing with thee! .. The Saviour is pleading! Is pleading with thee!
Plead-ing with thee!   Plead-ing with thee!

Alternative Tune (without Refrain), ST. ASAPH, No. 491.

212 Thou art not far from the kingdom of God.—MARK xii. 34.

1 So near to the Kingdom! yet what dost thou lack?
So near to the Kingdom! what keepeth thee back?
Renounce every idol, though dear it may be,
And come to the Saviour, now pleading with thee!
Plead - - - ing with thee! etc.

2 So near, that thou hearest the strains that resound
From those, who, believing, a pardon have found!
So near, yet unwilling to give up thy sin,
When Jesus is waiting to welcome thee in!

3 To die with no hope! hast thou counted the cost—
To die out of Christ, and thy soul to be lost?
So near to the Kingdom! oh, come, we implore!
While Jesus is pleading, come, enter the door! *Fanny J. Crosby.*

Greenland.　　　　　7.6.7.6., D.　　　　　J. M. HAYDN.

213

Rise; He calleth thee.—MARK X. 49.

1 To-DAY Thy mercy calls us
　To wash away our sin,
However great our trespass,
　Whatever we have been:
However long from mercy
　Our hearts have turned away,
Thy precious blood can cleanse us
　And make us white to-day.

2 To-day Thy gate is open,
　And all who enter in
Shall find a Father's welcome,
　And pardon for their sin.
The past shall be forgotten,
　A present joy be given,
A future grace be promised,
　A glorious crown in heaven.

3 To-day our Father calls us;
　His Holy Spirit waits;
The blessèd angels gather
　Around the heavenly gates:
No question will be asked us
　How often we have come;
Although we oft have wandered,
　It is our Father's home!

4 Oh, all-embracing mercy!
　Oh, ever-open door!
What should we do without thee
　When heart and eye run o'er?
When all things seem against us,
　To drive us to despair,
We know one gate is open,
　One ear will hear our prayer!
　　　　　　Oswald Allen.

214 St. Barnabas.　　　　　6.4.6.4.6.6.4.　　　　　W. R. BRAINE.

Yet is this still my plea, Je-sus hath died.

Alternative Tune, PROPIOR DEO, *No.* 365.

214

For Thy Name's sake, O Lord, pardon mine iniquity; for it is great.—PSALM xxv. 11.

1 No; not despairingly
Come I to Thee:
No; not distrustingly
Bend I the knee.
Sin hath gone over me,
Yet is this still my plea,
Jesus hath died.

2 Lord, I confess to Thee
Sadly my sin;
All I am tell I Thee,
All I have been.
Purge Thou my sin away,
Wash Thou my soul this day,
Lord, make me clean.

3 Faithful and just art Thou,
Forgiving all;
Low at Thy piercèd feet,
Saviour, I fall.
Oh, let the cleansing blood,
Blood of the Lamb of God,
Pass o'er my soul!

4 Then all is peace and light
This soul within:
Thus shall I walk with Thee
The Loved unseen,
Leaning on Thee, my God,
Guided along the road,
Nothing between. *H. Bonar.*

215 **Knocking, Knocking.**

With feeling.   P.M.   G. F. ROOT.

Alternative Tunes. MORECAMBE, *No.* 366, *and* ST. AGNES, *No.* 407.

215   *Behold, I stand at the door, and knock.*—Rev. iii. 20.

1 KNOCKING, knocking, who is there?
Waiting, waiting, oh, how fair!
'Tis a Pilgrim, strange and kingly,
Never such was seen before;
Ah! my soul, for such a wonder
Wilt thou not undo the door?

2 Knocking, knocking, still He's there;
Waiting, waiting, wondrous fair;
But the door is hard to open,
For the weeds and ivy-vine,
With their dark and clinging tendrils,
Ever round the hinges twine.

3 Knocking, knocking—what, still there!
Waiting, waiting, grand and fair:
Yes, the piercèd hand still knocketh,
And beneath the crownèd hair
Beam the patient eyes, so tender,
Of thy Saviour, waiting there.

4 Enter, enter, heavenly Guest,
Welcome, welcome to my breast.
I have long withstood Thy knocking,
For my heart was full of sin:
But Thy love has overcome me:
Blessèd Jesus, oh, come in!

Mrs. H. B. Stowe (arr.).

G

Have You any Room for Jesus?

8.7.8.7., with Chorus.

C. C. WILLIAMS.
ARR. GEO. C. STEBBINS.

CHORUS.

Room for Jesus, King of glo - ry! Has-ten
now, His word o - bey! Swing the heart's door wide-ly o - pen! Bid Him enter while you may!

By permission of Mrs. H. C. Dixon.

216   *Make haste, . . . for to-day I must abide at thy house.*—LUKE xix. 5.

1 HAVE you any room for Jesus—
   He who bore your load of sin?
   As He knocks and asks admission,
   Sinner, will you let Him in?
     Room for Jesus, King of glory! etc.

2 Room for pleasure, room for business;
   But for Christ, the crucified,
   Not a place that He can enter,
   In the heart for which He died!

3 Have you any time for Jesus,
   As in grace He calls again?
   Oh, "TO-DAY" is "time accepted,"
   To-morrow you may call in vain.

4 Room and time now give to Jesus;
   Soon will pass God's day of grace·
   Soon thy heart be cold and silent,
   And thy Saviour's pleadings cease.
            D. W. Whittle.

217 St. James.   C.M.   R. COURTEVILLE

217 *I am the Way, the Truth, and the Life.*—JOHN xiv. 6.

1 THOU art the Way,—to Thee alone
  From sin and death we flee ;
And he who would the Father seek,
  Must seek Him, Lord, by Thee.

2 Thou art the Truth,—Thy Word alone
  True wisdom can impart ;
Thou only canst inform the mind,
  And purify the heart.

3 Thou art the Life,—the rending tomb
  Proclaims Thy conquering arm ;
And those, who put their trust in Thee,
  Nor death nor hell shall harm.

4 Thou art the Way, the Truth, the Life ;
  Grant us that Way to know,
That Truth to keep, that Life to win
  Whose joys eternal flow.
                          G. W. Doane.

218 𝕳ark ! there Comes a 𝕎hisper.   P.M.   W. H. DOANE.

REFRAIN.

"Give thy heart to Me!
Just now !
Once I died for thee." Hark ! hark ! thy Saviour calls : Come, sinner, come !
Oh, come !

218 *Give Me thine heart.*—PROV. xxiii. 26.

1 HARK ! there comes a whisper
  Stealing on thine ear ;
'Tis the Saviour calling,
  Soft, soft and clear :
  "Give thy heart to Me !" etc.

2 With that voice so gentle,
  Dost thou hear Him say ?—
"Tell Me all thy sorrows ;
  Come, come away !"

3 Would'st thou find a refuge
  For thy soul opprest ?
Jesus kindly answers :
  "I am thy rest."

4 At the cross of Jesus
  Let thy burden fall,
While He gently whispers :
  "I'll bear it all."
                          Fanny J. Crosby.

Behold One Standing at the Door! L.M.

With feeling. (May be sung as a Solo.)

Mrs. J F. Knapp.

REFRAIN.

'Tis Je - sus stand-ing at the door, . . Oh, hear Him plead-ing ev - er-more; Come,

wea - ry heart, op-pressed with sin, . . Say, "En-ter in, Lord, en - ter in!"

Alternative Tune (without Refrain), STAINCLIFFE, *No.* 586.

219
Hear My voice, and open the door.—REV. iii. 20.

1 BEHOLD One standing at the door,
And hear Him pleading evermore
With gentle voice, oh, heart of sin,
"Let Me come in, let Me come in!"

'Tis Jesus standing at the door,
Oh, hear Him pleading evermore;
Come, weary heart, oppressed with sin,
Say, "Enter in, Lord, enter in!"

2 He bore the cruel thorns for thee,
Has waited long and patiently,
Say, weary heart, oppressed with sin,
Say, "Enter in, Lord, enter in!"

3 He brings thee joy from heaven above,
He brings thee pardon, peace, and love;
Say, weary heart, oppressed with sin,
Say, "Enter in, Lord, enter in!"

Fanny J. Crosby (alt.).

220 St. George.
S.M.

H. J. GAUNTLETT.

220 *Except a man be born again, he cannot see the kingdom of God.*—JOHN iii. 3.

1 How solemn are the words,
    And yet to faith how plain,
  Which Jesus uttered while on earth—
    "Ye must be born-again!"

2 "Ye must be born again,"
    And life in Christ must have;
  In vain the soul may elsewhere go—
    'Tis He alone can save.

3 "Ye must be born again,"
    Or never enter heaven:
  'Tis only blood-washed ones go there,
    The ransomed and forgiven.

4 "Ye must be born again!"
    Then look to Christ, and live;
  He is "the Life," and waits in heaven
    Eternal life to give.

A. Midlane.

221 Come to the Saviour. P.M.

Earnestly.

G. F. ROOT.

Joy-ful, joy-ful will the meet-ing be, When from sin our

hearts are pure and free; And we shall gath-er, Saviour, with Thee, In our e-ter-nal home.

221 *Incline your ear, and come unto Me.*—ISAIAH lv. 3.

1 COME to the Saviour, make no delay;
  Here in His Word He hath shown us the way;
  Here in our midst He's standing to-day,
    Tenderly saying, "Come!"
      Joyful, joyful will the meeting be, etc.

2 "Suffer the children"—oh! hear His voice,
  Let every heart leap forth and rejoice,
  And let us freely make Him our choice;
    Do not delay, but come.

3 Think once again, He's with us to-day;
  Heed now His blest command and obey;
  Hear now His accents tenderly say,
    "Will you, My children, come?" *G. F. Root.*

P.M.

222 The Ninety and Nine. [FIRST TUNE.]

IRA D. SANKEY.

1. There were nine-ty and nine that safe-ly lay In the shel-ter of the fold; But one was out on the hills a-way, Far off from the gates of gold— A-way on the mountains wild and bare, A-way from the ten-der Shep-herd's care, A-way from the ten-der Shep-herd's care.

By permission. From Sankey's *Sacred Songs and Solos.*

Rejoice with Me; for I have found My sheep which was lost.—LUKE xv. 6.

2 "Lord, Thou hast here Thy ninety and nine,
    Are they not enough for Thee?"
But the Shepherd made answer, "This of Mine
    Has wandered away from Me;
And although the road be rough and steep,
I go to the desert to find My sheep."

3 But none of the ransomed ever knew
    How deep were the waters crossed,
Nor how dark was the night that the Lord passed through
    Ere He found His sheep that was lost.
Out in the desert He heard its cry,
Sick, and helpless, and ready to die.

222 Compassion. [SECOND TUNE.] P.M.   FOUNTAIN MEEN.

1. There were nine-ty and nine that safe-ly lay In the shel-ter of the fold; But one was out on the hills a-way, Far off from the gates of gold— A-way on the moun-tains wild and bare, A-way from the ten-der Shep-herd's care.

4 "Lord, whence are those blood-drops all the way,
   That mark out the mountain's track?"
"They were shed for one who had gone astray
   Ere the Shepherd could bring him back."
"Lord, whence are Thy hands so rent and torn?"
"They are pierced to-night by many a thorn."

5 But all through the mountains, thunder-riven,
   And up from the rocky steep,
There arose a cry to the gate of heaven,
   "Rejoice! I have found My sheep!"
And the angels echoed around the throne:
   "Rejoice, for the Lord brings back His own!"

                                        E. C. Clephane.

Care must be taken in fitting the music to the syllables.

223 Princethorpe. [FIRST TUNE.] 6.5.6.5., D.

W. PITTS.

Hatherley. [SECOND TUNE.] 6.5.6.5., D.

J. J. DUGDALE

Copyright. By permission of the Composer.

223

I press toward the mark.—PHIL. iii. 14.

1 ONWARD, children, onward!
 Leave the paths of sin;
Hasten to the strait gate,
 Strive to enter in;
None can knock unheeded,
 None can strive in vain,
For the Saviour's welcome
 All that seek obtain.

2 Onward, children, onward!
 In the narrow way,
Christ your Lord shall lead you
 Safely day by day;
And with such a Leader
 What have you to fear?
Satan may oppose you,
 But your King is near.

3 Onward, ever, onward!
 Till you join the throng
Who in dazzling raiment
 Sing the triumph-song,
And to heavenly music
 Cry with one accord,
"Holy! holy! holy!
 Is our sovereign Lord."
    J. H. Brammall.

224 "Yet There is Room!" 10.10., with Refrain.

Slow, with expression.

IRA D. SANKEY.

REFRAIN.

By permission. From Sankey's *Sacred Songs and Solos.*

224 *It is done as thou hast commanded, and yet there is room.*—LUKE xiv. 22.

1 "Yet there is room!" the Lamb's bright hall of song,
 With its fair glory, beckons thee along,
  Room, room, still room! Oh, enter, enter now!

2 It fills, it fills, that hall of jubilee!
 Make haste, make haste; 'tis not too full for thee.

3 Yet there is room! still open stands the gate,
 The gate of love; it is not yet too late:

4 Pass in, pass in! that banquet is for thee;
 That cup of everlasting love is free:

5 Louder and sweeter sounds the loving call;
 Come, lingerer, come; enter that festal hall.

6 Ere night the gate may close, and seal thy doom:
 Then the last low, long cry: "No room, no room!"
  No room, no room! O woeful cry! "No room!"
            H. Bonar.

 * In verse 5 omit the rest and sing the following note as 𝅗𝅥

G*

Surrey Chapel.   12.11.12.11.   S. Tyler.

225

*I will forgive their iniquity, and I will remember their sin no more.—*Jer. xxxi. 34.

1 Oh, come to the merciful Saviour who calls you,
  Oh, come to the Lord who forgives and forgets;
  Though dark be the fortune on earth that befalls you,
    There's a bright home above, where the sun never sets.

2 Oh, come then to Jesus, whose arms are extended
    To fold His dear children in closest embrace.
  Oh, come, for your exile will shortly be ended,
    And Jesus will show you His beautiful face.

3 Then come to His feet and lay open your story
    Of suffering and sorrow, of guilt and of shame;
  For the pardon of sin is the crown of His glory,
    And the joy of our Lord to be true to His Name.

F. W. Faber.

Just as J am   8.8.8.6.   Sir Joseph Barnby.

By permission of Novello and Company, Limited.

226 *Say unto Him, take away all iniquity, and receive us graciously.*—Hosea xiv. 2.

1 Jesus, my Lord, to Thee I cry:
Unless Thou help me, I must die:
O bring Thy free salvation nigh,
And take me as I am!

2 Helpless I am, and full of guilt;
But yet for me Thy blood was spilt,
And Thou canst make me what Thou
And take me as I am!   [wilt,

3 No preparation can I make,
My best resolves I only break,
Yet save me for Thine own Name's sake,
And take me as I am!

4 Behold me, Saviour, at Thy feet;
Deal with me as Thou seest meet;
Thy work begin, Thy work complete,
But take me as I am!
E. H. Hamilton.

Agnus Dei.   8.8.8.6.   W. Blow.

227   *Behold the Lamb of God!*—John i. 29.

1 Just as I am—without one plea,
But that Thy blood was shed for me,
And that Thou bidd'st me come to Thee,
O Lamb of God, I come!

2 Just as I am—and waiting not,
To rid my soul of one dark blot,
To Thee whose blood can cleanse each
O Lamb of God, I come!   [spot,

3 Just as I am, though tossed about
With many a conflict, many a doubt,
Fightings and fears, within, without,
O Lamb of God, I come!

4 Just as I am—poor, wretched, blind—
Sight, riches, healing of the mind,
Yea, all I need, in Thee to find,
O Lamb of God, I come!

5 Just as I am—Thou wilt receive,
Wilt welcome, pardon, cleanse, relieve:
Because Thy promise I believe,
O Lamb of God, I come!

6 Just as I am—Thy love unknown
Hath broken every barrier down;
Now to be Thine, yea, Thine alone,
O Lamb of God, I come!   *C. Elliott.*

May also be sung to Just as I am, *as above.*

"Whosoever Will!"

P.M.   P. P. Bliss.

Joyfully.

1. "Who - so - ev - er hear - eth!" shout, shout the sound! Send the blessed ti - dings all the world a - round! Spread the joy - ful news wher - ev - er man is found,

CHORUS.

"Who - so - ev - er will may come." "Who - so - ev - er will! who - so - ev - er will!" Send the pro - cla - ma - tion o - ver vale and hill; 'Tis a lov-ing Fa - ther calls the wand'rer home: "Whoso - ev - er will may come!"

228   *Whosoever will, let him take the water of life freely.*—REV. xxii. **17**.

2 "Whosoever cometh!" need not delay;
  Now the door is open, enter while you may;
  Jesus is the true, the only Living Way,
  "Whosoever will may come."

3 "Whosoever will"—the promise is secure;
  "Whosoever will"—for ever shall endure;
  "Whosoever will"—'tis life for evermore;
  "Whosoever will may come."   *P. P. Bliss.*

Jesus, I Come!   P.M.   GEO. C. STEBBINS

By permission. From Sankey's *Sacred Songs and Solos*.

229   *Deliver me, O my God.*—PSALM lxxi. 4.

1 Out of my bondage, sorrow, and night,
    Jesus, I come! Jesus, I come!
Into Thy freedom, gladness, and light,
    Jesus, I come to Thee!
Out of my sickness into Thy health,
Out of my want and into Thy wealth,
Out of my sin and into Thyself,
    Jesus, I come to Thee!

2 Out of my shameful failure and loss,
    Jesus, I come! Jesus, I come!
Into the glorious gain of Thy cross,
    Jesus, I come to Thee!
Out of earth's sorrows into Thy balm,
Out of life's storm and into Thy calm,
Out of distress to jubilant psalm,
    Jesus, I come to Thee!

3 Out of unrest and arrogant pride,
    Jesus, I come! Jesus, I come!
Into Thy blessèd will to abide,
    Jesus, I come to Thee!
Out of myself to dwell in Thy love,
Out of despair into raptures above,
Upward for aye on wings like a dove,
    Jesus, I come to Thee!

4 Out of the fear and dread of the tomb,
    Jesus, I come! Jesus, I come!
Into the joy and light of Thy home,
    Jesus, I come to Thee!
Out of the depths of ruin untold,
Into the peace of Thy sheltering fold,
Ever Thy glorious face to behold,
    Jesus, I come to Thee!

W. T. Sleeper

Cyprus. 7.7.7.7. Adapted from MENDELSSOHN.

Alternative Tunes, VIENNA, No. 241, and WEBER, No. 199.

230

What wilt thou that I should do unto thee?—MARK x. 51.

1 JESUS Christ is passing by;
Sinner, lift to Him thine eye;
As the precious moments flee,
Cry, "Be merciful to me!"

2 Jesus Christ is passing by;
Will He always be so nigh?
Now is the accepted day,
Seek for healing while you may.

3 Lo! He stands and calls to thee,
"What wilt thou then have of Me?"

Rise, and tell Him all thy need;
Rise,—He calleth thee indeed.

4 "Lord, I would Thy mercy see;
Lord, reveal Thy love to me;
Let it penetrate my soul,
All my heart and life control."

5 Oh, how sweet! the touch of power
Comes—it is salvation's hour;
Jesus gives from guilt release:
"Faith hath saved thee, go in peace!"

J. Denham Smith.

St. Bernard. C.M. W. RICHARDSON.

231 *As many as received Him, to them gave He power to become the sons of God.*—JOHN i. 12.

1 HERE, Lord, relying on Thy Word,
I claim Thy promise true,
That whosoe'er receiveth Thee
At once is born anew.

2 I have no gift to offer Thee,
Nor dost Thou aught require,
'Tis Thine to give, and mine to take
The gift I most desire.

3 As Saviour from the guilt of sin,
And from its awful power,
As Lord of all, to reign within,
I take Thee from this hour.

4 The words I sing are nothing worth,
If words alone they be,
But Thou canst read my heart and know
The love none else can see.

5 My Saviour, I have taken Thee,
God's gift through perfect grace,
And now among the sons of God
By birth I have a place.

6 Help me to serve Thee faithfully,
And daily conquer sin,
Then let me hear the glad "Well done!"
The crown of glory win.

E. H. G. Sargent.

Invitation.   6.6.6.6., D.   F. C. MAKER.

Come unto Me.—MATT. xi. 28.

232

1 COME to the Saviour now!
  He gently calleth thee;
In true repentance bow,
  Before Him bend the knee.
He waiteth to bestow
  Salvation, peace, and love,
True joy on earth below,
  A home in heaven above.
    Come, come, come!

2 Come to the Saviour now!
  Gaze on that crimson tide—
Water and blood—that flow
  Forth from His wounded side.
Hark to that suffering One!—
  "'Tis finished!" now He cries:
Redemption's work is done;
  Then bows His head, and dies.
    Come, come, come!

3 Come to the Saviour now!
  He suffered all for thee,
And in His merits thou
  Hast an unfailing plea.
No vain excuses frame,
  For feelings do not stay;
None who to Jesus came
  Were ever sent away.
    Come, come, come!

4 Come to the Saviour now!
  Ye who have wandered far;
Renew your solemn vow,
  For His by right you are.
Come, like poor wandering sheep,
  Returning to His fold;
His arm will safely keep,
  His love will ne'er grow cold.
    Come, come, come!

5 Come to the Saviour, all!
  Whate'er your burdens be;
Hear now His loving call—
  "Cast all your care on Me."
Come, and for every grief
  In Jesus you will find
A sure and safe relief,
  A loving Friend, and kind.
    Come, come, come!
        J. M. Wigner.

Art Thou Longing?   8.5.8.3.   IRA D. SANKEY.

By permission. From Sankey's *Sacred Songs and Solos.*

233   *I will give you rest.*—MATT. xi. 28.

1 ART thou longing? Jesus calls thee
    To His wounded side;
"Come to Me," saith He, "and ever
    Safe abide."

2 Seeking Jesus? Jesus seeks thee—
    Wants thee as thou art;
He is knocking, ever knocking
    At thy heart.

3 If thou let Him, He will save thee—
    Make thee all His own;
Guide thee, keep thee, take thee, dying,
    To His throne.

4 Wilt thou still refuse His offer?
    Wilt thou say Him nay?
Wilt thou let Him, grieved, rejected,
    Go away?   *S. C. Morgan.*

Hartham.   8.5.8.3.   LIVESEY CARROTT.

Alternative Tune, BULLINGER, *No.* 417.

234   *Rise; He calleth thee.*—MARK x. 49.

1 Lo, a loving Friend is waiting,
    He is calling thee;
Listen to His voice so tender,
    "Come to Me.

2 "On the cross for thee I suffered,
    Death I bore for thee,
Canst thou still refuse My mercy?
    Trust to Me.

3 "Long hast thou been Satan's captive,
    I will set thee free;
Then, rejoicing in thy freedom,
    Follow Me."

4 Many times has Jesus spoken,
    Now He speaks again:
Shall thy Saviour's invitation
    Be in vain?

5 Soon that voice will cease its calling,
    Wilt thou still delay?
Wait no longer, sin grows stronger,
    Yield to-day.

6 Saviour, I will wait no longer,
    Now to Thee I come;
And when life's short voyage is over,
    Take me home.

        J. M. Wigner.

Stephanos.   8.5.8.3.   Sir H. W. Baker.

Alternative Tune, BULLINGER, *No. 417.*

235   *This is the rest wherewith ye may cause the weary to rest.*—ISAIAH xxviii. 12.

1 ART thou weary? art thou languid?
   Art thou sore distrest?
   "Come to Me," saith One; "and coming,
   Be at rest!"

2 Hath He marks to lead me to Him,
   If He be my Guide?
   "In His feet and hands are wound-prints,
   And His side."

3 Is there diadem as Monarch
   That His brow adorns?
   "Yea, a crown in very surety,
   But of thorns."

4 If I find Him, if I follow,
   What His guerdon here?

"Many a sorrow, many a labour,
   Many a tear."

5 If I still hold closely to Him,
   What hath He at last?
   "Sorrow vanquished, labour ended,
   Jordan passed."

6 If I ask Him to receive me,
   Will He say me nay?
   "Not till earth, and not till heaven,
   Pass away."

7 Finding, following, keeping, struggling.
   Is He sure to bless?
   "Saints, apostles, prophets, martyrs,
   Answer—Yes!"   *J. M. Neale.*

St. Ethelwald.   S.M.   W. H. MONK.

Alternative Tune, NARENZA, *No. 41.*

236   *Behold, now is the accepted time; behold, now is the day of salvation.*—
2 COR. vi. 2.

1 "Now is the accepted time!"
   Now is the day of grace;
   Now, children, come without delay,
   And seek the Saviour's face.

2 "Now is the accepted time,"
   The Saviour calls to-day;
   To-morrow it may be too late—
   Then why should you delay?

3 "Now is the accepted time,"
   And Jesus bids you come;
   And every promise in His Word
   Declares there yet is room.

4 Lord, draw our youthful hearts
   To seek a Saviour's love;
   Then shall rejoicing angels sing
   The joyful news above.   *J. Dobell.*

For You and for Me.

Slow. P.M. WILL L. THOMPSON.

CHORUS.

"Come home!.. come home!.. Ye who are wea-ry, come home!"

rit.

Earnestly, tender-ly, Je-sus is call-ing, Calling, "Oh, sinner, come home!"

237 *To-day if ye will hear His voice, harden not your hearts.*—HEB. iii. **7, 8.**

1 SOFTLY and tenderly Jesus is calling—
   Calling for you and for me;
 Patiently Jesus is waiting and watching—
   Watching for you and for me.
     "Come home!" etc.

2 Why should we tarry when Jesus is pleading—
   Pleading for you and for me?
 Why should we linger and heed not His mercies—
   Mercies for you and for me?

3 Time is now fleeting. the moments are passing—
   Passing from you and from me;
 Shadows are gathering, death may be coming—
   Coming for you and for me!

4 Oh, for the wonderful love He has promised—
   Promised for you and for me!
 Though we have sinned, He has mercy and pardon—
   Pardon for you and for me!
                         W. L. Thompson.

Tenderly Calling!   P.M.   GEO. C. STEBBINS.

Call - ing to - day! . .   call - ing to - day! . .
Call - ing, call-ing to - day, to-day!   Call - ing, call- ing to - day, to-day!

Je - sus is call - ing, is ten-der-ly call-ing to - day! .
Je - sus is ten-der - ly call -ing to-day!

238   *Ye shall find rest unto your souls.*—MATT. xi. 29.

1 JESUS is tenderly calling thee home—
    Calling to-day, calling to-day!
Why from the sunshine of love wilt thou roam,
    Farther and farther away?
      Calling to-day! etc.

2 Jesus is calling the weary to rest—
    Calling to-day, calling to-day!
Bring Him thy burden, and thou shalt be blest:
    He will not turn thee away.

3 Jesus is waiting, oh, come to Him now—
    Waiting to-day, waiting to-day!
Come with thy sins, at His feet lowly bow;
    Come, and no longer delay!

4 Jesus is pleading: oh, list to His voice—
    Hear Him to-day, hear Him to-day!
They who believe on His Name shall rejoice;
    Quickly arise and away!
            Fanny J. Crosby.

Seeking to Save.

6.5.6.4., with Chorus.

P. P. BLISS.

CHORUS.

Seek-ing to save, seek-ing to save; Lost one,'tis Je-sus seek-ing to save! .. Seek-ing to save, .. seek-ing to save; Lost one,'tis Je-sus seek-ing to save!

239 *The Son of man is come to seek and to save that which was lost.—*LUKE xix. **10.**

1 TENDERLY the shepherd,
　O'er the mountains cold,
Goes to bring his lost one
　Back to the fold.

　　Seeking to save,
　　Seeking to save;
　Lost one, 'tis Jesus
　　Seeking to save!

2 Patiently the owner
　Seeks, with earnest care,
In the dust and darkness,
　Her treasures rare.

3 Lovingly the father
　Sends the news around,
"He once dead, now liveth—
　Once lost, is found."

P. P. Bliss.

240 Response.

S.M., with Chorus.

L. HARTSOUGH.

CHORUS.

I am com-ing, Lord!

Com-ing now to Thee! Wash me, cleanse me, in the blood That flowed on Cal-va-ry.

Alternative Tune (without Chorus), ST. GEORGE, *No.* 220.

240 *Wash me throughly . . . and cleanse me from my sin.*—PSALM li. 2.

1 I HEAR Thy welcome voice,
That calls me, Lord, to Thee
For cleansing in Thy precious blood
That flowed on Calvary.
I am coming, Lord, etc.

2 'Tis Jesus calls me on
To perfect faith and love,
To perfect hope, and peace, and trust,
For earth and heaven above.

3 'Tis Jesus who confirms
The blessèd work within,

By adding grace to welcomed grace,
Where reigned the power of sin.

4 And He the witness gives
To loyal hearts and free,
That every promise is fulfilled,
If faith but brings the plea.

5 All hail, atoning blood!
All hail, redeeming grace!
All hail, the gift of Christ, our Lord,
Our Strength and Righteousness!

L. Hartsough.

Vienna.　　　　　7.7.7.7.　　　　　J. H. KNECHT.

241　*Knowing the time, that now it is high time to awake out of sleep.*—ROM. xiii. 11.

1 TIME is earnest, passing by;
Death is earnest, drawing nigh:
Sinner, wilt thou trifling be?
Time and death appeal to thee.

2 Life is earnest; when 'tis o'er,
Thou returnest nevermore;
Soon to meet eternity,
Wilt thou never serious be?

3 God is earnest: kneel and pray,
Ere the season pass away;

Ere He set His judgment throne;
Ere the day of grace be gone.

4 Christ is earnest, bids thee come,
Paid thy spirit's priceless sum;
Wilt thou spurn thy Saviour's love,
Pleading with thee from above?

5 Oh, be earnest, do not stay!
Thou may'st perish, e'en to-day:
Rise, thou lost one, rise and flee:
Lo! thy Saviour waits for thee. *S. Dyer.*

Vocation.
Tenderly and slowly.

8 7.8.7., D.

BOYTON SMITH.

Alternative Tune, DEERHURST, *No.* 557.

242   *I am not come to call the righteous, but sinners to repentance.*—MATT. ix. 13.

1 LOVING Saviour, Thou art calling
    Sinners to Thyself to-day;
They have wandered from the shelter
    Of Thy fold and gone astray.
Bring them back to peace and safety;
    May they hear Thy loving call;
Thou art waiting to receive them,
    Draw each one, receive them all.

2 Loving Saviour, I am coming,
    Bringing all my sins to Thee;
As I am, in shame and sorrow,
    Lord, receive and rescue me.

At the cross I lay my burden,
    Lowly at Thy feet I bow;
I no longer doubt and grieve Thee,
    Cleanse my heart: Lord, save me now!

3 Loving Saviour, Thou art pleading
    For my heart, my life, my all;
Long without I've kept Thee waiting,
    Now I open at Thy call.
Come Thou in, take full possession,
    Consecrated it shall be;
Take my life, direct and use it,
    I will live it all for Thee!

J. Stephens.

243 Pass Me Not.

P.M.

W. H. DOANE.

CHORUS.

Sa - viour, Sa - viour, Hear my hum - ble cry;

While on oth-ers Thou art call - ing, Do not pass me by.

Whosoever shall call upon the name of the Lord shall be saved.—ACTS ii. 21.

243

1 PASS me not, O gracious Saviour,
   Hear my humble cry;
   While on others Thou art calling,
   Do not pass me by.
   Saviour, Saviour, etc.

2 Let me at a throne of mercy
   Find a sweet relief;
   Kneeling there in deep contrition,
   Help my unbelief.

3 Trusting only in Thy merit,
   Would I seek Thy face;
   Heal my wounded, broken spirit,
   Save me by Thy grace.

4 Thou, the spring of all my comfort,
   More than life to me;
   Whom have I on earth beside Thee?
   Whom in heaven but Thee?
   Fanny J. Crosby.

Jesus is Calling. *With feeling.* 12.10.12.10. B. MANSELL RAMSEY.

Alternative Tune, SANCTISSIMUS, *No. 37.*

Jesus . . . saith unto him, Follow Me.—JOHN i. 43.

244

1 JESUS is calling in accents of tenderness,
   Jesus is calling, O sinner, to thee,
   Just as of old, by the waters of Galilee,
   Fell from His lips the command, "Follow Me."

2 Take to the Saviour thy sorrow and selfishness,
   Break from the fetters of sin, and be free;
   Jesus has promised thee strength as thou needest it,
   If thou obey the command, "Follow Me."

3 O Thou who knowest our wants and infirmities,
   Thou who hast promised our Helper to be,
   Grant us Thy grace, that with heart-searching earnestness
   We may respond to the call, "Follow Me." *B. M. Ramsey.*

"Verily! Verily!"   10.10.10.6., with Chorus.   J. McGRANAHAN

Chorus.

"Ver - i - ly, ver - i - ly,

I say un - to you;" "Ver - i - ly, ver - i - ly,"—mes-sage ev - er new!—

"He that be-liev-eth on the Son"—'tis true!—"*Hath* ev - er - last - ing life!"

245   *He that believeth on Me hath everlasting life.*—JOHN vi. 47.

1 OH, what a Saviour—that He died for me!
　　From condemnation He hath made me free;
　　"He that believeth on the Son," saith He,
　　　　"*Hath* everlasting life."
　　　　"Verily, verily," etc.

2 All my iniquities on Him were laid,
　　All my indebtedness by Him was paid;
　　All who believe on Him, the Lord hath said,
　　　　"*Have* everlasting life."

3 Though poor and needy, I can trust my Lord;
　　Though weak and sinful, I believe His word;
　　Oh, glad message; every child of God
　　　　"*Hath* everlasting life."

4 Though all unworthy, yet I will not doubt;
　　For him that cometh He will not cast out:
　　"He that believeth"—oh, the good news shout!—
　　　　"HATH everlasting life."

　　　　　　　　　　J. McGranahan.

Nothing to Pay!   P.M.   FRANCES R. HAVERGAL.

246   *And when they had nothing to pay, he frankly forgave them both.—*
   LUKE vii. 42.

1 NOTHING to pay! ah, nothing to pay!
   Never a word of excuse to say!
   Year after year thou hast filled the score,
   Owing thy Lord still more and more.
   Hear the voice of Jesus say,
   "Verily thou hast nothing to pay!
   Ruined, lost art thou, and yet
   I forgave thee all that debt!"

2 Nothing to pay! the debt is so great;
   What will you do with the awful weight?
   How shall the way of escape be made?
   Nothing to pay! yet it must be paid!
   Hear the voice of Jesus say,
   "Verily thou hast nothing to pay!
   All has been put to My account,
   I have paid the full amount."

3 Nothing to pay! yes, nothing to pay.
   Jesus has cleared all the debt away,
   Blotted it out with His bleeding hand!
   Free and forgiven, and loved, you stand.
   Hear the voice of Jesus say,
   "Verily thou hast nothing to pay!
   Paid is the debt and the debtor free!
   Now I ask thee, Lovest thou Me?"
          Frances R. Havergal.

Oh, Precious Words!   C.M., and Refrain.

IRA D. SANKEY.

1. "Who - ev - er he may be, Who - ev - er he may be;
2. "Have life for ev - er - more, Have life for ev - er - more;

I .. will in no wise cast him out, Who - ev - er he may be."
And all that en - ter in by Me Have life for ev - er - more."

Alternative Tune, BELMONT, *No.* 148.

247   *Him that cometh to Me I will in no wise cast out.*—JOHN vi. 37.

1 OH, precious words that Jesus said!—
  "The soul that comes to Me,
I will in no wise cast him out,
  Whoever he may be."
    "Whoever he may be,
    Whoever he may be;
  I will in no wise cast him out,
    Whoever he may be."

2 Oh, precious words that Jesus said!—
  "Behold, I am the Door;
And all that enter in by Me
  Have life for evermore."
    "Have life for evermore,
    Have life for evermore;
  And all that enter in by Me
    Have life for evermore."

3 Oh, precious words that Jesus said!—
  "Come, weary souls oppressed,
Come, take My yoke and learn of Me,
  And I will give you rest."
    "And I will give you rest,
    And I will give you rest;
  Come, take My yoke and learn of Me,
    And I will give you rest."

4 Oh, precious words that Jesus said!—
  "The world I overcame;
And they who follow where I lead
  Shall conquer in My Name."
    "Shall conquer in My Name,
    Shall conquer in My Name;
  And they who follow where I lead
    Shall conquer in My Name."

Fanny J. Crosby.

Lancashire. 7.6.7.6., D. HENRY SMART.

Alternative Tune, MUNICH, *No.* 91.

248 *Where your treasure is, there will your heart be also.*—LUKE xii. 34.

1 Go thou in life's fair morning,
    Go in the bloom of youth,
And buy, for thine adorning,
    The precious pearl of truth.
Secure this heavenly treasure,
    And bind it on thy heart,
And let not earthly pleasure
    E'er cause it to depart.

2 Go, while the day-star shineth,
    Go, while thy heart is light,
Go, ere thy strength declineth,
    While every sense is bright.
Sell all thou hast, and buy it;
    'Tis worth all earthly things,
Rubies and gold and diamonds,
    Sceptres and crowns of kings

3 Go, ere the clouds of sorrow
    Steal o'er the bloom of youth;
Defer not till to-morrow,
    Go now, and buy the truth.
Go, seek thy great Creator,
    Learn early to be wise;
Go, place upon His altar
    A morning sacrifice.
            I. B. Woodbury.

"Over the Line!" P.M. E. H. Phelps.

REFRAIN.

1, 2, 3. "O-ver the line!" Hear the sweet re-frain! Angels are chanting the hea-venly strain!
4. "O -ver the line!" Hear the sweet re-frain! Angels are chanting the hea-venly strain!

1,2,3. "O-ver the line!" Why should I re-main With a step be-tween me and Je - sus?
4. "O-ver the line!" I *will not* re-main; I'll cross it, and go to Je - sus.

249

Acquaint now thyself with Him, and be at peace.—Job xxii. 21.

1 Oh, tender and sweet was the Master's voice,
  As He lovingly called to me:
  "Come over the line! it is only a step;
  I am waiting, My child, for thee!"
  "Over the line!" etc.

2 "But my sins are many, my faith is small";
  Lo! the answer came quick and clear;
  "Thou needest not trust in thyself at all;
  Step over the line; I am here!"

3 "But my flesh is weak," I tearfully said,
  "And the way I cannot see;
  I fear if I try I may sadly fail,
  And thus may dishonour Thee."

4 Ah! the world is cold, and I cannot go back:
  Press forward I surely must:
  I will place my hand in His wounded palm,
  Step over the line and *trust.*
  "Over the line!" etc. *N. K. Bradford.*

There is Life for a Look.   P.M.   E. G. Taylor.

Refrain.

Look! look! look and live! There is life for a look at the Cru-ci-fied One; There is life at this mo-ment for thee.

250   *Look unto Me, and be ye saved, all the ends of the earth.*—Isa. xlv. 22.

1.

There is life for a look at the crucified One,
  There is life at this moment for thee;
Then look, sinner, look unto Him, and be saved,
  Unto Him who was nailed to the tree.
  Look! look! look and live! etc.

2.

Oh, why was He there as the Bearer of sin,
  If on Jesus thy sins were not laid?
Oh, why from His side flowed the sin-cleansing blood,
  If His dying thy debt has not paid?

3.

It is not thy tears of repentance, nor prayers,
  But the *blood*, that atones for the soul;
On Him then who shed it thou mayest at once
  Thy weight of iniquities roll.   [once

4.

We are "healed by His stripes";—wouldst thou add to the word?
  And He is our Righteousness made;
The best robe of heaven He bids thee put on:
  Oh, couldst thou be better arrayed?   [on:

5.

Then take with rejoicing from Jesus at once
  The life everlasting He gives;
And know with assurance thou never canst die,
  Since Jesus, thy Righteousness, lives. [die,

6.

There is life for a look at the crucified One,
  There is life at this moment for thee:
Then look, sinner, look unto Him, and be saved,
  And know thyself spotless as He.

A. M. Hull.

St. Catherine. [FIRST TUNE.]   8.8.8.8.8.8.   J. G. WALTON.

His knock is clear a-bove earth's din; Oh, shall I, shall I let Him in?

Southborough. [SECOND TUNE.]   L.M.   E. J. BELLERBY.

Alternative Tune, STAINCLIFFE, *No.* 586.

251   *Hear Me now therefore, O ye children.*—PROVERBS v. 7.

1 A KINGLY summons now I hear;
It is the Saviour drawing near:
His knock is clear above earth's **din**;
Oh, shall I, shall I let Him in?

2 His brow no longer crowned with thorn,
His hands with nails no longer torn:
"My child," saith He, "give up thy sin";
Oh, shall I, shall I let Him in?

3 Glory and honour crown Him now;
Shall my proud will refuse to bow?
Conscience to chide doth now begin;
Oh, shall I, shall I let Him in?

4 Again His knock is loud and clear;
His wondrous love casts out all fear:
Thy mighty arm my fight shall win;
Jesus, my Saviour, enter in.

Gibbard Hughes.

When singing the First Tune (*St. Catherine*) repeat the last two lines of each verse.

Redhead.   7.7.7.7.7.7.   R. REDHEAD.

Alternative Tune, WELLS, *No.* 181.

252   *I will put thee in a clift of the rock.*—EXODUS xxxiii. 22

1 ROCK of Ages, cleft for me,
　Let me hide myself in Thee;
　Let the water and the blood,
　From Thy riven side which flowed,
　Be of sin the double cure—
　Cleanse me from its guilt and power.

2 Not the labour of my hands
　Can fulfil Thy law's demands:
　Could my zeal no respite know,
　Could my tears for ever flow,
　All for sin could not atone;
　Thou must save, and Thou alone.

3 Nothing in my hand I bring,
　Simply to Thy cross I cling:
　Naked, come to Thee for dress;
　Helpless, look to Thee for grace;
　Foul, I to the fountain fly:
　Wash me, Saviour, or I die!

4 While I draw this fleeting breath,
　When mine eyelids close in death,
　When I soar to worlds unknown,
　See Thee on Thy judgment throne:
　Rock of Ages, cleft for me,
　Let me hide myself in Thee!
　　　　　　　A. M. Toplady.

Rousseau. 8.7.8.7.8.7. J. J. Rousseau.

253 *He that hath no money ; come ye, buy, and eat ; yea, come, buy wine and milk without money and without price.—Isaiah lv. 1.*

1 COME, ye sinners, poor and needy,
   Weak and wounded, sick and sore ;
Jesus ready stands to save you,
   Full of pity, love, and power :
     He is able,
  He is willing ; doubt no more.

2 Now, ye needy, come and welcome ;
   God's free bounty glorify :
True belief and true repentance—
   Every grace that brings you nigh—
     Without money,
  Come to Jesus Christ and buy.

3 Let not conscience make you linger,
   Nor of fitness fondly dream ;
All the fitness He requireth
   Is to feel your need of Him :
     This He gives you—
  'Tis the Spirit's rising beam.

4 Come, ye weary, heavy-laden,
   Bruised and ruined by the Fall ;
If you tarry till you're better,
   You will never come at all :
     Not the righteous—
  Sinners, Jesus came to call.

5 View Him prostrate in the garden,
   On the ground your Maker lies !
On the awful tree behold Him,
   Hear Him cry before He dies,
     " It is finished !"
  Sinner, will not this suffice ?

6 Lo, the incarnate God, ascended,
   Pleads the merit of His blood ;
Venture on Him, venture wholly,
   Let no other trust intrude :
     None but Jesus
  Can do helpless sinners good.

J. Hart.

254 All to Christ I owe. P.M. J. T. Grape.

1. I . . hear the Sa-viour say, "Thy strength in-deed is small ; Child of

CHORUS.

weakness, watch and pray, Find in Me thine all in all." Je - sus paid it all—

All to Him I owe; Sin had left a crimson stain ; He washed it white as snow.

254 *Who His own self bare our sins.*—1 PETER ii. 24.

2 Lord, now indeed I find
  Thy power, and Thine alone,
Can change the leper's spots,
  And melt the heart of stone.

3 For nothing good have I
  Whereby Thy grace to claim—

I'll wash my garments white
  In the blood of Calvary's Lamb.

4 And when before the throne
  I stand in Him complete,
I'll lay my trophies down,
  All down at Jesus' feet.

E. M. Hull.

Cairnbrook. 8.5.8.3. E. PROUT.

By permission of the Congregational Union of England and Wales.

Prove me now . . . saith the Lord of hosts.—MAL. iii. 10.

255

1 PROVE HIM! An almighty Saviour
  Is the Saviour still ;
Prove that He can save you fully—
  Can and will.

2 Prove Him! He is God eternal,
  An unchanging Friend,
With a love that never knoweth
  Bound or end.

3 Boundless is His love as ocean,
  Wide as heaven's own roof,
Put the riches of His mercy
  To the proof.

4 Prove Him now—for now you need Him ;
  Life is poor indeed

Lacking His great love that filleth
  All our need.

5 Prove Him—now the time of mercy,
  'Tis the Saviour's day ;
Make it yours, nor let it sadly
  Die away.

6 Prove Him—with your sin and sorrow,
  Come ; He longs to give
Pardon, freedom, with all gladness,
  Joys that live !

7 Heaven within you, heaven above you,
  Then your heart will raise
Glad thanksgiving for His mercies,
  Songs of praise ! *Anon.*

B

Dalkeith. 10.10.10.10. T. Hewlett.

256 *In whom we have redemption through His blood, the forgiveness of sins.*—Eph. i. 7.

1 WEARY of earth, and laden with my sin,
  I look at heaven, and long to enter in;
  But there no evil thing may find a home,
  And yet I hear a voice that bids me, "Come!"

2 So vile I am, how dare I hope to stand
  In the pure glory of that holy land?
  Before the whiteness of that throne appear?
  Yet there are hands stretched out to draw me near.

3 The while I fain would tread the heavenly way,
  Seems evil ever with me day by day;
  Yet on mine ears the gracious tidings fall:
  "Repent, confess, and thou art loosed from all."

4 It is the voice of Jesus that I hear,
  His are the hands outstretched to draw me near,
  And His the blood that can for all atone,
  And set me faultless there before the throne.

5 Yea, Thou wilt answer for me, righteous Lord;
  Thine all the merits, mine the great reward;
  Thine the sharp thorns, and mine the golden crown;
  Mine the life won, and Thine the life laid down.

6 Naught can I bring Thee, Lord, for all I owe,
  Yet let my full heart what it can bestow;
  Like Mary's gift, let my devotion prove,
  Forgiven greatly, how I greatly love.

S. J. Stone.

257 **The Love of Jesus.** P.M. T. E. Perkins.

CHORUS.

Je-sus' love, precious love, Bound-less and pure and free; Oh, turn to that love, weary wand'ring soul: Je-sus plead-eth with thee!

257

Greater love hath no man than this.—JOHN xv. 13.

1 THERE is no love like the love of Jesus—
  Never to fade or fall,
 Till into the fold of the peace of God
  He has gathered us all.
  Jesus' love, precious love, etc.

2 There is no heart like the heart of Jesus,
  Filled with a tender love;
 No throb nor throe that our hearts can know,
  But He feels it above.

3 There is no eye like the eye of Jesus,
  Piercing so far away;

Ne'er out of the sight of its tender light
  Can the wanderer stray.

4 There is no voice like the voice of Jesus—
  Tender and sweet its chime,
 Like musical ring of a flowing spring
  In the bright summer time.

5 Oh, let us hark to the voice of Jesus;
  Oh, may we never roam,
 Till safe we rest on His loving breast,
  In the dear heavenly home.
                    W. E. Littlewood.

Look Away to Jesus.   6.5.6.5., D.   P. P. BLISS.

Alternative Tune, WOODBROOK, *No.* 668.
Looking for the mercy of our Lord Jesus Christ.—JUDE 21.

258

1 LOOK away to Jesus,
  Soul by sin oppressed;
 'Twas for thee He suffered,
  Come to Him and rest:
 All thy griefs He carried;
  All thy sins He bore;
 Look away to Jesus,
  Trust Him evermore.

2 Look away to Jesus,
  Soldier in the fight,
 When the battle thickens,
  Keep thine armour bright:

Though thy foes be many,
  Though thy strength be small,
 Look away to Jesus;
  He will conquer all.

3 Look away to Jesus,
  When the skies are fair:
 Calm seas have their dangers;
  Mariner, beware!
 Earthly joys are fleeting,
  Going as they came:
 Look away to Jesus,
  Evermore the same.   *H. Burton.*

Even Me! [FIRST TUNE.] 8.7.8.7., and Refrain. W. B. BRADBURY.

E - ven me! e - ven me! Let some drops now fall on me!

Etiam et Mihi. [SECOND TUNE.] 8.7.8.7.3. J. B. DYKES.

By permission of Novello and Company, Limited.

259

Bless me, even me also, O my Father.—GEN. xxvii. 38.

1 LORD, I hear of showers of blessing
    Thou art scattering, full and free,
Showers the thirsty land refreshing:
    Let some drops now fall on me—
        Even me!

2 Pass me not, O gracious Father,
    Sinful though my heart may be;
Thou might'st leave me, but the rather
    Let Thy mercy light on me—
        Even me!

3 Pass me not, O tender Saviour,
    Let me love and cling to Thee;
I am longing for Thy favour,
    Whilst Thou'rt calling, oh, call me—
        Even me!

4 Pass me not, O mighty Spirit,
    Thou canst make the blind to see;
Witnesser of Jesus' merit,
    Speak the word of power to me—
        Even me!

5 Love of God, so pure and changeless;
    Blood of Christ, so rich and free;
Grace of God, so strong and boundless;
    Magnify them all in me—
        Even me!

6 Pass me not: Thy lost one bringing,
    Bind my heart, O Lord, to Thee;
Whilst the streams of life are springing
    Blessing others, oh, bless me—
        Even me!
            E. Codner.

All for You!   P.M.   LIVESEY CARROTT.

you! for you!

REFRAIN.

Yes, children,'twas for you! yes,
you! for you!

all   for   you!   Yes, children,'twas for you! yes,   all   for   you!
All, yes all, for   you! for you!

260

Who gave Himself for us.—TITUS ii. 14.

1 CHILDREN, think on Jesus' love—
        All for you!
    How He came from heaven above—
        All for you!
    He whom angels did adore,
    Full of wisdom, grace, and power,
    How He all your sorrows bore.
        Yes, children, 'twas for you! etc.

2 Think how He contrived the plan
        All for you!
    And, to save, became a Man—
        All for you!
    Left His glorious throne on high;
    Came to suffer, bleed, and die,
    You to raise above the sky.

3 See! He hangs upon the tree—
        All for you!
    Crowned with thorns in agony—
        All for you!
    Yes, for you all this He bore,
    And for thousands, thousands more,
    All to save from hell's dark door.   *Anon.*

Ibarwicb.　　　　　　5.5.11.5.5.11.　　　　　　B. MILGROVE.

261　*Is it nothing to you, all ye that pass by?*—LAMENTATIONS i. 12.

1.

ALL ye that pass by,
To Jesus draw nigh;
To you is it nothing that Jesus should die?
Your ransom and peace,
Your surety He is:
Come, see if there ever was sorrow like His.

2.

For what you have done
His blood must atone:　　　　[Son:
The Father hath punished for you His dear
The Lord, in the day
Of His anger, did lay　　　　[away.
Your sins on the Lamb, and He bore them

3.

He dies to atone
For sins not His own;　　　　[hath done.
Your debt He hath paid, and your work He
Ye all may receive
The peace He did leave,　　　　[give!"
Who made intercession, "My Father, for-

4.

For you and for me
He prayed on the tree;
The prayer is accepted, the sinner is free.
That sinner am I,
Who on Jesus rely,
And come for the pardon God cannot deny.

5.

My pardon I claim;
For a sinner I am,
A sinner believing in Jesus' dear Name.
He purchased the grace
Which now I embrace.
O Father, Thou know'st He hath died in my place.

C. Wesley.

Wonderful Words of Life! P.M. P. P. BLISS.

CHORUS.

Beau-ti-ful words! wonderful words! Wonderful words of life! .. life! ..

1st time. 2nd time.

262

The words that I speak unto you, they are spirit, and they are life.—
JOHN vi. 63.

1 SING them over again to me,
   Wonderful words of life!
Let me more of their beauty see,
   Wonderful words of life!
      Words of life and beauty,
      Teach me faith and duty!
         Beautiful words! wonderful words! **etc.**

2 Christ, the blessèd One. gives to all
   Wonderful words of life!
Sinner, list to the loving call,
   Wonderful words of life!
      All so freely given,
      Wooing us to heaven!

3 Sweetly echo the Gospel call,
   Wonderful words of life!
Offer pardon and peace to all,
   Wonderful words of life!
      Jesus, only Saviour,
      Sanctify for ever!
                  P. P Bliss.

Weeping Will not Save Me. P.M. R. LOWRY.

REFRAIN.

Je - sus wept and died for me;

Je - sus suf-fer'd on the tree; Je-sus waits to make me free, He a-lone can save me.

263 *By grace are ye saved through faith.*—EPH. ii. 8.

1 WEEPING will not save me;
Though my face were bathed in tears,
That could not allay my fears,
Could not wash the sins of years;
  Weeping will not save me.
    Jesus wept and died for me, etc.

2 Working will not save me;
Purest deeds that I can do,
Holiest thoughts and feelings too,
Cannot form my soul anew;
  Working will not save me.

3 Waiting will not save me;
Helpless, guilty, lost I lie,
In my ear is mercy's cry;
If I wait I can but die:
  Waiting will not save me.

4 Praying will not save me;
All the prayers that I could say
Could not wash my sins away—
The debt I owe could never pay:
  Praying will not save me.

5 Faith in Christ *will* save me;
Let me trust Thy gracious Son,
Trust the work that He has done,
To His arms, Lord, help me run;
  Faith in Christ *will* save me.
          R. Lowry.

264 Saving Power. P.M. G. F. ROOT.

CHORUS.

Oh, touch the hem of His gar-ment! And thou too shalt be free; His sav-ing pow'r this ve-ry hour Shall give new life to thee!

264 *If I may but touch His garment, I shall be whole.*—MATT. ix. 21.

1 SHE only touched the hem of His garment,
As to His side she stole,
Amid the crowd that gathered around Him
And straightway she was whole.
Oh, touch the hem of His garment, etc.

2 She came in fear and trembling before Him,
She knew her Lord had come;
She felt that from Him virtue had healed her;
The mighty deed was done.

3 He turned with, "Daughter, be of good comfort;
Thy faith hath made thee whole!"
And peace that passeth all understanding
With gladness filled her soul.

G. F. Root.

Almost Persuaded. P.M.

P. P. BLISS.

265 *Almost thou persuadest me to be a Christian.*—ACTS xxvi. 28.

1 "ALMOST persuaded"—now to believe:
"Almost persuaded"—Christ to receive:
Seems now some soul to say—
"Go, Spirit, go Thy way;
Some more convenient day
On Thee I'll call"?

2 "Almost persuaded," come, come to-day;
"Almost persuaded," turn not away:
Jesus invites you here.
Angels are lingering near,
Prayers rise from hearts so dear;
Oh, wanderer, come!

3 "Almost persuaded,"—harvest is past!
"Almost persuaded"—doom comes at last:
"Almost" cannot avail;
"Almost" is but to fail!
Sad, sad that bitter wail—
"Almost"—*but lost.*

P. P. Bliss.

H*

Look and Live!

Tenderly.

P.M.

P. P. BLISS.

Look! the Lord is lift-ed high,

Look to Him, He's ev-er nigh: Look and live! why will ye die? Look and live!

266

As Moses lifted up the serpent in the wilderness, even so must the Son of Man be lifted up.—JOHN iii. 14.

1 LOOK to Jesus, weary one,
  Look and live! look and live!
Look at what the Lord has done,
  Look and live!
See Him lifted on the tree,
  Look and live! look and live!
Hear Him say, "Look unto Me!"
  Look and live!
    Look! the Lord, etc.

2 Though unworthy. vile, unclean,
  Look and live! look and live!
Look away from self and sin,
  Look and live!
Long by Satan's power enslaved,
  Look and live! look and live!
Look to Him, ye shall be saved,
  Look and live.

3 Though you've wandered far away,
  Look and live! look and live!
Harden not your heart to-day,
  Look and live!
'Tis thy Father calls thee home,
  Look and live! look and live!
Whosoever will may come.
  Look and live!

P. P. Bliss.

One There is Who Loves Thee. P.M.

W. H. DOANE.

REFRAIN.

One there is who loves thee,

Oh, re-ceive Him now!.. He has wait-ed all thy days; Why wait-est thou?

267 *Therefore will the Lord wait, that He may be gracious unto you.*—ISA. xxx. 18.

1 ONE there is who loves thee,
    Waiting still for thee:
Can'st thou yet reject Him?
    None so kind as He!
Do not grieve Him longer,
    Come and trust Him now!
He has waited all thy days:
    Why waitest thou?
    One there is, etc

2 Tenderly he woos thee,
    Do not slight His call;
Though thy sins are many,
    He'll forgive them all.
Turn to Him, repenting,
    He will cleanse thee now;
He is waiting at thy heart:
    Why waitest thou?

3 Jesus still is waiting;
    Sinner, why delay?
To His arms of mercy
    Rise and haste away!
Only come believing,
    He will save thee now;
He is waiting at the door:
    Why waitest thou?

        H. C. Ayers.

Redemption. 9.8.9.8., and Chorus. P. BILHORN.

CHORUS.

Be - lieve it, O sinner, be - lieve it; Re - ceive the glad message—'tis true;

rit.

Trust now in the cru-ci-fied Sa - viour, Sal - va - tion He offers to you.

268   *In whom we have redemption through His blood.*—EPH. i. 7.

1 REDEMPTION! oh, wonderful story—
    Glad message for you and for me:
  That Jesus has purchased our pardon,
    And paid all the debt on the tree.
      Believe it, O sinner, believe it, etc.

2 From death unto life He hath brought us,
    And made us by grace sons of God;
  A fountain is opened for sinners:
    Oh, wash and be cleansed in the blood!

3 No longer shall sin have dominion,
    Though present to tempt and annoy;
  For Christ, in His blessèd redemption,
    The power of sin shall destroy.

4 Accept now God's offer of mercy;
    To Jesus, oh, hasten to-day;
  For He will receive him that cometh,
    And never will turn him away.
                        S. M. Sayford.

The Gospel of Thy Grace. 6.6.6.6., and Chorus. J. McGranahan.

CHORUS.

That "Who - so - ev - er will be-lieve, Shall

ev - er last-ing life receive! Shall ev - - er - last - ing life re - ceive!"

Alternative Tune, St. Godric, *No.* 63.

269 *God so loved the world that He gave His only-begotten Son.*—John iii. 16.

1 THE Gospel of Thy grace
     My stubborn heart has won;
   For God so loved the world,
     He gave His only Son,
   That "Whosoever will believe,
   Shall everlasting life receive!"

2 The serpent "lifted up"
     Could life and healing give,
   So Jesus on the cross
     Bids me to look and live;
   For "Whosoever will believe,
   Shall everlasting life receive!"

3 "The soul that sinneth dies:"
     My awful doom I heard;
   I was for ever lost,
     But for Thy gracious word
   That "Whosoever will believe,
   Shall everlasting life receive!"

4 "Not to condemn the world"
     The "Man of Sorrows" came;
   But that the world might have
     Salvation through His Name;
   For "Whosoever will believe,
   Shall everlasting life receive!"

5 "Lord, help my unbelief!"
     Give me the peace of faith,
   To rest with childlike trust
     On what Thy Gospel saith,
   That "Whosoever will believe,
   Shall everlasting life receive!"
                    A. T. Pierson.

SECTION VII.—The Christian Life.
(1.) Assurance.

Vox Dilecti.   C.M.D.   J. B. DYKES.

270   *If any man thirst, let him come unto Me, and drink.*—JOHN vii. 37.

1 I HEARD the voice of Jesus say,
  "Come unto Me and rest:
Lay down, thou weary one, lay down
  Thy head upon My breast."
I came to Jesus as I was,
  Weary, and worn, and sad,
I found in Him a resting-place,
  And He has made me glad.

2 I heard the voice of Jesus say,
  "Behold I freely give
The living water—thirsty one,
  Stoop down, and drink, and live."
I came to Jesus, and I drank
  Of that life-giving stream;
My thirst was quenched, my soul revived,
  And now I live in Him.

3 I heard the voice of Jesus say,
  "I am this dark world's Light;
Look unto Me; thy morn shall rise,
  And all thy day be bright."
I looked to Jesus, and I found
  In Him my Star, my Sun;
And in that light of life I'll walk,
  Till travelling days are done.
                    H. Bonar.

What a Wonderful Saviour!   P.M.   E. A. HOFFMANN.

CHORUS.

What a won - der - ful Sa - viour is Je - sus, my Je - sus!

What a won - der - ful Sa - viour is Je - sus, my Lord!

271   *Now . . . hath He appeared to put away sin by the sacrifice of Himself.—*
HEB. ix. 26.

1 CHRIST has for sin atonement made,
 What a wonderful Saviour!
We are redeemed! the price is paid!
What a wonderful Saviour!
 What a wonderful Saviour! etc.

2 I praise Him for the cleansing blood,
 What a wonderful Saviour!
That reconciled my soul to God,
 What a wonderful Saviour!

3 He dwells within me day by day,
 What a wonderful Saviour!
And keeps me faithful all the way,
 What a wonderful Saviour!

4 He gives me overcoming power,
 What a wonderful Saviour!
And triumph in each conflict hour,
 What a wonderful Saviour!

5 To Him I've given all my heart,
 What a wonderful Saviour!
The world shall never share a part,
 What a wonderful Saviour!
      E. A. Hoffmann.

Standing on the Promises.   P.M.

R. KELSO CARTER.

CHORUS.

Stand - ing, stand - ing, Standing on the promis-es of God my Saviour;
Standing on the promises, standing on the promises,

Stand - ing, stand - ing, I'm stand-ing on the promises of God.
Standing on the promises, standing on the promises,

272   *All the promises of God in Him are yea and . . . Amen.*—2 COR. i. 20.

1 STANDING on the promises of Christ my King,
  Through eternal ages let His praises ring;
  Glory in the highest, I will shout and sing,
  Standing on the promises of God.
    Stand- . . . ing, . . stand- . . . ing, . . etc.

2 Standing on the promises that cannot fail,
  When the howling storms of doubt and fear assail,
  By the living Word of God I shall prevail,
  Standing on the promises of God.

3 Standing on the promises I now can see
  Perfect, present cleansing in the blood for me;
  Standing in the liberty where Christ makes free,
  Standing on the promises of God.

4 Standing on the promises of Christ the Lord,
  Bound to Him eternally by love's strong cord,
  Overcoming daily with the Spirit's sword,
  Standing on the promises of God.

5 Standing on the promises I cannot fall,
  Listening every moment to the Spirit's call,
  Resting in my Saviour as my All-in-all,
  Standing on the promises of God.   *R. Kelso Carter.*

Trusting More.   8.7.8.7., with Chorus.   F. A. BLACKMER.

Oh, the peace my Saviour gives! Peace I never knew be - fore: . .

For my way has brighter grown, Since I learn'd to trust Him more. . .

273   *The peace of God, which passeth all understanding.*—PHIL. iv. 7.

1 ONCE I thought I walked with Jesus,
    Yet such changeful moods I had;
Sometimes trusting, sometimes doubting,
    Sometimes joyful, sometimes sad.
        Oh, the peace my Saviour gives! etc.

2 For He called me closer to Him,
    Bade my doubting tremors cease:
And when I had fully trusted—
    Filled my soul with perfect peace.

3 Now I'm trusting every moment,
    Less than this is not enough;
And my Saviour bears me gently,
    O'er the places once so rough.

4 Blessèd Saviour, Thou dost keep me
    By Thy power from day to day,
And my heart is full of gladness;
    Thou wilt keep me all the way!
                        F. A. Blackmer.

It Is Well. P.M. P. P. Bliss.

CHORUS.
It is well, ... with my soul, . .

well . . . . with my soul, It is well, it is well with my soul.

274 *He hath delivered my soul in peace.*—Psalm lv. 18.

1.
When peace, like a river, attendeth my way,
When sorrows, like sea-billows, roll;
Whatever my lot, Thou hast taught me to know,
It is well, it is well with my soul.
It is well . . . with my soul, . . .
It is well, it is well with my soul.

2.
Though Satan should buffet, though trials
should come,
Let this blest assurance control,
That Christ hath regarded my helpless estate!
And hath shed His own blood for my soul.

3.
My sin—oh, the bliss of this glorious thought!
My sin—not in part, but the whole,
Is nailed to His cross: and I bear it no
more:
Praise the Lord, praise the Lord, O my
soul!

4.
For me, be it Christ, be it Christ hence to
live!
If Jordan above me shall roll,
No pang shall be mine, for in death as in life
Thou wilt whisper Thy peace to my soul.

5.
But, Lord, 'tis for Thee, for Thy coming, we wait;
The sky, not the grave, is our goal:
Oh, trump of the angel! oh, voice of the Lord!
Blessèd hope! blessèd rest of my soul!

H. G. Spafford.

St. Michael.   S.M.   Arr. by W. H. HAVERGAL.

275   *We have peace with God through our Lord Jesus Christ.*—ROM. v. i.

1 I HEAR the words of love,
    I gaze upon the blood,
I see the mighty Sacrifice,
    And I have peace with God.

2 'Tis everlasting peace!
    Sure as Jehovah's Name;
'Tis stable as His steadfast throne,
    For evermore the same.

3 The clouds may go and come,
    And storms may sweep my sky—

This blood-sealed friendship changes not:
    The cross is ever nigh.

4 My love is oft-times low,
    My joy still ebbs and flows;
But peace with Him remains the same—
    No change Jehovah knows.

5 I change, He changes not,
    The Christ can never die;
His love, not mine, the resting-place,
    His truth, not mine, the tie.

H. Bonar.

St. Oswald.   8.7.8.7.   J. B. DYKES.

Alternative Tune, STUTTGART, *No.* 434.
In Thee is my trust.—PSALM cxli. 8.

276

1 ALL my doubts I give to Jesus!
    I've His gracious promise heard—
I "shall never be confounded"—
    I am trusting in that word.

2 All my sins are laid on Jesus!
    He doth wash me in His blood;
He will keep me pure and holy,
    And will bring me home to God.

3 All my fears I give to Jesus!
    Rest my weary soul on Him;

Though my way be hid in darkness
    Never can His light grow dim.

4 All my joys I give to Jesus!
    He is all I want of bliss;
He of all the worlds is Master—
    He has all I need in this.

5 All I am I give to Jesus!
    All my body, all my soul;
All I have, and all I hope for,
    While eternal ages roll.

J. C. Morgan.

Winsford. C.M., with Chorus. R. Hudson Pope.

CHORUS.

Free .. in - deed, .. free .. in - deed, ..
I .. shall be, I .. shall be free ... in - deed, ... For, if the Son shall
I shall be free indeed,
Free in - deed, ... I shall be free in - deed. ....

set me free, I shall .. be free .. in - deed. ....
set me free, I shall, I shall be free, I shall be free in - deed. ...
I shall, I shall be free in - deed. ....

Alternative Tune (without Chorus), BEATITUDO, No. 571.

277 *If the Son therefore shall make you free, ye shall be free indeed.*—JOHN viii. 36.

1.
O SON of God, my Saviour dear,
    If Thou dost meet my need,
And loose my bonds of guilt and fear,
    I shall be free indeed.
        Free indeed, free indeed, etc.

2.
Lord, I would know the daily power
    That keeps Thy children free,
The glorious liberty of sons,
    From all iniquity.

3.
Then let me know the saving grace
    That conquers every foe,
That opens wide the prison door
    And bids the captive go.

4.
Call me with Thy life-giving voice,
    That I may rise again;
And from the grave-clothes set me free,
    In life by Thee to reign.

G. Goodman.

Saved by Grace.
SOLO OR DUET.

L.M., and Chorus.

GEO. C. STEBBINS.

CHORUS.

And I shall see   Him face to   face,   And tell the sto-ry—Saved by grace!

shall see   to face,

And I shall see   Him face to   face,   And tell the sto-ry—Saved   by grace!

rit.

shall see   to face,

278

By grace ye are saved.—EPH. ii. 5.

1 SOME day the silver cord will break,
   And I no more as now shall sing;
But, oh, the joy when I shall wake
   Within the palace of the King!
      And I shall see . . . Him face to face, . . .
      And tell the story—Saved by grace!

2 Some day my earthly house will fall,
   I cannot tell how soon 'twill be;
But this I know—my All-in-all
   Has now a place in heaven for me.

3 Some day, when fades the golden sun
   Beneath the rosy-tinted west,
My blessèd Lord shall say, "Well done!"
   And I shall enter into rest.

4 Some day; till then I'll watch and wait—
   My lamp all trimmed and burning bright—
That when my Saviour opes the gate,
   My soul to Him may take its flight.

Fanny J. Crosby.

Blessed Assurance.

P.M.

Mrs. J. F. Knapp.

Chorus.

This is my sto - ry, this is my song, Praising my Sa-viour all the day long;

This is my sto - ry, this is my song, Praising my Sa-viour all the day long.

279

Beloved, now are we the sons of God.—1 John iii. 2.

1 Blessèd assurance—Jesus is mine!
Oh, what a foretaste of glory divine!
Heir of salvation, purchase of God;
Born of His Spirit, washed in His blood.
This is my story, this is my song,
Praising my Saviour all the day long.

2 Perfect submission, perfect delight,
Visions of rapture burst on my sight;
Angels descending, bring from above
Echoes of mercy, whispers of love.

3 Perfect submission, all is at rest,
I in my Saviour am happy and blest;
Watching and waiting, looking above,
Filled with His goodness, lost in His love.

Fanny J. Crosby.

Celeste.   8.8.8.8. (amphibrachic).   Anon.

280   *He is the Mediator of a better covenant.*—HEB. viii. 6.

1 A DEBTOR to mercy alone,
    Of covenant mercy I sing;
Nor fear to draw near to Thy throne,
    My person and offerings to bring.

2 The wrath of a sin-hating God
    With me can have nothing to do;
My Saviour's obedience to blood
    Hides all my transgressions from view.

3 The work which His goodness began,
    The arm of His strength will complete;
His promise is "Yea and Amen,"
    And never was forfeited yet.

4 Things future, nor things that are now,
    Not all things below or above,
Can make Him His promise forego,
    Or sever my soul from His love.

5 My name from the palms of His hands
    Eternity will not erase:
Impressed on His heart it remains,
    In marks of indelible grace.

6 And I to the end shall endure,
    As sure as the earnest is given;
More happy, but not more secure,
    When glorified with Him in heaven.
                         A. M. Toplady.

281 The Unchangeable Friend.
      To be sung to the above Tune.

For Thou, Lord, art good.—PSALM lxxxvi. **5.**

1 How good is the God we adore,
    Our faithful unchangeable Friend!
His love is as great as His power,
    And knows neither measure nor end!

2 'Tis Jesus the First and the Last,
    Whose Spirit shall guide us safe home;
We'll praise Him for all that is past,
    We'll trust Him for all that's to come.
                         J. Hart.

At the Cross! C.M., with Chorus.

R. E. HUDSON.

Chorus.

At the cross! at the cross! where I first saw the light, And the bur-den of my heart roll'd a - way; roll'd a-way; It was there by faith I re-ceived my sight, And now I am hap-py all the day!

Alternative Tune (without Chorus), DUNDEE, *No.* 284.

282   *I am not ashamed: for I know whom I have believed.*—2 TIM. i. 12.

1 I'M not ashamed to own my Lord,
   Or to defend His cause,
Maintain the honour of His Word,
   The glory of His cross.
      At the cross! etc.

2 Jesus, my God! I know His Name—
   His Name is all my trust;
Nor will He put my soul to shame,
   Nor let my hope be lost.

3 Firm as His throne His promise stands,
   And He can well secure
What I've committed to His hands,
   Till the decisive hour.

4 Then will He own my worthless name
   Before His Father's face;
And, in the New Jerusalem,
   Appoint my soul a place.

Isaac Watts.

Festus. L.M. German.

Alternative Tune, MAINZER, *No.* 60.

283 *We have a great High Priest, that is passed into the heavens.*—HEB. iv. 14.

1 BEFORE the throne of God above
   I have a strong, a perfect plea;
   A great High Priest, whose Name is Love,
   Who ever lives and pleads for me.

2 My name is graven on His hands,
   My name is written on His heart;
   I know that while in heaven He stands
   No tongue can bid me thence depart.

3 When Satan tempts me to despair,
   And tells me of the guilt within,
   Upward I look, and see Him there
   Who made an end of all my sin.

4 Because the sinless Saviour died,
   My sinful soul is counted free;
   For God, the Just, is satisfied
   To look on Him and pardon me.

5 Behold Him there! the risen Lamb!
   My perfect, spotless Righteousness,
   The great unchangeable I AM,
   The King of glory and of grace!

6 One with Himself, I cannot die;
   My soul is purchased by His blood;
   My life is hid with Christ on high,
   With Christ, my Saviour and my God.

   C. L. Bancroft.

Dundee. C.M. Scotch Psalter.

Alternative Tune, MARTYRDOM, *No.* 404.

284 *Ye . . . are made nigh by the blood of Christ.*—EPH. ii. 13.

1 A MIND at "perfect peace" with God;
   Oh, what a word is this!
   A sinner reconciled through blood;
   This, this indeed is peace!

2 By nature and by practice far—
   How very far from God!
   Yet now by grace brought nigh to Him,
   Through faith in Jesus' blood.

3 So nigh, so very nigh to God,
   I cannot nearer be;
   For in the person of His Son
   I am as near as He.

4 So dear, so very dear to God,
   More dear I cannot be;
   The love wherewith He loves the Son—
   Such is His love to me!

5 Why should I ever anxious be,
   Since such a God is mine?
   He watches o'er me night and day,
   And tells me "Mine is thine."

   Catesby Paget.

Will your Anchor hold?   P.M.   WM. J. KIRKPATRICK

CHORUS.

We have an an-chor that keeps the soul Steadfast and sure while the bil - lows roll;

Fasten'd to the Rock which can - not move, Ground-ed firm and deep in the Saviour's love.

285

An anchor of the soul, both sure and steadfast.—HEB. vi. 19.

1 WILL your anchor hold in the storms of life?
   When the clouds unfold their wings of strife;
   When the strong tides lift and the cables strain,
   Will your anchor drift or firm remain?
   We have an anchor that keeps the soul, etc.

2 Will your anchor hold in the straits of fear?
   When the breakers roar and the reef is near;
   While the surges rave and the wild winds blow,
   Shall the angry waves then your bark o'erflow?

3 Will your anchor hold in the floods of death,
   When the waters cold chill your latest breath?
   On the rising tide you can never fail,
   While your anchor holds within the vail.

4 Will your eyes behold through the morning light
   The city of gold, and the harbour bright?
   Will you anchor safe by the heavenly shore,
   When life's storms are past for evermore?

P. J. Owens (alt.).

Trusting Jesus. 7.7.7.7., and Chorus. IRA D. SANKEY.

CHORUS.

Trust-ing Him while life shall last, Trust-ing Him till earth is past,

Till with-in the jas-per wall— Trust-ing Je - sus, that is all.

By permission. From Sankey's *Sacred Songs and Solos.*

*Though He slay me, yet will I trust in Him.—*JOB xiii. 15.

286

1 SIMPLY trusting every day,
Trusting through a stormy way;
Even when my faith is small,
Trusting Jesus, that is all.
　Trusting Him while life shall last, etc.

2 Brightly doth His Spirit shine
Into this poor heart of mine:
While He leads I cannot fall,
Trusting Jesus, that is all.

3 Singing if my way be clear:
Praying if the path be drear:
If in danger, for Him call;
Trusting Jesus, that is all.

4 Trusting as the moments fly,
Trusting as the days go by,
Trusting Him, whate'er befall;
Trusting Jesus, that is all.

E. Page Stites.

Boylston.   S.M.   L. Mason.

Alternative Tunes, SILCHESTER, No. 105, and ST. BRIDE, No. 157.

287   *By one offering He hath perfected for ever them that are sanctified.*—HEB. x. 14.

1 NOT all the blood of beasts,
On Jewish altars slain,
Could give the guilty conscience peace
Or wash away its stain.

2 But Christ, the heavenly Lamb,
Takes all our sins away;
A sacrifice of nobler Name,
And richer blood than they.

3 My faith would lay her hand
On that dear head of Thine,
While like a penitent I stand,
And there confess my sin.

4 My soul looks back to see
The burden Thou didst bear,
When hanging on the accursèd tree,
And knows her guilt was there.

5 Believing, we rejoice
To see the curse remove;
We bless the Lamb with cheerful voice,
And sing His wondrous love.

Isaac Watts.

Winchester New.   L.M.   CRASSELIUS.

Alternative Tune, WAREHAM, No. 189.

288   *The Lord our Righteousness.*—JER. xxiii. 6.

1 JESUS, Thy blood and righteousness
My beauty are, my glorious dress;
'Midst flaming worlds, in these arrayed,
With joy shall I lift up my head.

2 Bold shall I stand in that great day,
For who aught to my charge shall lay?
Fully absolved through these I am,
From sin and fear, from guilt and shame.

3 When from the dust of death I rise,
To claim my mansion in the skies,
E'en then shall this be all my plea,
"Jesus hath lived, and died, for me."

4 This spotless robe the same appears,
When ruined nature sinks in years;
No age can change its glorious hue,
The robe of Christ is ever new.

5 Oh, let the dead now hear Thy voice,
Bid, Lord, Thy banished ones rejoice;
Their beauty this, their glorious dress,
Jesus, the Lord our Righteousness!

Zinzendorf, tr. *J. Wesley*

"If God be for us!"   P.M.   JAMES McGRANAHAN.

CHORUS.

"If God be for us, if God be for us, if God be for us, Who can be a-
"If God be for us,   if God be for us,

- gainst us? Who? who? who? . . Who can be against us, a - gainst us?"
Who? who? Who can be against us?

Words and Music by permission of Mrs. H. C. Dixon.

289   *If God be for us, who can be against us?*—ROM. viii. **31.**

1 REJOICE in the Lord! oh, let His mercy cheer;
    He sunders the bands that enthrall;
  Redeemed by His blood, why should we ever fear—
    Since Jesus is our "all in all"?
      "If God be for us," etc.

2 Be strong in the Lord! rejoicing in His might,
    Be loyal and true day by day;
  When evils assail, be valiant for the right,
    And He will be our strength and stay.

3 Confide in His Word—His promises so sure;
    In Christ they are "yea and amen;"
  Though earth pass away, they ever shall endure,
    'Tis written o'er and o'er again.

4 Abide in the Lord: secure in His control,
    'Tis life everlasting begun;
  To pluck from His hand the weakest, trembling soul—
    It never, never can be done!
        G. M. J.

St. Catherine.   8.8.8.8.8.8.   J. G. WALTON.

Alternative Tune, MELITA, *No.* 689.

290

For other foundation can no man lay than that is laid, which is Jesus Christ.—1 COR. iii. 11.

1 MY hope is built on nothing less
   Than Jesus' blood and righteousness;
   I dare not trust the sweetest frame
   But wholly lean on Jesus' Name.
     On Christ, the solid Rock, I stand;
     All other ground is sinking sand.

2 When darkness seems to veil His face,
   I rest on His unchanging grace;
   In every high and stormy gale
   My anchor holds within the veil.
     On Christ, the solid Rock, I stand;
     All other ground is sinking sand.

3 His oath, His covenant, and blood
   Support me in the 'whelming flood:
   When all around my soul gives way,
   He then is all my hope and stay.
     On Christ, the solid Rock, I stand;
     All other ground is sinking sand.

E. Mote.

291 No Other Plea.   C.M., with Chorus.   Norse Air.
Arr. by WM. J. KIRKPATRICK.

CHORUS.

I need no oth - er   ar - gu - ment, I need no oth - er

plea,.. It is e-nough that Je-sus died, And that He died for me.

291 *There is none other Name under heaven . . . whereby we must be saved.*—ACTS iv. 12.

1 My faith has found a resting-place,
   Not in a form or creed;
I trust the Ever-living One,
   His wounds for me shall plead.
      I need no other argument, etc.

2 Enough for me that Jesus saves,
   This ends my fear and doubt;
A sinful soul I come to Him,
   He'll never cast me out.

3 My heart is leaning on the Word,
   The written Word of God,
Salvation by my Saviour's Name,
   Salvation through His blood.

4 My great Physician heals the sick,
   The lost He came to save;
For me His precious blood He shed,
   For me His life He gave.

L. H. Edmunds.

Dir.   7.7.7.7.7.7.   C. KOCHER.

292   *Now are we the sons of God.*—1 JOHN iii. 2.

1 BLESSÈD are the sons of God.
   They are bought with Jesus' blood;
   They are ransomed from the grave,
   Life eternal they shall have.
      With them numbered may I be,
      Now and through eternity!

2 God did love them in His Son,
   Long before the world begun:
   They the seal of this receive
   When on Jesus they believe.
      With them numbered may I be,
      Now and through eternity!

3 They are justified by grace,
   They enjoy a solid peace;
   All their sins are washed away,
   They shall stand in God's great day.
      With them numbered may I be,
      Now and through eternity!

4 They produce the fruits of grace
   In the works of righteousness;
   Born of God, they hate all sin,
   God's pure Word remains within.
      With them numbered may I be,
      Now and through eternity!

5 They have fellowship with God,
   Through the Mediator's blood;
   One with God, through Jesus one,
   Glory is in them begun.
      With them numbered may I be,
      Now and through eternity!

J Humphreys.

Section VII.—The Christian Life.
(2.) Guidance and Safety.

All the Way. 8.7.8.7., D. R. Lowry.

For I know what'er be-fall me, Je-sus do-eth all things well.

Alternative Tune, Bethany, No. 362.

293 *Thou shalt remember all the way which the Lord thy God led thee.—*
DEUT. viii. 2.

1 ALL the way my Saviour leads me:
  What have I to ask beside?
Can I doubt His tender mercy,
  Who through life has been my Guide?
Heavenly peace, divinest comfort,
  Here by faith in Him to dwell!
For I know whate'er befall me,
  Jesus doeth all things well.

2 All the way my Saviour leads me:
  Cheers each winding path I tread;
Gives me grace for every trial,
  Feeds me with the living bread.
Though my weary steps may falter,
  And my soul a-thirst may be,
Gushing from the rock before me,
  Lo! a spring of joy I see.

3 All the way my Saviour leads me;
  Oh, the fulness of His love!
Perfect rest to me is promised
  In my Father's house above.
When my spirit, clothed immortal,
  Wings its flight to realms of day,
This, my song through endless ages—
  Jesus led me all the way.

Fanny J. Crosby.

Pastor Bonus.

S.M.D.

A. J. Caldicott.

All we like sheep have gone astray.—Isa. liii. 6.

294

1 I was a wandering sheep,
   I did not love the fold,
I did not love my Shepherd's voice,
   I would not be controlled:
   I was a wayward child,
   I did not love my home,
I did not love my Father's voice,
   I loved afar to roam.

2 The Shepherd sought His sheep,
   The Father sought His child;
They followed me o'er vale and hill,
   O'er deserts waste and wild:
   They found me nigh to death,
   Famished, and faint, and lone;
They bound me with the bands of love,
   They saved the wandering one.

3 Jesus my Shepherd is;
   'Twas He that loved my soul,
'Twas He that washed me in His blood,
   'Twas He that made me whole:
   'Twas He that sought the lost,
   That found the wandering sheep;
'Twas He that brought me to the fold,
   'Tis He that still doth keep.

4 I was a wandering sheep,
   I would not be controlled;
But now I love my Shepherd's voice,
   I love, I love the fold:
   I was a wayward child,
   I once preferred to roam;
But now I love my Father's voice,
   I love, I love His home.

H. Bonar.

295 Lux Benigna. [FIRST TUNE.] 10.4.10.4.10.10. J. B. DYKES.

Sandon. [SECOND TUNE.] 10.4.10.4.10.10. C. H. PURDAY.

295

He that followeth Me shall not walk in darkness, but shall have the light of life.—JOHN viii. 12.

1 LEAD, kindly Light, amid the encircling gloom,
  Lead Thou me on;
The night is dark, and I am far from home;
  Lead Thou me on.
Keep Thou my feet; I do not ask to see
The distant scene; one step enough for me.

2 I was not ever thus, nor prayed that Thou
  Shouldst lead me on;
I loved to choose and see my path; but now
  Lead Thou me on.
I loved the garish day, and, spite of fears,
Pride ruled my will: remember not past years.

3 So long Thy power hath blest me, sure it still
  Will lead me on
O'er moor and fen, o'er crag and torrent, till
  The night is gone,
And with the morn those angel-faces smile,
Which I have loved long since and lost awhile.

J. H. Newman.

Victoria Street. 8.4.8.4. P. G. LARBALESTIER.

Copyright. By permission of the Composer.

296 *The inward man is renewed day by day.*—2 COR. iv. 16.

1 LORD, for to-morrow and its needs
    I do not pray;
  Keep me, my God, from stain of sin—
    Just for to-day.

2 Let me do faithfully Thy work,
    And duly pray;
  Let me be kind in word and deed,
    Just for to-day.

3 Let me no wrong or idle word,
    Unthinking, say;
  Set Thou a seal upon my lips—
    Just for to-day.

4 So for to-morrow and its needs
    I do not pray;
  But keep me, guide me, hold me, Lord—
    Just for to-day.

S. M. X.

St. Ishmael.   S.M.D.   CHARLES VINCENT HARMONY.

UNISON.

Be - yond . .

. . our

Alternative Tune, DIADEMATA, *No. 2.*

297   *The path of the just is as the shining light.*—PROV. iv. 18.

1 ALONG the shining road
   That leads to life so free,
I tread with glad and glowing heart,
   For Jesus leadeth me ;
   Though long ago He passed
   Beyond our mortal sight,
The very pathway that He went
   Still shines with heavenly light.

2 I know that but for Him
   The road would darkened be,
And shapes and shadows dark and dread
   Might gather threateningly ;
   But He has trodden first
   The long, the changeful way,
And left His light upon it all
   To turn the night to day.

3 The shining road may seem
   To lose itself in night ;
The valley mist, the winter cloud
   May hide it from my sight.
   I know full well it winds,
   Until, or soon or late,
It finds upon the hills of God
   His shining City gate.

F. Goldsmith French.

298 Submission.   10.4.10.4.   GEORGE LOMAS.

298   *I am . . . thy God . . . which leadeth thee by the way that thou shouldest go.—*
Isa. xlviii. 17.

1.

I do not ask, O Lord, that life may be
    A pleasant road;
I do not ask that Thou would'st take from me
    Aught of its load:

2.

I do not ask that flowers should always spring
    Beneath my feet;
I know too well the poison and the sting
    Of things too sweet.

3.

For one thing only, Lord, dear Lord, I plead:
    Lead me aright,
Though strength should falter, and though
    heart should bleed,
    Through peace to light.

4.

I do not ask, O Lord, that Thou should'st
    Full radiance here;   [shed
Give but a ray of peace, that I may tread
    Without a fear.

5.

I do not ask my cross to understand,
    My way to see;
Better in darkness just to feel Thy hand,
    And follow Thee.

6.

Joy is like restless day, but peace divine
    Like quiet night:
Lead me, O Lord, till perfect day shall shine
    Through peace to light.
        A. A. Procter.

St. Aëlred.   8.8.8.3.   J. B. Dykes.

299   *He arose, and rebuked the wind, and said unto the sea, Peace, be still.—*
Mark iv. 39.

1 Fierce raged the tempest o'er the deep;
    Watch did Thine anxious servants keep,
    But Thou wast wrapped in guileless sleep,
        Calm and still.

2 "Save, Lord, we perish," was their cry,
    "Oh, save us in our agony!"
    Thy word above the storm rose high,
        "Peace, be still."

3 The wild winds hushed; the angry deep
    Sank, like a little child, to sleep;
    The sullen billows ceased to leap,
        At Thy will.

4 So, when our life is clouded o'er,
    And storm-winds drift us from the shore
    Say, lest we sink to rise no more,
        "Peace, be still."   *G. Thring.*

The Heavenly Pilot.   6.5.6.5. D., with Chorus.   Anon., *circa* 1864.

Je - sus is our Pi - lot,

Guid-ed by His hand,   We shall reach the ha - ven   On the gold - en   strand.

Alternative Tune (without Chorus), VESPERS, *No.* 13.

300   *So He bringeth them unto their desired haven.*—PSALM cvii. 30.

1 JESUS is our Pilot:
   No one else can guide
   Our frail barque in safety
   O'er life's stormy tide:
   When the waves of trouble
   Baffle human skill,
   He can always calm them
   With His " Peace, be still."
   Jesus is our Pilot, etc.

2 Jesus is our Pilot:
   Through His mighty arm
   We are safe from danger—
   Safe from fear and harm:
   In His strong protection
   We may ever rest;
   Refuge from all sorrow
   Is His faithful breast.

3 Jesus is our Pilot:
   Well He knows the way
   From this vale of shadows
   To the realm of day:
   He can find the harbour
   Others seek in vain;
   There, the Lord of glory,
   Evermore He'll reign.
         Kate Cameron.

Never Lose Sight of Jesus!   P.M.   ROBERT HARKNESS.

Never lose sight of Je - sus! Nev - er lose sight of Je - sus!

Day and night He will lead you right; Nev - er lose sight of Je - sus!

Words and Music by permission of Mrs. H. C. Dixon.

301

Looking unto Jesus.—HEB. xii. 2.

1 O PILGRIM bound for the heavenly land,
   Never lose sight of Jesus!
   He'll lead you gently with loving hand:
   Never lose sight of Jesus!
       Never lose sight of Jesus! etc.

2 When you are tempted to go astray,
   Never lose sight of Jesus!
   Press onward, upward, the narrow way;
   Never lose sight of Jesus!

3 Though dark the pathway may seem ahead,
   Never lose sight of Jesus!
   "I will be with you," His Word hath said:
   Never lose sight of Jesus!

4 When death is knocking outside the door,
   Never lose sight of Jesus!
   Till safe with Him on the golden shore:
   Never lose sight of Jesus!

                    J. Oatman (arr.).

He Leadeth Me.   P.M.   W. B. BRADBURY.

REFRAIN.

He lead-eth me! He lead-eth me! By His own hand He lead-eth me! His

faith-ful fol-lower I would be; For by His hand He lead-eth me!

302   *For I the Lord thy God will hold thy right hand.*—ISA. xli. 13.

1 HE leadeth me! Oh, blessèd thought!
Oh, words with heavenly comfort fraught!
Whate'er I do, where'er I be,
Still 'tis God's hand that leadeth me!
   He leadeth me! He leadeth me! etc.

2 Sometimes 'mid scenes of deepest gloom,
Sometimes where Eden's bowers bloom,
By waters still, o'er troubled sea,
Still 'tis His hand that leadeth me!

3 Lord, I would place my hand in Thine,
Nor ever murmur nor repine;
Content, whatever lot I see,
Since 'tis my God that leadeth me.

4 And when my task on earth is done,
When, by Thy grace, the victory's won,
E'en death's cold wave I will not flee;
Since Thou through Jordan leadest me.
                              J. H. Gilmore.

He Will Hold Me Fast.

P.M.

Robert Harkness.

Refrain. *a tempo.*

He will hold me fast,
He will hold, me, hold me fast,

He will hold me fast;
He will hold me, hold me fast;

rall.

For my Sa-viour loves me so, . . He will hold me fast.

Words and Music by permission of Mrs. H. C. Dixon.

303

Thy right hand shall hold me.—Psalm cxxxix. 10.

1 When I fear my faith will fail,
  Christ can hold me fast!
  When the tempter would prevail,
  He can hold me fast!
  He will hold me fast, etc.

2 I could never keep my hold,
  He must hold me fast!
  For my love is often cold,
  He must hold me fast!

3 I am precious in His sight,
  He will hold me fast!
  Those He saves are His delight,
  He will hold me fast!

4 He'll not let my soul be lost,
  Christ will hold me fast;
  Bought by Him at such a cost,
  He will hold me fast!

Ada R. Habershon.

1*

The Life=Boat. P.M. P. P. Bliss.

CHORUS.

Pull for the shore, sail - or, pull for the shore ; Heed not the roll - ing waves, but

bend to the oar ; Safe in the life-boat, sail - or, cling, to self no more!

Leave the poor old strand - ed wreck and pull for the shore.

304 *Wherefore, my beloved, . . work out your own salvation with fear and trembling.*—PHIL. ii. 12.

1 LIGHT in the darkness, sailor, day is at hand!
  See o'er the foaming billows fair haven's land;
  Drear was the voyage, sailor, now almost o'er;
  Safe within the life-boat, sailor, pull for the shore.
    Pull for the shore, sailor, etc.

2 Trust in the life-boat, sailor, all else will fail;
  Stronger the surges dash and fiercer the gale;
  Heed not the stormy winds, though loudly they roar;
  Watch the "Bright and Morning Star," and pull for the shore.

3 Bright gleams the morning, sailor, uplift the eye;
  Clouds and darkness disappearing, glory is nigh:
  Safe in the life-boat, sailor; sing evermore,
  "Glory in so great salvation!" Pull for the shore! *P. P. Bliss.*

Constant Companion. P.M. GRANT COLFAX TULLAR.

CHORUS. ♩=♩

Lord, . . I am Thine, . . Sa - - viour Di - vine! . . .
Lord, I am Thine, Lord, I am Thine, Saviour Di-vine, Saviour Di-vine!

Oh, . . . what a joy . . . just to know . . Thou art mine! . .
Oh, what a joy, oh, what a joy, just to know Thou art mine!

305

I will never leave thee, nor forsake thee.—HEB. xiii. 5.

1 JESUS the Saviour, dying on Calvary,
    Purchased my pardon, setting me free:
  Love so abundant, should I not serve Him,
    When He so gladly suffered for me?
      Lord, I am Thine, etc

2 Oh, what a Saviour, tender and loving,
    Guarding my footsteps lest I should stray:
  Love so abundant, leading me ever
    Out of the darkness into the day.

3 Constant Companion, leaving me never,
    Bidding me follow close by His side:
  He is my Refuge, safely I shelter,
    Knowing He loves me, whate'er betide.

              G. C. Tullar.

He knows.   P.M.   P. P. Bliss.

CHORUS.

Where He .. may lead I'll fol-low, ..

My trust in Him re-pose; .. And ev-'ry hour in per-fect peace, I'll sing,

"He knows, He knows;" And ev-'ry hour in per-fect peace, I'll sing, "He knows, He knows."

306   *He knoweth the way that I take.*—Job xxiii. 10.

1 I KNOW not what awaits me,
    God kindly veils my eyes,
And o'er each step of my onward way
    He makes new scenes to rise;
And every joy He sends me comes
    A sweet and glad surprise.
        Where He may lead I'll follow, etc.

2 One step I see before me,
    'Tis all I need to see,
The light of heaven more brightly shines
    When earth's illusions flee;
And sweetly through the silence comes,
    His loving, "Follow Me!"

3 Oh, blissful lack of wisdom!
    'Tis blessèd not to know;
He holds me with His own right hand,
    And will not let me go,
And lulls my troubled soul to rest
    In Him who loves me so.

4 So on I go not knowing;
    I would not if I might;
I'd rather walk in the dark with God
    Than go alone in the light;
I'd rather walk by faith with Him
    Than go alone by sight.
        Mary G. Brainard (altd.).

Hanover.　　　　5.5.5.5.6.5.6.5.　　　　W. Croft.

Alternative Tune, Houghton, *No.* 18.

307 *God will provide.*—Gen. xxii. 8.

1 Though troubles assail,
　And dangers affright,
Though friends should all fail,
　And foes all unite—
Yet one thing secures us,
　Whatever betide:
The Scripture assures us,
　"The Lord will provide."

2 The birds, without barn
　Or storehouse, are fed;
From them let us learn
　To trust for our bread:
His saints what is fitting
　Shall ne'er be denied,
So long as 'tis written,
　"The Lord will provide."

3 His call we obey,
　Like Abram of old,
Not knowing our way;
　But faith makes us bold:
For though we are strangers
　We have a good Guide;
And trust, in all dangers,
　"The Lord will provide."

4 No strength of our own,
　Or goodness we claim;
Yet, since we have known
　The Saviour's great Name,
In this our strong tower
　For safety we hide,
Almighty His power:
　"The Lord will provide."

J. Newton.

308 *Why are ye fearful, O ye of little faith?*—Matt. viii. 26.

1 Begone, unbelief!
　My Saviour is near,
And for my relief
　Will surely appear.
By prayer let me wrestle,
　And He will perform:
With Christ in the vessel,
　I smile at the storm.

2 If dark be my way,
　Since He is my guide,
'Tis mine to obey,
　'Tis His to provide:
Though cisterns be broken,
　And creatures all fail,
The word He hath spoken
　Shall surely prevail.

3 His love in time past
　Forbids me to think
He'll leave me at last
　In trouble to sink:
Each sweet Ebenezer
　I have in review,
Confirms His good pleasure
　To help me quite through.

4 Since all that I meet
　Shall work for my good,
The bitter is sweet,
　The medicine is food;
Though painful at present,
　'Twill cease before long;
And then, oh, how pleasant
　The conqueror's song!

J. Newton.

Bentley   7.3.7.6., D.   J. P. HULLAH.

Alternative Tune, ST. THEODULPH, *No.* 39.

I will rejoice in the Lord.—HAB. iii. 18.

309

1 SOMETIMES a light surprises
    The Christian while he sings :
It is the Lord who rises
    With healing in His wings,
When comforts are declining,
    He grants the soul again
A season of clear shining,
    To cheer it after rain.

2 In holy contemplation
    We sweetly then pursue
The theme of God's salvation,
    And find it ever new.
Set free from present sorrow,
    We cheerfully can say,
E'en let the unknown morrow
    Bring with it what it may.

3 It can bring with it nothing,
    But He will bear us through ;
Who gives the lilies clothing,
    Will clothe His people too :
Beneath the spreading heavens,
    No creature but is fed ;
And He, who feeds the ravens,
    Will give His children bread.

4 Though vine nor fig-tree neither
    Their wonted fruit should bear,
Though all the fields should wither,
    Nor flocks nor herds be there ;
Yet God the same abiding,
    His praise shall tune my voice ;
For, while in Him confiding,
    I cannot but rejoice !

W. Cowper.

Christ Shall Lead us.   P.M.   H. ERNEST NICHOL.

Tho' the way be long and drea - ry,   Tho' in darkest night we roam,

By His side we nev - er wea - - ry, Christ shall lead us home.

Words and Music by permission of H. E. Nichol, Charlotte Street, Hull.

310   *I am the Lord . . . which leadeth thee by the way that thou shouldest go.* —
Isa. xlviii. 17.

1 CHRIST shall lead us in the time of youth,
   Christ shall lead us in the way of truth,
   Christ shall lead us in the love of right,
     Homeward to the light.
       Though the way be long and dreary, etc.

2 Christ shall lead us in the hour of gloom,
   He hath known it, Victor o'er the tomb;
   When from grief we vainly seek release,
     He can give us peace.

3 Christ shall lead us in the hour of strife,
   Fill our hearts with everlasting life,
   Give us, even with our latest breath,
     Victory over death.

4 Christ shall lead us when the fight shall cease,
   To the fields of everlasting peace,
   Where the soul that all the way hath trod,
     Resteth calm in God.
               Colin Sterne.

St. Faith. 7.6.7.6., D. E. Husband

Alternative Tunes, Bentley, *No.* 309, *and* Dies Dominica, *No.* 484.

311 *Fear not, little flock.*—Luke xii. 32.

1 In heavenly love abiding,
  No change my heart shall fear ;
And safe is such confiding,
  For nothing changes here.
The storm may roar without me,
  My heart may low be laid,
But God is round about me,
  And can I be dismayed ?

2 Wherever He may guide me,
  No want shall turn me back ;
My Shepherd is beside me,
  And nothing can I lack.
His wisdom ever waketh,
  His sight is never dim ;
He knows the way He taketh,
  And I will walk with Him.

3 Green pastures are before me,
  Which yet I have not seen ;
Bright skies will soon be o'er me,
  Where the dark clouds have been.
My hope I cannot measure ;
  My path to life is free ;
My Saviour has my treasure,
  And He will walk with me.

A. L. Waring.

St. Raphael.   8.7.8.7.4.7.   E. J. Hopkins.

Alternative Tune, KENSINGTON NEW, *No.* 110.

312

He will be our Guide even unto death.—PSALM xlviii. 14.

1 GUIDE me, O Thou great Jehovah,
    Pilgrim through this barren land;
 I am weak, but Thou art mighty;
    Hold me with Thy powerful hand:
       Bread of heaven,
    Feed me till I want no more.

2 Open now the crystal fountain,
    Whence the healing waters flow;
 Let the fiery, cloudy pillar,
    Lead me all my journey through:
       Strong Deliverer,
    Be Thou still my strength and shield.

3 When I tread the verge of Jordan,
    Bid my anxious fears subside;
 Bear me through the swelling current,
    Land me safe on Canaan's side:
       Songs of praises
    I will ever give to Thee.
                    W. Williams.

Heber. 7.6.7.6., D. R. HEBER.

Alternative Tune, LANCASHIRE, *No.* 248.

313 *Blessed are all they that put their trust in Him.*—PSALM ii. 12.

1 OH, trust thyself to Jesus
    When conscious of thy sin—
Its heavy weight upon thee,
    Its mighty power within :
Then is the hour for pleading
    His finished work for thee ;
Then is the time for singing,
    "His blood was shed for me."

2 Oh, trust thyself to Jesus
    When tempted to transgress,
By word or look of anger,
    Or thought of bitterness :
Then is the hour for claiming
    Thy Lord to fight for thee ;
Then is the time for singing,
    "He doth deliver me."

3 Oh, trust thyself to Jesus
    When thou art wearied sore,
When head or hand refuses
    To think or labour more :
Then is the hour for leaning
    Upon the Master's breast ;
Then is the time for singing,
    "My Saviour gives me rest."

4 Oh, trust thyself to Jesus
    When thou art full of care,
For loved ones still refusing
    Our blessèd hope to share :
Then is the hour for trusting
    Thy Lord to bring them nigh ;
Then is the time for singing,
    "He loves them more than I."

Anon.

Dearer Home.   S.M.D.   I. B. WOODBURY.
Arr. by Sir A. SULLIVAN.

By permission of Novello and Company, Limited.

314

And so shall we ever be with the Lord.—1 THESS. iv. 17.

1 "FOR ever with the Lord!"
    Amen, so let it be!
Life from the dead is in that word,
    'Tis immortality.
    Here in the body pent,
    Absent from Him I roam,
Yet nightly pitch my moving tent
    A day's march nearer home.

2 My Father's house on high,
    Home of my soul, how near
At times to faith's foreseeing eye
    Thy golden gates appear!
    Ah! then my spirit faints
    To reach the land I love,
The bright inheritance of saints,
    Jerusalem above.

3 "For ever with the Lord!"
    Father, if 'tis Thy will,
The promise of that faithful word
    E'en here to me fulfil.
    Be Thou at my right hand,
    Then I can never fail;
Uphold Thou me, and I shall stand;
    Fight, and I must prevail.

4 So when my latest breath
    Shall rend the veil in twain,
By death I shall escape from death
    And life eternal gain.
    That resurrection-word,
    That shout of victory;
Once more, "For ever with the Lord!"
    Amen, so let it be!
                        J. Montgomery

Toulon.   10.10.10.10.   Adapted from F. C. GOUDIMEL.

Alternative Tunes, MORECAMBE, No. 366, and ST. AGNES, No. 407.

315

Lo, I am with you alway.—MATT. xxviii. 20.

1 I TAKE Thy promise, Lord, in all its length,
  And breadth and fulness, as my daily strength,
  Into life's future fearless I may gaze,
  For, Jesus, Thou art with me all the days.

2 Days may be coming fraught with loss and change,
  New scenes surround my life and faces strange;
  I thank Thee that no day can ever break,
  Saviour, when Thou wilt leave me or forsake.

3 There may be days of darkness and distress,
  When sin has power to tempt, and care to press—
  Yet in the darkest day I will not fear,
  For, 'mid the shadows, Thou wilt still be near.

4 Days there may be of joy, and deep delight,
  When earth seems fairest, and her skies most bright;
  Then draw me closer to Thee, lest I rest
  Elsewhere, my Saviour, than upon Thy breast.

5 And all the other days that make my life,
  Marked by no special joy or grief or strife,
  Days filled with quiet duties, trivial care,
  Burdens too small for other hearts to share;

6 Spend Thou these days with me, all shall be Thine—
  So shall the darkest hour with glory shine.
  Then when these earthly years have passed away,
  Let me be with Thee in the perfect day.   *Rev. H. L. R. Deck.*

316 Southgate.   8.4.8.4.8.8.8.4.   T. B. SOUTHGATE.

316   *All things work together for good to them that love God.—*Rom. viii. 28.

1 THROUGH the love of God our Saviour,
      All will be well;
  Free and changeless is His favour,
      All, all is well:
  Precious is the blood that healed us,
  Perfect is the grace that sealed us,
  Strong the hand stretched out to shield us,
      All must be well.

2 Though we pass through tribulation,
      All will be well;
  Ours is such a full salvation,
      All, all is well:

Happy, still in God confiding,
Fruitful, if in Christ abiding,
Holy, through the Spirit's guiding,
    All must be well.

3 We expect a bright to-morrow,
      All will be well;
  Faith can sing, through days of sorrow,
      All, all is well:
  On our Father's love relying,
  Jesus every need supplying,
  Or in living or in dying,
      All must be well.

                                        M. Peters.

The Book of Life.   7.7.7.7., with Chorus.   Wm. J. KIRKPATRICK.

CHORUS.

Write my name in the book of life, Lamb of God,

write it there; Where Thy saved Thou dost re-cord, Write my name, my name, O Lord.

Alternative Tune (without Chorus), BUCKLAND, No. 687.
       *They which are written in the Lamb's book of life.—*REV. xxi. 27.

317

1 IN Thy book, where glory bright
  Shines with never-fading light,
  Where Thy saved Thou dost record,
  Write my name, my name, O Lord.
      Write my name in the book of life, etc.

2 In the book, whose pages tell
  Who have tried to serve Thee well,
  O'er my name let mercy trace,
  "Child of God, redeemed by grace."

3 In the book, where Thou dost keep
  Record still of years that sleep,
  Let my name be written down,
  Heir to life's immortal crown.

4 O my Saviour, Thou canst show
  What I long so much to know:
  Let my faith behold and see
  That my life is hid with Thee.

                                        L. Edwards.

Ash Grove.　　　　　12.11.12.11., D.　　　　　Welsh Melody.

Alternative Tune, ST. ASAPH, *No.* 491.

Follow thou Me.—JOHN xxi. 22.

318

1 THE Master hath come, and He calls us to follow
　　The track of the footprints He leaves on our way;
　Far over the mountain, and through the deep hollow,
　　The path leads us on to the mansions of day.
　The Master hath called us, the children who fear Him,
　　Who march 'neath Christ's banner, His own little band;
　We love Him, and seek Him, we long to be near Him,
　　And rest in the light of His beautiful land.

2 The Master hath called us; the road may be dreary,
  And dangers and sorrows are strewn on the track;
But God's Holy Spirit shall comfort the weary—
  We follow the Saviour, and cannot turn back.
The Master hath called us: though doubt and temptation
  May compass our journey, we cheerfully sing.
"Press onward, look upward," through much tribulation
  The children of Zion must follow their King.

8 The Master hath called us: in life's early morning
  With spirits as fresh as the dew on the sod:
We turn from the world, with its smiles and its scorning,
  To cast in our lot with the people of God.
The Master hath called us, His sons and His daughters,
  We plead for His blessing, and trust in His love;
And through the green pastures, beside the still waters,
  He'll lead us at last to His kingdom above.

Sarah Doudney.

Ibold Tbou my Ibano.

11.10.11.10.

H. P. Main.

Words and Music by permission of Mrs. H. C. Dixon.

319   *I the Lord have called thee, . . . and will hold thine hand.*—Isa. xlii. 6.

1 Hold Thou my hand! so weak I am, and helpless,
  I dare not take one step without Thy aid;
Hold Thou my hand! for then, O loving Saviour,
  No dread of ill shall make my soul afraid.

2 Hold Thou my hand! and closer, closer draw me
  To Thy dear self—my hope, my joy, my all:
Hold Thou my hand, lest haply I should wander;
  And missing Thee, my trembling feet should fall.

3 Hold Thou my hand! the way is dark before me
  Without the sunlight of Thy face divine:
But when by faith I catch its radiant glory,
  What heights of joy, what rapturous songs are mine!

4 Hold Thou my hand! that when I reach the margin
  Of that lone river Thou didst cross for me,
A heavenly light may flash along its waters,
  And every wave, like crystal, bright shall be.

Grace J. Frances.

Refuge. 8.7.8.7., with Chorus. J. McGRANAHAN.

He will hide me! He will hide me! Where no
He will hide me! He will hide me!

harm . . can e'er be-tide me;.. He will hide me! safe-ly
Where no harm He will hide me!

hide me In .. the sha - - dow of His hand.
safe-ly hide me In the sha-dow

Alternative Tune (without Chorus), CROSS OF JESUS, *No.* 94.
In the shadow of His hand hath He hid me.—ISA. xlix. 2.

320

1 WHEN the storms of life are raging,
    Tempests wild on sea and land,
  I will seek a place of refuge
    In the shadow of God's hand.
      He will hide me! etc.

2 Though He may send some affliction,
    'Twill but make me long for home;
  For in love, and not in anger,
    All His chastenings will come.

3 Enemies may strive to injure,
    Satan all his arts employ;
  God will turn what seems to harm me
    Into everlasting joy.

4 So, while here the cross I'm bearing,
    Meeting storms and billows wild,
  Jesus for my soul is caring,
    Naught can harm His Father's child.
      M. E. Servoss.

Jesus is a Friend of Mine. C.M., with Chorus.   D. B. TOWNER.

CHORUS.

Yes, He's a Friend of mine, And He with me doth all things share; Since all is Christ's and Christ is mine, Why should I have a care? For Je - sus is a Friend of mine. . .

Words and Music by permission of Mrs. H. C. Dixon.

Alternative Tune (without Chorus), SAWLEY, *No.* 370.

321

And ye are Christ's; and Christ is God's.—1 COR. iii. **23.**

1 WHY should I charge my soul with care?
    The wealth in every mine
Belongs to Christ, God's Son and Heir,
    And He's a Friend of mine.
        Yes, He's a Friend of mine, etc.

2 The silver moon, the golden sun,
    And all the stars that shine,
Are His alone, yes, every one,
    And He's a Friend of mine.

3 He daily spreads a glorious feast,
    And at His table dine
The whole creation, man and beast,
    And He's a Friend of mine.

4 And when He comes in bright array,
    And leads the conquering line,
It will be glory then to say,
    That He's a Friend of mine.
                    J. H. Sammis.

Ein' Feste Burg. P.M. MARTIN LUTHER.

322 *The Lord is my Rock and my Fortress.*—2 SAM. xxii. 2.

1 A MIGHTY fortress is our God,
   A bulwark never failing;
Our Helper He, amid the flood
   Of mortal ills prevailing.
      For still our ancient foe
      Doth seek to work his woe;
      His craft and power are great,
      And armed with cruel hate—
   On earth is not his equal.

2 Did we in our own strength confide,
   Our striving would be losing;
Were not the right Man on our side,
   The Man of God's own choosing.
      Doth ask who that may be?
      Christ Jesus, it is He!
      Lord Sabaoth is His Name,
      From age to age the same;
   And He must win the battle.

3 And though this world, with devils filled,
      Should threaten to undo us,
   We will not fear, for God hath willed
      His truth to triumph through us.
         Let goods and kindred go,
         This mortal life also:
         The body they may kill,
         God's truth abideth still,
      His kingdom is for ever.
            M. Luther. (Tr. *F. H. Hedge.*)

Open my Eyes. P.M. CLARA H. SCOTT.

Arrangement of Words Copyright, by Mrs. H. C. Dixon.

323 *Open Thou mine eyes, that I may behold wondrous things out of Thy law.*—PSALM cxix. 18.

1 OPEN my eyes that I may see
Glimpses of truth Thou hast for me;
Place in my hands the wonderful key
That shall unclasp and set me free.
  Silently now I wait for Thee,
  Ready, my God, Thy will to see;
  Open my eyes, illumine me,
    Spirit Divine!

2 Open my ears that I may hear
Voices of truth Thou sendest clear;
And while the wave-notes fall on my ear,
Everything false will disappear.
  Silently now I wait for Thee,
  Ready, my God, Thy will to see;
  Open my ears, illumine me,
    Spirit Divine!

3 Open my mouth and let me bear
Tidings of mercy everywhere;
Open my heart and let me prepare
Love with Thy children thus to share.
  Silently now I wait for Thee,
  Ready, my God, Thy will to see;
  Open my heart, illumine me,
    Spirit Divine!

4 Open my mind, that I may read
More of Thy love in word and deed:
What shall I fear while yet Thou dost
Only for light from Thee I plead. [lead?
  Silently now I wait for Thee,
  Ready, my God, Thy will to see;
  Open my mind, illumine me,
    Spirit Divine!
        C. H. Scott and F. P. Morris.

Christian, Walk Carefully! 10.10.10.10., with Refrain.

GEO. C. STEBBINS.

REFRAIN.

1st time.

2nd time.

Christian, walk care-ful-ly, Christian, walk care-ful-ly, dan-ger is near!
Christian, walk cheer-ful-ly, Christian, walk cheer-ful-ly, thro' the fierce storm.
Christian, walk prayerful-ly, Christian, walk prayerful-ly, fear lest thou fall.
Christian, walk hope-ful ly, Christian, walk hope-ful-ly, rest thou shalt gain.

By permission. From Sankey's *Sacred Songs and Solos.*

324

Walk worthy of the vocation wherewith ye are called.—EPH. iv. 1.

1 CHRISTIAN, walk carefully, danger is near!
On in thy journey with trembling and fear;
Snares from without, and temptations within,
Seek to entice thee once more into sin.
  Christian, walk carefully, danger is near!

2 Christian, walk cheerfully, through the fierce storm,
Dark though the sky with its threats of alarm;
Soon will the clouds and the tempest be o'er,
Then with thy Saviour thou'lt rest evermore.
  Christian, walk cheerfully, through the fierce storm.

3 Christian, walk prayerfully; oft wilt thou fall,
If thou forget on thy Saviour to call;
Safe thou shalt walk through each trial and care,
If thou art clad in the armour of prayer.
  Christian, walk prayerfully—fear lest thou fall.

4 Christian, walk hopefully; sorrow and pain
Cease when the haven of rest thou shalt gain;
Then from the lips of the Judge thy reward:
"Enter thou into the joy of thy Lord."
  Christian, walk hopefully, rest thou shalt gain.

Arr. *G. C. Stebbins.*

325 Ibstone.

6.6.6.6.

MARIA TIDDEMAN.

325

Not as I will, but as Thou wilt.—MATT. xxvi. 39.

1 THY way, not mine, O Lord,
However dark it be;
Lead me by Thine own hand,
Choose Thou the path for me.

2 Smooth let it be or rough,
It will be still the best;
Winding or straight, it leads
Right onward to Thy rest.

3 I dare not choose my lot;
I would not if I might;
Choose Thou for me, my God,
So shall I walk aright.

4 Take Thou my cup, and it
With joy or sorrow fill,
As best to Thee may seem;
Choose Thou my good or ill.

5 Choose Thou for me my friends,
My sickness or my health:
Choose Thou my cares for me,
My poverty or wealth.

6 Not mine, not mine the choice,
In things or great or small:
Be Thou my Guide, my Strength,
My Wisdom and my All.   *H. Bonar.*

My Grace is Sufficient.   12.8.12.8.   From HANDEL.

326

My grace is sufficient for thee.—2 COR. xii. 9.

1 "My grace is sufficient"—The Saviour hath spoken—
I rest on the truth of His word;
I know that His promise hath never been broken,
The faithful, unchangeable Lord.

2 "*My* grace is sufficient"—no word of a stranger
Could give me this confidence deep;
But He is my succour in doubt or in danger,
Almighty to save and to keep.

3 "My *grace* is sufficient"—unmerited favour
To me full of failure and sin;
Though I am but weakness, my glorious Saviour
Will finish what He did begin.

4 "My grace *is* sufficient"—I tremble no longer;
My best resolutions may fail;
Yet I trust Him with faith ever stronger and stronger,
His promise must ever prevail.

5 "My grace is *sufficient*"—exhaustless in measure,
Though millions appeal in their need;
My Saviour, I praise Thee, I take of the treasure,
Thy grace is sufficient indeed.   *S. F. Forrest.*

Oh, how He Loves! 8.4.8.4.8.8.8.4. H. P. MAIN.

327 *His great love wherewith He loved us.*—EPH. ii. 4.

1 ONE there is above all others—
  Oh, how He loves!
His is love beyond a brother's—
  Oh, how He loves!
Earthly friends may fail or leave us,
One day soothe, the next day grieve us,
But this Friend will ne'er deceive us:
  Oh, how He loves!

2 'Tis eternal life to know Him—
  Oh, how He loves!
Think, oh think, how much we owe Him—
  Oh, how He loves!
With His precious blood He bought us,
In the wilderness He sought us,
To His fold He safely brought us:
  Oh, how He loves!

3 We have found a Friend in Jesus—
  Oh, how He loves!
'Tis His great delight to bless us—
  Oh, how He loves!
How our hearts delight to hear Him
Bid us dwell in safety near Him!
Why should we distrust or fear Him?
  Oh, how He loves!

4 Through His Name we are forgiven—
  Oh, how He loves!
Backward shall our foes be driven—
  Oh, how He loves!
Best of blessings He'll provide us,
Naught but good shall e'er betide us,
Safe to glory He will guide us:
  Oh, how He loves!
                              M. Nunn.

328 Cassel. 7.7.7.7.7.7. German.

328

My soul is even as a weaned child.—PSALM cxxxi. 2.

1 QUIET, Lord, my froward heart;
　Make me teachable and mild,
Upright, simple, free from art;
　Make me as a little child—
From distrust and envy free,
Pleased with all that pleases Thee.

2 What Thou shalt to-day provide,
　Let me as a child receive;
What to-morrow may betide,
　Calmly to Thy wisdom leave:
'Tis enough that Thou wilt care—
Why should I the burden bear?

3 As a little child relies
　On a care beyond his own,
Knows he's neither strong nor wise,
　Fears to stir a step alone—
Let me thus with Thee abide,
As my Father, Guard, and Guide!

John Newton.

O Quanta Qualia.　　　　　10.10.10.10.　　　　　*Paris Melody.*

329

He careth for you.—1 PETER v. 7.

1 GOD will take care of you: all through the day
　Jesus is near you to keep you from ill;
Waking or resting, at work or at play,
　Jesus is with you, and watching you still.

2 He will take care of you: all through the night
　Jesus, the Shepherd, His little one keeps;
Darkness to Him is the same as the light;
　He never slumbers, and He never sleeps.

3 He will take care of you: all through the year,
　Crowning each day with His kindness and love,
Sending you blessings, and shielding from fear,
　Leading you on to the bright home above.

4 He will take care of you: yes, to the end:
　Nothing can alter His love for His own;
Children, be glad that you have such a Friend;
　He will not leave you one moment alone.

Frances R. Havergal.

Tenderly Guide Us. P.M. G. F. Root.

CHORUS.

Nev-er! . . . Nev-er! . . . Nev-er! oh, nev-er, for Thou art the Way;
Nev-er! oh, nev-er, for Thou art the Way;

Nev-er! . . . Nev-er! . . . Nev-er from Thee would we stray!
Nev-er, oh, nev-er from Thee would we stray!

330

Hold up my goings in Thy paths.—PSALM xvii. 5.

1 TENDERLY guide us, O Shepherd of love,
To the green pastures and waters above;
Guarding us ever by night and by day,
Never from Thee would we stray.
Never! . . . Never! . . . etc.

2 What though the heavens with clouds be o'ercast?—
Fearful the tempest, and bitter the blast?
Still with the light of Thy Word on the way,
Never from Thee would we stray.

3 Over our weakness Thy strength has been cast;
Keep us in meekness, Thy own till the last:
Then, safely folded, with joy we shall say,
Never from Thee would we stray.

Mrs. W. R. Griswold.

Newington.   7.7.7.7.   Archbishop W. D. MACLAGAN.

331

And they shall be Mine, saith the Lord of hosts, in that day when I make up My jewels.—MAL. iii. 17.

1 THINE for ever: God of love,
  Hear us from Thy throne above;
  Thine for ever may we be,
  Here and in eternity.

2 Thine for ever: Lord of life,
  Shield us through our earthly strife;
  Thou the Life, the Truth, the Way,
  Guide us to the realms of day.

3 Thine for ever: oh, how blest
  They who find in Thee their rest;

Saviour, Guardian, heavenly Friend,
Oh, defend us to the end!

4 Thine for ever: Shepherd, keep
  These Thy frail and trembling sheep;
  Safe alone beneath Thy care,
  Let us all Thy goodness share.

5 Thine for ever: Thou our Guide,
  All our wants by Thee supplied,
  All our sins by Thee forgiven,
  Lead us, Lord, from earth to heaven.

Mary F. Maude.

Wiltshire.   **C.M.**   Sir GEORGE T. SMART.

Alternative Tune, BEDFORD, *No.* 75.

332   *I will bless the Lord at all times.*—PSALM xxxiv. 1.

1 THROUGH all the changing scenes of life,
  In trouble and in joy,
  The praises of my God shall still
  My heart and tongue employ.

2 Oh, magnify the Lord with me!
  With me exalt His Name;
  When in distress to Him I called,
  He to my rescue came.

3 The hosts of God encamp around
  The dwellings of the just;

Deliverance He affords to all
Who on His succour trust.

4 Oh, make but trial of His love!
  Experience will decide
  How blest they are, and only they,
  Who in His truth confide.

5 Fear Him, ye saints; and you will then
  Have nothing else to fear;
  Make you His service your delight,
  Your wants shall be His care.

Tate and Brady.

K

Wye Valley.
Joyful.

6.5.6.5., D., with Chorus.

J. MOUNTAIN.

CHORUS.

Stayed up-on Je - ho - vah, Hearts are ful - ly blest; Find-ing, as He prom - ised, Per-fect peace and rest.

333 *Thus saith the Lord, . . . I will extend peace to her like a river.*—ISA. lxvi. 12.

1 LIKE a river glorious
  Is God's perfect peace,
Over all victorious
  In its bright increase ;
Perfect, yet it floweth
  Fuller every day ;
Perfect, yet it groweth
  Deeper all the way.
    Stayed upon Jehovah, etc.

2 Hidden in the hollow
  Of His blessèd hand,
Never foe can follow,
  Never traitor stand ;
Not a surge of worry,
  Not a shade of care,
Not a blast of hurry
  Touch the spirit there.

3 Every joy or trial
  Falleth from above,
Traced upon our dial
  By the Sun of Love :
We may trust Him fully
  All for us to do ;
They who trust Him wholly
  Find Him wholly true.

Frances R. Havergal.

334 The Path Divine.

6.4.6.4.6.6.6.4.

B. MANSELL RAMSEY.

334

Teach me Thy way, O Lord, and lead me.—PSALM xxvii. 11.

1 TEACH me Thy way, O Lord,
  Teach me Thy way!
 Thy gracious aid afford,
  Teach me Thy way!
 Help me to walk aright,
 More by faith, less by sight;
 Lead me with heavenly light:
  Teach me Thy way!

2 When doubts and fears arise,
  Teach me Thy way!
 When storms o'erspread the skies,
  Teach me Thy way!

Shine through the cloud and rain,
Through sorrow, toil, and pain;
Make Thou my pathway plain:
  Teach me Thy way!

3 Long as my life shall last,
  Teach me Thy way!
 Where'er my lot be cast,
  Teach me Thy way!
 Until the race is run,
 Until the journey's done,
 Until the crown is won,
  Teach me Thy way!

B. M. Ramsey.

The Good Shepherd.   8.7.8.7.8.7.   W. B. BRADBURY.

Alternative Tunes, ST. WERBURGH, *No.* 337, *and* REQUIEM, *No.* 367.

335   *He shall feed His flock like a shepherd.*—ISA. xl. 11.

1 SAVIOUR, like a shepherd lead us,
  Much we need Thy tender care;
 In Thy pleasant pastures feed us,
  For our use Thy fold prepare:
   Blessèd Jesus,
 Thou hast bought us, Thine we are.

2 We are Thine, do Thou befriend us;
  Be the Guardian of our way:
 Keep Thy flock, from sin defend us,
  Seek us when we go astray:
   Blessèd Jesus,
 Hear Thy children when they pray.

3 Thou hast promised to receive us,
  Poor and sinful though we be;
 Thou hast mercy to relieve us,
  Grace to cleanse, and power to free:
   Blessèd Jesus,
 Let us early turn to Thee.

4 Early let us seek Thy favour,
  Early let us do Thy will;
 Blessèd Lord and only Saviour,
  With Thyself our bosoms fill:
   Blessèd Jesus,
 Thou hast loved us—love us still.

H. F. Lyte.

I Know Whom I have Believed. C.M., with Chorus.

JAMES McGRANAHAN.

CHORUS.

But "I know whom I have be-liev-ed; and am per-suad-ed that He is a-ble to keep that which I've com-mit-ted un-to Him against that day."

Words and Music by permission of Mrs. H. C. Dixon.

336

I know Whom I have believed.—2 TIM. 1. 12.

1 1 KNOW not why God's wondrous grace
　To me hath been made known;
Nor why—unworthy as I am—
　He claimed me for His own.
　But "I know," etc.

2 I know not how this saving faith
　To me He did impart;
Or how believing in His Word
　Wrought peace within my heart.

3 1 know not how the Spirit moves,
　Convincing men of sin;

Revealing Jesus through the Word,
　Creating faith in Him.

4 I know not what of good or ill
　May be reserved for me—
Of weary ways or golden days
　Before His face 1 see.

5 I know not when my Lord may come;
　I know not how, nor where;
If I shall pass the vale of death,
　Or "meet Him in the air."
　　　　　　　　El Nathan.

337 St. Werburgh.　　8.7.8.7.8.7.　　S. WEBBE.

337 · *Thou art the Guide of my youth.*—Jer. iii. 4.

1 FATHER, let Thy benediction,
   Gently falling as the dew,
And Thy ever-gracious presence
   Bless us all our journey through :
      May we ever,
   In our lives keep Christ in view !

2 Young in years, we need the wisdom
   Which can only come from Thee ;
In the morn of our existence
   Let us Thy salvation see :
      Changed in spirit,
   We shall then Thy children be.

3 When temptations shall assail us,
   When we falter by the way,
Let Thine arm of strength defend us ;
   Saviour, hear us when we pray :
      Thou art mighty,
   Be Thou then our rock and stay.

4 Praise and blessing, power and glory,
   Will we render, Lord, to Thee ;
For the news of Thy salvation
   Shall extend from sea to sea ;
      And the nations,
   Joyfully shall worship Thee.

M. E. Shelley.

Pax Tecum. 10.10. G. T. CALDBECK.

338 *Thou wilt keep him in perfect peace, whose mind is stayed on Thee ; because he trusteth in Thee.*—Isa. xxvi. 3.

1 PEACE, perfect peace, in this dark world of sin?
   The blood of Jesus whispers peace within.

2 Peace, perfect peace, by thronging duties pressed?
   To do the will of Jesus, this is rest.

3 Peace, perfect peace, with sorrows surging round?
   On Jesus' bosom naught but calm is found.

4 Peace, perfect peace, with loved ones far away?
   In Jesus' keeping we are safe, and they.

5 Peace, perfect peace, our future all unknown?
   Jesus we know, and He is on the throne.

6 Peace, perfect peace, death shadowing us and ours?
   Jesus has vanquished death and all its powers.

7 It is enough : earth's struggles soon shall cease,
   And Jesus call to heaven's perfect peace.

E. H. Bickersteth.

Petros. 8.7.8.7., and Chorus. L. HARTSOUGH.

In the high-er Rock, I'm trusting, Restful, peace-ful, saved, and free; 'Tis the test-ed Rock of A-ges, Its dear shad-ow shelters me.

Alternative Tune (without Chorus), LUCERNE, *No.* 412.

Thou art my Rock and my Fortress.—PSALM xxxi. 3.

339

1 LEAD me to the Rock that's higher
   Than the rock poor self can show;
   Lead me to its perfect "shelter,"
   The "strong tower" from every foe.
      In the higher Rock, etc.

2 Yes, the higher Rock, so towering,
   Gives, amid life's rudest storms,
   Perfect refuge, surest safety,
   Sweetest rest amid alarms.

3 'Tis the higher Rock that gives me
   Faith's glad strength for every hour;
   Oh! to measure all its gladness,
   All its preciousness of power!

4 'Tis the higher Rock sustains me
   Joyously from day to day;
   Lifting heart and soul and spirit
   To the purer, holier way.

5 'Tis the higher Rock that saves me,
   'Tis the higher Rock I've found,
   Where abide the crowning graces—
   Faith and hope and love abound.

6 So will I sing praises to Thee
   For Thy wondrous power to save;
   Daily 'neath Thy shadow resting,
   'Till the victor's palm I wave.
                              L. Hartsough.

340 Ashburton. 7.7.7.7.7.7. R. JACKSON.

340

That your joy might be full.—JOHN xv. 11.

1 LIFE and light and joy are found
   In the presence of the Lord;
Life, with richest blessings crowned,
   Light, from many fountains poured :
Life and light and holy joy
None can darken or destroy.

2 Bring to Him life's brightest hours,
   He will make them still more bright;
Give to Him your noblest powers,
   He will hallow all your might;
Come to Him with eager quest,
You shall hear His high behest.

3 All your questions large and deep,
   All the open thoughts of youth,
Bring to Him, and you shall reap

All the harvest of His truth;
   You shall find in that great store
Largest love and wisest lore.

4 Then, when comes life's wider sphere
   And its busier enterprise,
You shall find Him ever near,
   Looking with approving eyes
On all honest work and true
His dear servants' hands can do.

5 And if care should dim your eye,
   And life's shadows come apace,
You shall find Him ever nigh
   In His all-abounding grace,
Changing sorrow's darkest night
Into morning clear and bright.

C. E. Mudie.

Walking with Jesus.   P.M.   MRS. L. SHOREY. Arr. by H. A. MCKENZIE.

Words and music copyright of the National Sunday School Union.

Walk in newness of life.—ROM. vi. 4.

341

1 WALKING with Jesus day by day,
   Taking Him for our Guide;
Holding His hand we can never stray
   Far from His wounded side.

2 Looking to Jesus day by day,
   Ever for fresh supply,
Never a blessing will He delay,
   Naught but in love deny.

3 Speaking for Jesus day by day,
   Telling what He has done

Helping some wanderer to find the way,
   Guiding some erring one.

4 Singing for Jesus day by day,
   Praising His Name in song;
Telling His love in a happy lay
   Gladly the whole day long.

5 Living for Jesus day by day,
   Sharing His grace and love,
Bearing His cross, that by this we may
   Share in His joy above.   *L. Shorey*

Crosby.

P.M.

W. H. Doane.

REFRAIN.

Safe in the arms of Je - sus,

Safe on His gentle breast, There by His love o'ersha - ded, Sweetly my soul shall rest.

342   *Underneath are the everlasting arms.*—DEUT. xxxiii. 27.

1 SAFE in the arms of Jesus,
  Safe on His gentle breast,
There by His love o'ershaded,
  Sweetly my soul shall rest:
Hark! 'tis the voice of angels
  Borne in a song to me,
Over the fields of glory,
  Over the jasper sea.
    Safe in the arms of Jesus, etc.

2 Safe in the arms of Jesus,
  Safe from corroding care,
Safe from the world's temptations,
  Sin cannot harm me there:
Free from the blight of sorrow,
  Free from my doubts and fears;
Only a few more trials,
  Only a few more tears.

3 Jesus, my heart's dear Refuge,
  Jesus has died for me;
Firm on the Rock of Ages
  Ever my trust shall be:
Here let me wait with patience,
  Wait till the night is o'er;
Wait till I see the morning
  Break on the golden shore.

Fanny J. Crosby.

The Saviour With Me.   8.7.8.7., with Chorus.   JNO. R. SWENEY.

DUET.

CHORUS. *A little faster.*

Then my soul . . . . . shall fear no ill,   Let Him
Then my soul   fear no ill,

lead . . . . . me where He will,   I will
Let Him lead   where He will,

go . . . . . with-out a mur-mur, And His foot-steps fol-low still.
I will go

343   *I will never leave thee, nor forsake thee.*—HEB. xiii. 5.

1 I MUST have the Saviour with me,
   For I dare not walk alone;
I must feel His presence near me,
   And His arm around me thrown.
     Then my soul shall fear no ill, etc.

2 I must have the Saviour with me,
   For my faith, at best, is weak;
He can whisper words of comfort
   That no other voice can speak.

3 I must have the Saviour with me,
   In the onward march of life,
Through the tempest and the sunshine,
   Through the battle and the strife.

4 I must have the Saviour with me,
   And His eye the way must guide;
Till I reach the vale of Jordan,
   Till I cross the rolling tide.

L. Edwards.

K *

Charlesworth. P.M. IRA D. SANKEY.

CHORUS.

Oh, Je-sus is a Rock in a wea-ry land, A wea-ry land, a wea-ry land; Oh,

Je-sus is a Rock in a wea-ry land, A shel-ter in the time of storm.

344 *My God is the Rock of my refuge.*—PSALM xciv. 22.

1 THE Lord's our Rock, in Him we hide,
  A shelter in the time of storm;
Secure, whatever ill betide,
  A shelter in the time of storm.
    Oh, Jesus is a Rock, etc.

2 A shade by day, defence by night,
  A shelter in the time of storm;
No fears alarm, no foes affright,
  A shelter in the time of storm.

3 The raging storms may round us beat,
  A shelter in the time of storm;
We'll never leave our safe retreat,
  A shelter in the time of storm.

4 O Rock divine, O Refuge dear,
  A shelter in the time of storm;
Be Thou our Helper, ever near,
  A shelter in the time of storm.

V. J. Charlesworth.

345 Jesus, Lord and Master. P.M. C. FISHWICK

345 *I . . . am persuaded that He is able to keep that which I have committed unto Him.*—2 Tim. i. 12.

1 Jesus, Lord and Master,
    Keep me now, I pray;
  If I but resist him
    Satan cannot stay.
  When the storm-clouds gather
    When temptation's nigh,
  Thou wilt then protect me,
    And whisper, "It is I."

2 Though I fain would follow,
    Where my Lord once trod,
  Drawing ever nearer
    To the throne of God;
  Yet I often stumble
    On my upward way,
  Come, then, loving Saviour,
    Help me to watch and pray.

3 Though my faith is feeble,
    Though my strength is small,
  I will ever trust Thee,
    Who art over all.
  I am now persuaded
    Thou wilt keep me true;
  If looking unto Jesus
    Then I can all things do.

4 On that last great morning
    When all men shall meet,
  Shall I dare to face Him
    Kneeling at His feet?
  Yes! for now I'll serve Him
    Till my life is gone,
  That I may lead men to Him,
    And hear Him say, "Well done!"

J. F. Spink.

St. Ann.   **C.M.**   W. Croft.

346 *Lord, Thou hast been our dwelling place in all generations.*—Psalm xc. 1.

1 O God, our help in ages past,
    Our hope for years to come;
  Our shelter from the stormy blast,
    And our eternal home.

2 Under the shadow of Thy throne
    Thy saints have dwelt secure;
  Sufficient is Thine arm alone,
    And our defence is sure.

3 Before the hills in order stood,
    Or earth received her frame,
  From everlasting Thou art God,
    To endless years the same.

4 A thousand ages in Thy sight
    Are like an evening gone;
  Short as the watch that ends the night
    Before the rising sun.

5 Time, like an ever-rolling stream,
    Bears all its sons away;
  They fly, forgotten, as a dream
    Dies at the opening day.

6 O God, our help in ages past,
    Our hope for years to come;
  Be Thou our guard while life shall last,
    And our eternal home.

Isaac Watts.

Hiding in Thee. 11.11.11.11., with Refrain. IRA D. SANKEY.

Hiding in Thee, hi-ding in Thee, Thou blest "Rock of A-ges," I'm hi-ding in Thee.

By permission. From Sankey's *Sacred Songs and Solos.*

347 *My strong Rock, for an house of defence.*—PSALM xxxi. 2.

1 OH, safe to the Rock that is higher than I,
My soul in its conflicts and sorrows would fly;
So sinful, so weary, Thine, Thine would I be;
Thou blest "Rock of Ages," I'm hiding in Thee.
    Hiding in Thee, etc.

2 In the calm of the noontide, in sorrow's lone hour,
In times when temptation casts o'er me its power;
In the tempests of life, on its wide, heaving sea,
Thou blest "Rock of Ages," I'm hiding in Thee.

3 How oft in the conflict, when pressed by the foe,
I have fled to my Refuge and breathed out my woe;
How often, when trials like sea-billows roll,
Have I hidden in Thee, O Thou Rock of my soul.

W. O. Cushing.

Providence.   7.7.7.7.   PLEYEL.

Alternative Tune, LUBECK, *No.* 659.
He careth for you.—1 PETER v. 7.

348

1 POOR and needy though I be,
God Almighty cares for me;
Gives me clothing, shelter, food,
Gives me all I have of good.

2 He will hear me when I pray—
He is with me night and day;
When I sleep and when I wake—
For the Lord my Saviour's sake.

3 He who reigns above the sky
Once became as poor as I;

He whose blood for me was shed
Had not where to lay His head.

4 Though I labour here awhile,
He will bless me with His smile,
And when this short life is past
I shall rest with Him at last.

5 Then to Him I'll tune my song,
Happy as the day is long:
This my joy for ever be—
God Almighty cares for me.

D. A. Thrupp.

Innocents.   7.7.7.7.   Composed or adapted by JOSEPH SMITH.

349   *The ransomed of the Lord shall . . . come to Zion with songs.*—ISA. XXXV. 10.

1 CHILDREN of the heavenly King,
As ye journey gladly sing;
Sing your Saviour's worthy praise,
Glorious in His works and ways.

2 We are travelling home to God,
In the way the fathers trod:
They are happy now; and we
Soon their happiness shall see.

3 Shout, ye little flock and blest;
You on Jesus' throne shall rest:
There your seat is now prepared,
There your kingdom and reward.

4 Lift your eyes, ye sons of light;
Zion's city is in sight;
There our endless home shall be,
There our Lord we soon shall see.

5 Fear not, brethren; joyful stand
On the borders of your land;
Christ, the everlasting Son,
Bids you undismayed go on.

6 Lord, obediently we go,
Gladly leaving all below;
Only Thou our Leader be,
And we still will follow Thee.

J. Cennick.

Olivet.   6.6.4.6.6.6.4.   L. MASON.

350   *The life which I now live . . . I live by the faith of the Son of God.—*
GAL. ii. 20.

1 My faith looks up to Thee,
  Thou Lamb of Calvary,
    Saviour Divine:
  Now hear me while I pray,
  Take all my guilt away,
  Oh, let me from this day
    Be wholly Thine!

2 May Thy rich grace impart
  Strength to my fainting heart,
    My zeal inspire;
  As Thou hast died for me,
  Oh, may my love to Thee
  Pure, warm, and changeless be,
    A living fire!

3 When life's dark maze I tread,
  And griefs around me spread,
    Be Thou my Guide;
  Bid darkness turn to day,
  Wipe sorrow's tears away,
  Nor let me ever stray
    From Thee aside.

4 When ends life's transient dream,
  When death's cold, sullen stream
    Shall o'er me roll;
  Blest Saviour, then in love
  Fear and distrust remove;
  Oh, bear me safe above,
    A ransomed soul.

Ray Palmer.

351 God holds the Key.   8.4.8.8.4.   GEO. C. STEBBINS.

By permission. From Sankey's *Sacred Songs and Solos.*

351 *Casting all of your care upon Him; for He careth for you.*—1 PETER v. 7.

1 GOD holds the key of all unknown,
 And I am glad:
If other hands should hold the key,
Or if He trusted it to me,
 I might be sad.

2 What if to-morrow's cares were here
 Without its rest?
I'd rather He unlocked the day,
And, as the hours swing open, say,
 "My will is best."

3 The very dimness of my sight
 Makes me secure;
For, groping in my misty way,
I feel His hand; I hear Him say,
 "My help is sure."

4 I cannot read His future plans;
 But this I know:
I have the smiling of His face,
And all the refuge of His grace,
 While here below.

5 Enough: this covers all my wants;
 And so I rest!
For what I cannot, He can see,
And in His care I saved shall be,
 For ever blest. *J. Parker.*

The Journey of Life. 7.7.7.7.7.7. J. E. GOULD.

352 *He guided them by the skilfulness of His hands.*—PSALM lxxviii. 72.

1 JESUS, Saviour, pilot me
 Over life's tempestuous sea;
 Unknown waves before me roll,
 Hiding rock and treacherous shoal;
 Chart and compass come from Thee:
 Jesus, Saviour, pilot me!

2 As a mother stills her child,
 Thou canst hush the ocean wild;
 Boisterous waves obey Thy will
 When Thou say'st to them, "Be still!"
 Wondrous Sovereign of the sea—
 Jesus, Saviour, pilot me!

3 When at last I near the shore,
 And the fearful breakers roar
 'Twixt me and the peaceful rest—
 Then, while leaning on Thy breast,
 May I hear Thee say to me—
 "Fear not, I will pilot thee!" *E. Hopper.*

Thy Will in Me.   P.M.   CHAS. H. GABRIEL.

CHORUS.

Thy will be done in me, Lord! My all I yield to Thee, Lord! In life, in death, Be Thou my Guide And I shall be sat-is - fied! . .

Words and Music by permission of Mrs. H. C. Dixon.

353

*I delight to do Thy will, O my God.—*PSALM xl. 8.

1 DEAR LORD, I cannot see
  Where Thou art leading me!
I cannot tell if thorns or roses strew the
  My future is concealed;   [way;
  Thou hast not yet revealed
Thy will in me, nor do I for the knowledge
      pray.
    Thy will be done in me, Lord! etc.

2 What streams I have to cross,
  Of sorrow, pain, or loss,   [mayed;
Are not for me to fear—I shall not be dis-
  Content if Thou, my Guide,
  Art ever near my side,
That I may hear Thee whisper, "Child, be
      not afraid!"

3   Rejoicing, on I go:
      I do not ask to know
  The path I tread, or whither be the way I take.
      Thy will be done in me;
      This is my only plea:
  Forgive, and love, and guide me, for Thy mercy's sake.
                                    Charlotte G. Homer.

Courage, Brother!   8.7.8.7. D.   Sir ARTHUR S. SULLIVAN.

"Trust in God, trust in God, trust in God, and .. do the right."

By permission of Novello and Company, Limited.
Alternative Tune, BETHANY, *No.* 362.

354   *Be strong and of a good courage.*—JOSH. i. 6.

1 COURAGE, brother! do not stumble,
   Though thy path be dark as night;
There's a star to guide the humble;
   "Trust in God, and do the right."
Let the road be rough and dreary,
   And its end far out of sight,
Foot it bravely! strong or weary,
   "Trust in God, and do the right."

2 Perish policy and cunning,
   Perish all that fears the light!
Whether losing, whether winning,
   "Trust in God, and do the right."
Simple rule, and safest guiding,
   Inward peace, and inward light,
Star upon our path abiding—
   "Trust in God, and do the right."

3 Some will hate thee, some will love thee,
   Some will flatter, some will slight:
Cease from man, and look above thee:
   "Trust in God, and do the right."
Courage, brother! do not stumble,
   Though thy path be dark as night;
There's a star to guide the humble;
   "Trust in God, and do the right."

Norman Macleod.

Mannheim. 8.7.8.7.8.7. F. Filitz.

355 *He led them forth by the right way.*—Psalm cvii. 7.

1 Lead us, heavenly Father, lead us
    O'er the world's tempestuous sea;
  Guard us, guide us, keep us, feed us,
    For we have no help but Thee;
  Yet possessing every blessing,
    If our God our Father be.

2 Saviour, breathe forgiveness o'er us;
    All our weakness Thou dost know;
  Thou didst tread this earth before us,
    Thou didst feel its keenest woe;
  Lone and dreary, faint and weary,
    Through the desert Thou didst go.

3 Spirit of our God, descending,
    Fill our hearts with heavenly joy;
  Love with every passion blending,
    Pleasure that can never cloy:
  Thus provided, pardoned, guided,
    Nothing can our peace destroy.

                              J. Edmeston.

356 St. Flavian. C.M. T. Ravenscroft.

Alternative Tune, Nox Præcessit, *No.* 111.

356

If we walk in the light, as He is in the light, we have fellowship one with another.—1 JOHN i. 7.

1 WALK in the light, so shalt thou know
　That fellowship of love
His Spirit only can bestow,
　Who reigns in light above.

2 Walk in the light, and thou shalt find
　Thy heart made truly His,
Who dwells in cloudless light enshrined,
　In whom no darkness is.

3 Walk in the light—and sin abhorred
　Shall not defile again;
The blood of Jesus Christ the Lord
　Shall cleanse from every stain.

4 Walk in the light, and e'en the tomb
　No fearful shade shall wear;
Glory shall chase away its gloom,
　For Christ hath conquered there.

5 Walk in the light, and thou shalt own
　Thy darkness passed away,
Because that light hath on thee shone,
　In which is perfect day.

6 Walk in the light—thy path shall be
　Peaceful, serene, and bright;
For God, by grace, shall dwell in thee,
　And God Himself is Light.

Bernard Barton.

Montgomery.　　　11.11.11.11.　　　J. STANLEY.

Alternative Tunes, ADESTE FIDELES, *No. 117, and* ST. LUKE, *No. 46.*

357

Fear not: for I am with thee.—ISA. xliii. 5

1 How firm a foundation, ye saints of the Lord,
Is laid for your faith in His excellent Word!
What more can He say than to you He hath said,
You who unto Jesus for refuge have fled?

2 "In every condition—in sickness, in health,
In poverty's vale, or abounding in wealth;
At home and abroad, on the land, on the sea,
As thy days may demand, shall thy strength ever be.

3 "Fear not, I am with thee, oh, be not dismayed!
For I am thy God and will still give thee aid:
I'll strengthen thee, help thee, and cause thee to stand,
Upheld by My righteous, omnipotent hand.

4 "When through fiery trials thy pathway shall lie,
My grace all-sufficient shall be thy supply;
The flame shall not hurt thee; I only design
Thy dross to consume, and thy gold to refine.

5 "The soul that on Jesus hath leaned for repose,
I will not, I will not, desert to its foes;
That soul, though all hell should endeavour to shake,
I'll never, no, never, no, never forsake!"

George Keith.

No, not One!

P.M.

GEO. C. HUGG, arr.

With feeling.

CHORUS.

Je - sus knows all a - bout our struggles, He will guide till the day is done.

There's not a friend like the low - ly Je - sus, No, not one! no, not one!

358 *Christ also hath loved us, and hath given Himself for us.—EPH. v. 2.*

1 THERE'S not a friend like the lowly Jesus,
 No, not one! no, not one!
None else could heal all our soul's diseases,
 No, not one! no, not one!
  Jesus knows, etc.

2 No friend like Him is so high and holy,
 No, not one! no, not one!
And yet no friend is so meek and lowly,
 No, not one! no, not one!

3 There's not an hour that He is not near us,
 No, not one! no, not one!
No night so dark but His love can cheer us,
 No, not one! no, not one!

4 Did ever saint find this Friend forsake him?
 No, not one! no, not one!
Or sinner find that He would not take him?
 No, not one! no, not one!

5 Was e'er a gift like the Saviour given?
 No, not one! no, not one!
Will He refuse us a home in heaven?
 No, not one! no, not one!

J. Oatman, Jun.

Section VII.—The Christian Life.
(8.) Fellowship with God and Union with Christ.

Jesus! I am Resting.   P.M.   Rev. J. Mountain.

Joyfully.

CHORUS.

Je-sus! I am rest-ing, rest-ing

In the joy of what *Thou* art; I am find-ing out the greatness Of Thy loving heart.

359

My Beloved is mine, and I am His.—Song of Sol. ii. 16.

1 Jesus! I am resting, resting
  In the joy of what *Thou* art;
I am finding out the greatness
  Of Thy loving heart.
Thou hast bid me gaze upon Thee,
  And Thy beauty fills my soul,
For, by Thy transforming power,
  Thou hast made me whole.
    Jesus! I am resting, etc.

2 Oh, how great Thy loving-kindness,
  Vaster, broader than the sea!
Oh, how marvellous Thy goodness,
  Lavished all on me!
Yes, I rest in Thee, Belovèd,
  Know what wealth of grace is Thine,
Know Thy certainty of promise,
  And have made it mine.

3 Simply trusting Thee, Lord Jesus,
  I behold Thee as Thou art,
And Thy love so pure, so changeless,
  Satisfies my heart;
Satisfies its deepest longings,
  Meets, supplies its every need,
Compasseth me round with blessings;
  Thine is love indeed!

4 Ever lift Thy face upon me,
  As I work and wait for Thee;
Resting 'neath Thy smile, Lord Jesus,
  Earth's dark shadows flee.
Brightness of my Father's glory,
  Sunshine of my Father's face,
Keep me ever trusting, resting,
  Fill me with Thy grace.
        Jean Sophia Pigott.

Keswick. P.M. A. J. GORDON.

CHORUS.

Oh, the love that sought me! Oh, the blood that bought me! Oh, the grace that

brought me to the fold, . . Wondrous grace that brought me to the fold! . .

360 *The precious blood of Christ.*—1 PETER i. 19.

1 IN tenderness He sought me,
  Weary and sick with sin,
And on His shoulders brought me
  Back to His fold again.
While angels in His presence sang,
Until the courts of heaven rang.
  Oh, the love that sought me! etc.

2 He found me bruised and dying,
  And poured in oil and wine;
He whispered to assure me,
  "I've found thee—thou art Mine;"
I never heard a sweeter voice,
It made my aching heart rejoice.

3 He pointed to the nail-prints,
  For me His blood was shed,
A mocking crown so thorny,
  Was placed upon His head:
I wondered what He saw in me,
To suffer such deep agony.

4 I'm sitting in His presence,
  The sunshine of His face,
While with adoring wonder
  His blessings I retrace.
It seems as if eternal days
Are far too short to sound His praise.

5 So while the hours are passing,
  All now is perfect rest;
I'm waiting for the morning,
  The brightest and the best.
When He will call us to His side
To be with Him, His spotless Bride.

  W. Spencer Walton.

Hollingside.   7.7.7.7., D.   J. B. Dykes.

361   *I flee unto Thee to hide me.*—Psalm cxliii. 9.

1 Jesus, Lover of my soul,
    Let me to Thy bosom fly,
While the nearer waters roll,
    While the tempest still is high:
Hide me, O my Saviour, hide,
    Till the storm of life be past!
Safe into the haven guide,
    Oh, receive my soul at last!

2 Other refuge have I none,
    Hangs my helpless soul on Thee:
Leave, ah, leave me not alone,
    Still support and comfort me.
All my trust on Thee is stayed,
    All my help from Thee I bring;
Cover my defenceless head
    With the shadow of Thy wing.

3 Thou, O Christ, art all I want;
    More than all in Thee I find:
Raise the fallen, cheer the faint,
    Heal the sick, and lead the blind;
Just and holy is Thy Name,
    I am all unrighteousness;
Vile. and full of sin I am,
    Thou art full of truth and grace.

4 Plenteous grace with Thee is found,
    Grace to pardon all my sin;
Let the healing streams abound,
    Make and keep me pure within.
Thou of life the fountain art,
    Freely let me take of Thee,
Spring Thou up within my heart,
    Rise to all eternity.

                    C. Wesley.

Bethany. 8.7.8.7. D. HENRY SMART.

362 *He that dwelleth in love dwelleth in God, and God in him.*—1 JOHN iv. **16.**

1 LOVE divine, all loves excelling,
    Joy of heaven, to earth come down!
Fix in us Thy humble dwelling,
    All Thy faithful mercies crown.
Jesus, Thou art all compassion,
    Pure, unbounded love Thou art;
Visit us with Thy salvation,
    Enter every trembling heart.

2 Breathe, oh, breathe Thy loving Spirit
    Into every troubled breast!
Let us all in Thee inherit,
    Let us find Thy promised rest;
Take away the love of sinning;
    Alpha and Omega be;
End of faith, as its beginning,
    Set our hearts at liberty.

3 Come, almighty to deliver,
    Let us all Thy grace receive!
Suddenly return, and never,
    Never more Thy temples leave;
Thee we would be always blessing,
    Serve Thee as Thy hosts above,
Pray, and praise Thee without ceasing,
    Glory in Thy perfect love.

4 Finish then Thy new creation,
    Pure and spotless may we be;
Let us see our whole salvation
    Perfectly restored in Thee!
Changed from glory into glory,
    Till in heaven we take our place;
Till we cast our crowns before Thee,
    Lost in wonder, love, and praise.

C. Wesley.

Day of Rest.   7.6.7.6. D.   J. W. ELLIOTT.

VOICES IN UNISON.   HARMONY.

Man.   Ped.   By permission of Novello and Company, Limited.

363   *I have said that I would keep Thy words.*—PSALM cxix. 57.

1 O JESUS, I have promised
   To serve Thee to the end;
Be Thou for ever near me,
   My Master and my Friend;
I shall not fear the battle
   If Thou art by my side,
Nor wander from the pathway
   If Thou wilt be my Guide.

2 Oh, let me feel Thee near me:
   The world is ever near;
I see the sights that dazzle,
   The tempting sounds I hear;
My foes are ever near me,
   Around me and within;
But, Jesus, draw Thou nearer,
   And shield my soul from sin.

3 Oh, let me hear Thee speaking,
   In accents clear and still,
Above the storms of passion,
   The murmurs of self-will

Oh, speak to reassure me,
   To hasten, or control;
Oh, speak, and make me listen,
   Thou Guardian of my soul.

4 O Jesus, Thou hast promised
   To all who follow Thee
That where Thou art in glory
   There shall Thy servant be;
And, Jesus, I have promised
   To serve Thee to the end;
Oh, give me grace to follow
   My Master and my Friend.

5 Oh, let me see Thy footmarks,
   And in them plant mine own:
My hope to follow duly
   Is in Thy strength alone.
Oh, guide me, call me, draw me,
   Uphold me to the end;
And then in heaven receive me,
   My Saviour and my Friend.

J. E. Bode.

Ernan.   L.M.   L. MASON.

Alternative Tune, WHITBURN, *No.* 443.

364

I am not ashamed of the gospel of Christ.—ROM. i. 16.

1 JESUS! and shall it ever be,
A sinful child ashamed of Thee?
Ashamed of Thee whom angels praise,
Whose glories shine through endless days?

2 Ashamed of Jesus! that dear Friend
On whom my hopes of heaven depend!
No; when I blush, be this my shame,
That I no more revere His Name.

3 Ashamed of Jesus! yes, I may,
When I've no guilt to wash away,
No tears to wipe, no joys to crave,
No fears to quell, no soul to save.

4 Till then, nor is my boasting vain,
Till then I'll boast a Saviour slain!
And, oh, may this my glory be,
That Christ is not ashamed of me!

Joseph Grigg.

365 Horbury. [FIRST TUNE.]   6.4 6.4.6.6.4.   J. B. DYKES.

rall.   *a tempo.*

Propior Deo. [SECOND TUNE.]   6.4.6.4.6.6.4.   Sir ARTHUR S. SULLIVAN.

By permission of Novello and Company, Limited.

365

*Behold, a ladder set up on the earth, and the top of it reached to
heaven.*—GEN. xxviii. 12.

1 NEARER, my God, to Thee,
  Nearer to Thee;
E'en though it be a cross
  That raiseth me;
Still all my song shall be—
Nearer, my God, to Thee,
  Nearer to Thee.

2 Though, like the wanderer,
  The sun gone down,
Darkness comes over me,
  My rest a stone:
Yet in my dreams I'd be
Nearer, my God, to Thee,
 · Nearer to Thee.

3 There let my way appear
  Steps unto heaven;
All that Thou sendest me,
  In mercy given;
Angels to beckon me
Nearer, my God, to Thee,
  Nearer to Thee.

4 Then, with my waking thoughts
  Bright with Thy praise,
Out of my stony griefs
  Bethel I'll raise;
So by my woes to be
Nearer, my God, to Thee,
  Nearer to Thee.

5 Or if on joyful wing,
  Cleaving the sky,
Sun, moon, and stars forgot,
  Upward I fly;
Still all my song shall be,
Nearer, my God, to Thee,
  Nearer to Thee.
       Sarah F. Adams.

Morecambe. 10.10.10.10. F. C. Atkinson.

366 *If any man hear My voice, and open the door, I will come in to Him.—*
Rev. iii. 20.

1 Come in, O come! the door stands open now;
I knew Thy voice: Lord Jesus, it was Thou;
The sun has set long since; the storms begin;
'Tis time for Thee, my Saviour, O come in!

2 Alas, ill-ordered shows the dreary room;
The household-stuff lies heaped amidst the gloom;
The table empty stands, the couch undressed;
Ah, what a welcome for the Eternal Guest!

3 Yet welcome, and to-day; this doleful scene
Is e'en itself my cause to hail Thee in;
This dark confusion e'en at once demands
Thine own bright presence, Lord, and ordering hands.

4 I seek no more to alter things, or mend,
Before the coming of so great a Friend;
All were at best unseemly; and 'twere ill
Beyond all else to keep Thee waiting still.

5 Come, not to find, but make this troubled heart
A dwelling worthy of Thee as Thou art;
To chase the gloom, the terror, and the sin:
Come, all Thyself, yea come, Lord Jesus, in!

H. C. G. Moule.

367 Requiem. 8.7.8.7.7.7. W. Schulthes.

Org.

367 *Thou shalt call His Name Jesus; for He shall save His people from their sins.*—MATT. i. 21.

1 THOU whose Name is callèd Jesus,
  Risen Lord of life and power,
Oh, it is so sweet to trust Thee!
  Every day and every hour.
    Of Thy wondrous grace I sing,
    Saviour, Counsellor, and King.

2 Thou canst keep my feet from falling,
  Even my poor wayward feet.—
Thou who dost present me faultless,
  In Thy righteousness complete,
    Jesus, Lord. in knowing Thee,
    Oh, what strength and victory!

3 All the sin in me, my Saviour,
  Thou canst conquer and subdue;
With Thy sanctifying power
  Permeate my spirit through;
    Let Thy government increase,
    Risen, crownèd, Prince of Peace.

4 Thou canst keep me upward looking;
  Ever upward in Thy face;
Thou canst make me stand, upholden
  By the greatness of Thy grace;
    Every promise of Thy Word
    Now I claim from Thee, dear Lord.

5 Oh! what joy to trust Thee, Jesus,
  Mighty Victor o'er the grave,
And to learn amid earth's shadows
  Thine unceasing power to save!
    Only those who prove Thee know
    What the grace Thou dost bestow.

6 Make my life a bright outshining
  Of Thy life, that all may see
Thine own resurrection power
  Mightily put forth in me;
    Ever let my heart become
    Yet more consciously Thy home.

Jean Sophia Pigott.

St. Silas.   8.6.8.6.8.6.   J. LANCASTER.

368 *Ordered in all things.*—2 SAM. xxiii. 5.

1 FATHER, I know that all my life
  Is portioned out for me;
The changes that will surely come
  I do not fear to see:
I ask Thee for a present mind
  Intent on pleasing Thee.

2 I ask Thee for a thoughtful love,
  Through constant watching wise,
To meet the glad with joyful smiles,
  And wipe the weeping eyes;
A heart at leisure from itself
  To soothe and sympathise.

3 I would not have the restless will
  That hurries to and fro,
Seeking for some great thing to do,
  Or secret thing to know;
I would be treated as a child,
  And guided where I go.

4 Wherever in the world I am,
  In whatsoe'er estate,
I have a fellowship with hearts
  To keep and cultivate;
A work of lowly love to do
  For Him on whom I wait.

Anna L. Waring.

O Happy Day!   L.M., with Chorus.   Anon.

CHORUS.

Hap-py day, hap-py day When Je-sus wash'd my sins a-way! He teaches me to watch and pray; And live re-joic-ing ev-'ry day. Hap-py day, hap-py day, When Je-sus wash'd my sins a-way!

Alternative Tunes (without Chorus), GIDEON, *No.* 143, *and* OMBERSLEY, *No.* 391.

369 *Whoso trusteth in the Lord, happy is he.*—PROVERBS xvi. 20.

1 O HAPPY day! that fixed my choice
  On Thee, my Saviour and my God;
Well may this glowing heart rejoice,
  And tell its raptures all abroad.
    Happy day, happy day, etc.

2 'Tis done! the great transaction's done!
  I am my Lord's, and He is mine;
He drew me, and I followed on,
  Charmed to confess the voice divine.

3 Now rest, my long-divided heart;
  Fixed on this blissful centre, rest;
Nor ever from thy Lord depart,
  With Him of every good possessed.

4 High heaven that heard the solemn vow,
  That vow renewed shall daily hear;
Till in life's latest hour I bow,
  And bless in death a bond so dear.

                                 P. Doddridge.

Sawley. C.M. J. WALCH.

Alternative Tune, BEATITUDO, *No.* 571.

370 *Create in me a clean heart, O God.*—PSALM li. 10.

1 OH, for a heart to praise my God,
   A heart from sin set free;
A heart that's sprinkled with the blood
   So freely shed for me:

2 A heart resigned, submissive, meek,
   My dear Redeemer's throne;
Where only Christ is heard to speak,
   Where Jesus reigns alone:

3 A humble, lowly, contrite heart,
   Believing, true, and clean;

Which neither death nor life can part
   From Him that dwells within:

4 A heart in every thought renewed,
   And filled with love divine;
Perfect, and right, and pure, and good:
   A copy, Lord, of Thine!

5 Thy nature, gracious Lord, impart!
   Come quickly from above;
Write Thy new Name upon my heart,
   Thy new, best Name of Love.
              C. Wesley.

Manoab. C.M. ARR. from ROSSINI.

Alternative Tunes, IRISH, *No.* 593, *and* LYNTON, *No.* 578.

371 *Whom having not seen, ye love.*—1 PETER i. 8.

1 JESUS, these eyes have never seen
   That radiant form of Thine;
The veil of sense hangs dark between
   Thy blessèd face and mine.

2 I see Thee not, I hear Thee not,
   Yet art Thou oft with me;
And earth hath ne'er so dear a spot
   As where I meet with Thee.

3 Like some bright dream that comes un-
   When slumbers o'er me roll, [sought

Thine image ever fills my thought,
   And charms my ravished soul.

4 Yet, though I have not seen, and still
   Must rest in faith alone,
I love Thee, dearest Lord, and will,
   Unseen, but not unknown.

5 When death these mortal eyes shall seal,
   And still this throbbing heart,
The rending veil shall Thee reveal
   All-glorious as Thou art.
             Ray Palmer.

Kelsey Park. D.C.M. E. H. G. SARGENT.

Alternative Tune, PETERSHAM, *No. 383.*

372

For by grace are ye saved through faith.—EPH. ii. 8.

1 FAITH looks to Jesus crucified and risen from the dead.
Faith rests upon His promises, believing all He said.
Faith makes confession of His Name, holds forth the faithful Word.
Faith takes her cross and follows Him, her Saviour and her Lord.

2 Faith sees beyond this passing world, with open vision keen.
Faith all endures as seeing Him, beloved, but yet unseen.
Faith suffers with her Lord below to reign with Him above.
Faith ever seeks to walk in light and ever works by love.

3 Faith loves to be obedient, for she hears her Master's voice.
Faith walks in separation, and a pilgrim is by choice.
Faith hastens to His coming—oh, the rapture and the bliss!
Faith knows she will be like Him when she sees Him as He is.

4 O grant us, Lord, like precious faith, with them that went before,
That we may keep our garments white until the conflict's o'er;
Nor lose our crown, nor faint until the race is fully run,
When we at last shall see Thy face and hear Thee say, "Well done!"

Geo. Goodman.

Sicilian Mariners. [FIRST TUNE.] 8.7.8.7. MERRICK AND TATTERSALL'S Psalms.

Batty. [SECOND TUNE.] 8.7.8.7. German.

Alternative Tunes, SHARON, No. 550, and EVENING PRAYER, No. 607.

373

Peace through the blood of His cross.—COL. i. 20.

1 SWEET the moments, rich in blessing,
  Which before the cross I spend,
Life, and health, and peace possessing,
  From the sinner's dying Friend !

2 Here I rest, in wonder viewing
  All my sins on Jesus laid,
And a full redemption flowing
  From the sacrifice He made.

3 Here I find my hope of heaven,
  While upon the Lamb I gaze;

Loving much, and much forgiven,
  Let my heart o'erflow in praise.

4 Love and grief my heart dividing,
  With my tears His feet I'll bathe ;
Constant still in faith abiding—
  Life deriving from His death.

5 Lord, in ceaseless contemplation
  Fix my thankful heart on Thee !
Till I taste Thy full salvation,
  And Thine unveiled glory see.

W. Shirley.

L

St. George's, Bolton.　　　7.6.7.6., D.　　　J. WALCH.

374　　　*Unto you therefore which believe, He is precious.*—1 PETER ii. 7.

1 I NEED Thee, precious Jesus!
　For I am full of sin :
My soul is dark and guilty,
　My heart is dead within :
I need the cleansing fountain,
　Where I can always flee,
The blood of Christ most precious,
　The sinner's perfect plea.

2 I need Thee, precious Jesus!
　For I am very poor ;
A stranger and a pilgrim,
　I have no earthly store :
I need the love of Jesus
　To cheer me on my way,
To guide my doubting footsteps,
　To be my strength and stay.

3 I need Thee, precious Jesus !
　I need a friend like Thee ;
A Friend to soothe and comfort—
　A Friend to care for me :
I need the heart of Jesus
　To feel each anxious care,
To tell my every trouble
　And all my sorrows share.

4 I need Thee, precious Jesus !
　And hope to see Thee soon,
Encircled with the rainbow,
　And seated on Thy throne ;
There with Thy blood-bought children
　My joy shall ever be,
To sing Thy praise, Lord Jesus—
　To gaze, my Lord, on Thee.

F. Whitfield.

Llanthony Abbey. [FIRST TUNE.] 9.6.9.6. J. H. LESTER.

Slowly.

Whitchester. [SECOND TUNE.] 9.6.9.6. E. J. BELLERBY.

Slowly.

Org.

375 *Hide me under the shadow of Thy wings—PSALM xvii. 8.*

1 LET me come closer to Thee, Jesus,
　　Oh, closer day by day;
　Let me lean harder on Thee, Jesus,
　　Yes, harder all the way.

2 Let me show forth Thy beauty, Jesus,
　　Like sunshine on the hills;
　Oh, let my lips pour forth Thy sweetness
　　In joyous sparkling rills!

3 Yes, like a fountain, precious Jesus.
　　Make me and let me be;
　Keep me and use me daily, Jesus,
　　For Thee, for only Thee.

4 In all my heart and will, O Jesus,
　　Be altogether King;
　Make me a loyal subject, Jesus,
　　To Thee in everything.

5 Thirsting and hungering for Thee, Jesus,
　　With blessèd hunger here;
　Looking for home on Zion's mountain—
　　No thirst, no hunger there.

J. L. Lyne.

The author permits the ascription "Lord Jesus," when preferred, to the first line of verses (and line 3 in
verses 1, 3, 4) ; but as the additional word alters the rhythm, it cannot be printed thus.

Magdalena. 7.6.7.6., D. Sir J. STAINER.

376 *Without Me ye can do nothing.*—JOHN xv. 5.

1 I COULD not do without Thee,
   O Saviour of the lost,
Whose precious blood redeemed me
   At such tremendous cost;
Thy righteousness, Thy pardon,
   Thy precious blood must be
My only hope and comfort,
   My glory and my plea.

2 I could not do without Thee,
   I cannot stand alone,
I have no strength or goodness,
   No wisdom of my own;
But Thou, belovèd Saviour,
   Art all in all to me,
And perfect strength in weakness
   Is theirs who lean on Thee.

3 I could not do without Thee,
   For, oh, the way is long!
And I am often weary,
   And sigh replaces song.

How could I do without Thee?
   I do not know the way;
Thou knowest, and Thou leadest,
   And wilt not let me stray.

4 I could not do without Thee,
   O Jesus, Saviour dear;
E'en when my eyes are holden,
   I know that Thou art near;
How dreary and how lonely
   This changeful life would be
Without the sweet communion,
   The secret rest with Thee!

5 I could not do without Thee,
   For years are fleeting fast,
And soon in solemn loneliness
   The river must be passed;
But Thou wilt never leave me,
   And though the waves roll high,
I know Thou wilt be near me,
   And whisper, "It is I."

Frances R. Havergal.

Nothing Between.   P.M.   J. MOUNTAIN.

Nothing be-tween, nothing be - tween.

377 *The vail shall be taken away.*—2 COR. iii. 16.

1 NOTHING between, Lord, nothing between;
  Let me Thy glory see,
  Draw my soul close to Thee;
  Then speak in love to me—
  Nothing between.

2 Nothing between, Lord, nothing between;
  Let not earth's din and noise
  Stifle Thy still small voice;
  In it let me rejoice—
  Nothing between.

3 Nothing between, Lord, nothing between;
  Unbelief disappear,
  Vanish each doubt and fear,
  Fading when Thou art near—
  Nothing between.

4 Nothing between, Lord, nothing between;
  Till Thine eternal light,
  Rising on earth's dark night,
  Bursts on my open sight—
  Nothing between.

E. H. Hamilton.

Holley.   L.M.   G. HEWS.

Alternative Tune, MARYTON, *No.* 68.

378 *I am that Bread of Life.*—JOHN vi. 48.

1 JESUS, Thou joy of loving hearts,
  Thou Fount of Life, Thou Light of men,
  From the best bliss that earth imparts,
  We turn unfilled to Thee again.

2 Thy truth unchanged hath ever stood;
  Thou savest those that on Thee call;
  To them that seek Thee, Thou art good;
  To them that find Thee, All in all.

3 We taste Thee, O Thou living Bread,
  And long to feast upon Thee still;

  We drink of Thee, the Fountain-head,
  And thirst our souls from Thee to fil'

4 Our restless spirits yearn for Thee,
  Where'er our changeful lot is cast:
  Glad, when Thy gracious smile we see;
  Blest, when our faith can hold Thee fast.

5 O Jesus, ever with us stay;
  Make all our moments calm and bright;
  Chase the dark night of sin away;
  Shed o'er the world Thy holy light.

Ray Palmer (tr.).

Tichfield.　　　　　7.7.7.7., D.　　　　　R. W. Beaty.

Alternative Tune, St. Martin, *No.* 634.

379　　*We love Him because He first loved us.*—1 John iv. 19.

1 Saviour, teach me, day by day,
Love's sweet lesson to obey:
Sweeter lesson cannot be—
Loving Him who first loved me.
Teach me, I am not my own,
I am Thine and Thine alone:
May I serve and copy Thee,
Loving Him who first loved me.

2 With a child's glad heart of love,
At Thy bidding may I move,
Prompt to serve and follow Thee,
Loving Him who first loved me.
Teach me thus Thy steps to trace,
Strong to follow in Thy grace,
Learning how to love from Thee,
Loving Him who first loved me.

8 Love, in loving, finds employ,
In obedience all her joy;
Ever new that joy will be,
Loving Him who first loved me.
Thus may I rejoice to show
That I feel the love I owe;
Singing, till Thy face I see,
Of His love who first loved me.
　　　　　　　　　　　Jane E. Leeson.

Stella.   8.8.8.8.8.8.   Easy Hymn Tunes.

380

To know the love of Christ . . . that ye might be filled with all the fulness of God.—Eph. iii. 19.

1 O Love, who formedst me to wear
    The image of Thy Godhead here;
  Who soughtest me with tender care
    Through all my wanderings wild and drear;
  O Love, I give myself to Thee,
  Thine ever, only Thine to be.

2 O Love, who once in time wast slain,
    Pierced through and through with bitter woe;
  O Love, who wrestling thus did'st gain,
    That we eternal joy might know;
  O Love, I give myself to Thee,
  Thine ever, only Thine to be.

3 O Love, who lovest me for aye,
    Who for my soul dost ever plead;
  O Love, who didst my ransom pay,
    Whose power sufficeth in my stead;
  O Love, I give myself to Thee,
  Thine ever, only Thine to be.

4 O Love, whose voice shall bid me rise
    From out this dying life of ours;
  O Love, whose hand o'er yonder skies
    Shall set me in the fadeless bowers;
  O Love, I give myself to Thee,
  Thine ever, only Thine to be.

                              C. Winkworth (tr.).

381 Never Alone. P.M. J. C. H. and V. A. WHITE.

No, nev-er a -
Nev-er a-lone,

- lone, . . . No, nev-er a - lone; He prom-ised never to leave me,
nev-er a-lone,

Never to leave me a lone. No, never a-lone, . . . No, never a -
Never a-lone, never a-lone,

- lone; He promised nev-er to leave me, Nev-er to leave me a - lone.

381   *I will never leave thee, nor forsake thee.*—HEB. xiii. 5.

1 " FEAR not, I am with thee";
    Blessèd golden ray,
Like a star of glory,
    Lighting up my way!
Through the clouds of midnight,
    This bright promise shone,
" I will never leave thee,
    Never will leave thee alone."
      No, never alone, etc.

2 Roses fade around me,
    Lilies bloom and die,
Earthly sunbeams vanish—
    Radiant still the sky!

Jesus, Rose of Sharon,
    Blooming for His own,
Jesus, heaven's sunshine,
    Never will leave me alone.

3 Steps unseen before me,
    Hidden dangers near;
Nearer still my Saviour,
    Whispering, "Be of cheer,"
Joys, like birds of spring-time,
    To my heart have flown,
Singing all so sweetly,
    "He will not leave me alone.
              E. E. Hewitt.

I Need Thee Every Hour.

P.M.   R. LOWRY.

REFRAIN.

I need Thee, oh, I need Thee!

Ev - 'ry hour I need Thee: Oh, bless me now, my Sa-viour! I come to Thee.

382   *Hear me, for I am poor and needy.*—PSALM lxxxvi. 1.

1 I NEED Thee every hour,
    Most gracious Lord;
No tender voice like Thine
    Can peace afford.
      I need Thee, etc.

2 I need Thee every hour:
    Stay Thou near by;
Temptations lose their power
    When Thou art nigh.

3 I need Thee every hour,
    In joy or pain;
Come quickly and abide,
    Or life is vain.

4 I need Thee every hour;
    Teach me Thy will;
And Thy rich promises
    In me fulfil.

5 I need Thee every hour,
    Most Holy One;
Oh, make me Thine indeed,
    Thou blessèd Son!
            Mrs. A. S. Hawks.

C.M., with Chorus.

None but Christ can Satisfy! [FIRST TUNE.]

J. McGranahan.

Now none but Christ can sat-is-fy, None o-ther name for me; There's for me;

love and life and last-ing joy, Lord Je-sus, found in Thee.

Words and Music by permission of Mrs. H. C. Dixon.

383 *We also joy in God, through our Lord Jesus Christ, by whom we have now received the atonement.*—ROM. v. 11.

1 O CHRIST, in Thee my soul hath found,
   And found in Thee alone,
The peace, the joy I sought so long,
   The bliss till now unknown.
      Now none but Christ can satisfy, etc.

2 I sighed for rest and happiness,
   I yearned for them, not Thee;
But, while I passed my Saviour by,
   His love laid hold on me.

3 I tried the broken cisterns, Lord,
   But, ah, the waters failed!
E'en as I stooped to drink they fled,
   And mocked me as I wailed.

4 The pleasures lost I sadly mourned,
   But never wept for Thee,
Till grace the sightless eyes received,
   Thy loveliness to see.
                              B. E. (arr.)

Petersham. [SECOND TUNE.]   C.M.D.   C. W. Poole.

CHORUS.

Now none but Christ can sat-is-fy,

None other name for me; There's love and life and lasting joy, Lord Jesus, found in Thee.

Copyright by W. Garrett Horder.

Raynolds.　　　　　　11.10.11.10.　　　　　　MENDELSSOHN (arr.)

384

Sir, we would see Jesus.—JOHN xii. 21.

1 WE would see Jesus—for the shadows lengthen
　　Across this little landscape of our life;
　We would see Jesus, our weak faith to strengthen,
　　For the last weariness—the final strife.

2 We would see Jesus—the great Rock-foundation,
　　Whereon our feet were set with sovereign grace;
　Not life, nor death, with all their agitation,
　　Can thence remove us, if we see His face.

3 We would see Jesus; sense is all too blinding,
　　And heaven appears too dim, too far away:
　We would see Thee Thyself, our hearts reminding
　　What Thou hast suffered our great debt to pay.

4 We would see Jesus—this is all we're needing,
　　Strength, joy, and willingness come with the sight;
　We would see Jesus, dying, risen, pleading,
　　Then welcome, day, and farewell, mortal night!
　　　　　　　　　　　　　　　　Anna B. Warner.

More about Jesus. L.M., with Refrain. JNO. R. SWENEY.

REFRAIN.

More, more a-bout Je - sus, More, more a-bout Je - sus;

More of His sav - ing ful - ness see, More of His love who died for me.

385 *Follow on to know the Lord.*—HOSEA vi. 3.

1 MORE about Jesus would I know,
   More of His grace to others show;
   More of His saving fulness see,
   More of His love who died for me.
   More, more about Jesus, etc.

2 More about Jesus let me learn,
   More of His holy will discern;
   Spirit of God, my Teacher be,
   Showing the things of Christ to me.

3 More about Jesus in His Word,
   Holding communion with my Lord;
   Hearing His voice in every line,
   Making each faithful saying mine.

4 More about Jesus, on His throne,
   Riches in glory all His own;
   More of His kingdom's sure increase;
   More of His coming, Prince of Peace.

E. E. Hewitt.

Everlasting Love.
Smoothly.

7.7.7.7., D.

J. MOUNTAIN.

Alternative Tune, TICHFIELD, *No. 379.*

386

Yea, I have loved thee with an everlasting love.—JER. xxxi. 3.

1 LOVED with everlasting love,
   Led by grace that love to know,
Spirit, breathing from above,
   Thou hast taught me it is so.
Oh, this full and perfect peace!
   Oh, this transport all divine!
In a love which cannot cease,
   I am His, and He is mine.

2 Heaven above is softer blue,
   Earth around is sweeter green;
Something lives in every hue
   Christless eyes have never seen:
Birds with gladder songs o'erflow,
   Flowers with deeper beauties shine,
Since I know, as now I know,
   I am His, and He is mine.

3 Things that once were wild alarms
   Cannot now disturb my rest;
Closed in everlasting arms,
   Pillowed on the loving breast:
Oh, to lie for ever here!
   Doubt and care and self resign,
While He whispers in my ear—
   I am His, and He is mine.

4 His for ever, only His;
   Who the Lord and me shall part?
Ah, with what a rest of bliss,
   Christ can fill the loving heart!
Heaven and earth may fade and flee;
   Firstborn light in gloom decline;
But while God and I shall be,
   I am His, and He is mine.

G. Wade Robinson.

It passeth Knowledge.   P.M.   IRA D. SANKEY.

By permission. From Sankey's *Sacred Songs and Solos*.

387   *The love of Christ, which passeth knowledge.*—EPH. iii. 19.

1 IT passeth knowledge, that dear love of Thine,
My Jesus, Saviour; yet this soul of mine
Would of Thy love, in all its breadth and length,
Its height and depth, its everlasting strength,
    Know more and more.

2 It passeth telling, that dear love of Thine,
My Jesus, Saviour; yet these lips of mine
Would fain proclaim to sinners, far and near,
A love which can remove all guilty fear,
    And love beget.

3 It passeth praises, that dear love of Thine,
My Jesus, Saviour; yet this heart of mine
Would sing that love, so full, so rich, so free,
Which brings a rebel sinner, such as me,
    Nigh unto God.

4 But though I cannot sing, or tell, or know
The fulness of Thy love, while here below,
My empty vessel I may freely bring:
O Thou, who art of love the living spring,
    My vessel fill.

5 I am an empty vessel—not one thought,
Or look of love, I ever to Thee brought;
Yet I may come, and come again to Thee,
With this, the empty sinner's only plea—
    Thou lovest me.

6 Oh, fill me, Jesus, Saviour, with Thy love!
Lead, lead me to the living fount above;
Thither may I, in simple faith, draw nigh,
And never to another fountain fly,
    But unto Thee.
           Mary Shekleton.

Overstrand.   P.M.   English Air.

Moderato.

From my heart the burden roll'd a-way—Happy day!

388   *Casting all your care upon Him; for He careth for you.*—1 PETER v. **7.**

1 I LEFT it all with Jesus long ago;
    All my sin I brought Him, and my woe:
    When by faith I saw Him on the tree,
    Heard His still, small whisper, "'Tis for thee,"
    From my heart the burden rolled away—
       Happy day!

2 I leave it all with Jesus; for He knows
    How to steal the bitter from life's woes,
    How to gild the tear-drop with His smile,
    Make the desert garden bloom awhile:
    When my weakness leaneth on His might,
       All seems light.

3 I leave it all with Jesus day by day:
    Faith can firmly trust Him, come what may:
    Hope has dropped her anchor, found her rest,
    In the calm, sure haven of His breast:
    Love esteems it heaven to abide
       At His side.

4 Oh, leave it all with Jesus, drooping soul!
    Tell not half thy story, but the whole:
    Worlds on worlds are hanging on His hand,
    Life and death are waiting His command;
    Yet His tender bosom makes *thee* room:
       Oh, come home!

             E. H. Willis.

Adelboden.   C.M.D.   Swiss Melody.

Smoothly.

Alternative Tune, CASTLE RISING, *No.* 563.

389   *My servants shall sing for joy of heart.*—ISA. lxv. 14.

1 MY heart is resting, O my God,
    I will give thanks and sing:
  My heart is at the secret source
    Of every precious thing.
  Now the frail vessel Thou hast made,
    No hand but Thine shall fill;
  The waters of the earth have failed,
    And I am thirsty still.

2 I thirst for springs of heavenly life,
    And here all day they rise;
  I seek the treasure of Thy love,
    And close at hand it lies.
  And a "new song" is in my mouth,
    To long-loved music set;
  Glory to Thee for all the grace
    I have not tasted yet!

3 I have a heritage of joy,
    That yet I must not see;
  The hand that bled to make it mine
    Is keeping it for me.
  My heart is resting on Thy truth,
    Who hath made all things mine;
  That draws my captive will to Thee,
    And makes it one with Thine.

4 My heart is resting, oh my God,
    My heart is in Thy care;
  I hear the voice of joy and health
    Resounding everywhere.
  "Thou art my portion, saith my soul,"
    Ten thousand voices say,
  The music of their glad Amen
    Will never die away.

Anna L. Waring

Dominus Regit Me. 8.7.8.7. J. B. DYKES.

390

The Lord is my Shepherd.—PSALM xxiii. 1.

1 THE King of love my Shepherd is,
    Whose goodness faileth never;
I nothing lack if I am His,
    And He is mine for ever.

2 Where streams of living water flow
    My ransomed soul He leadeth,
And, where the verdant pastures grow,
    With food celestial feedeth.

3 Perverse and foolish oft I strayed,
    But yet in love He sought me,
And on His shoulder gently laid,
    And home rejoicing brought me.

4 In death's dark vale I fear no ill
    With Thee, dear Lord, beside me;
Thy rod and staff my comfort still,
    Thy cross before to guide me.

5 Thou spread'st a table in my sight;
    Thy unction grace bestoweth:
And oh, what transport of delight
    From Thy pure chalice floweth!

6 And so through all the length of days
    Thy goodness faileth never;
Good Shepherd, may I sing Thy praise
    Within Thy house for ever.

Sir H. W. Baker.

Ombersley. L.M. W. H. GLADSTONE.

By permission of Novello and Company, Limited.

Alternative Tunes, MELCOMBE, *No. 104, and* WARRINGTON, *No. 72.*
Jesus Himself drew near, and went with them.—LUKE xxiv. 15.

391

1 Oh, walk with Jesus, would'st thou know
How deep, how wide His love can flow!
They only fail His love to prove
Who in the ways of sinners rove.

2 Walk thou with Him; that way is light,
All other pathways end in night:
Walk thou with Him; that way is rest,
All other pathways are unblest.

3 Oh, walk with Jesus! to thy view
He will make all things sweet and new;
Will bring new fragrance from each flower,
And hallow every passing hour.

4 Jesus, a great desire have we
To walk life's troubled path with Thee:
Come to us now, in converse stay;
And oh! walk with us day by day.

E. Paxton Hood.

Moment by Moment.　　10.10.10.10., with Chorus.　　MARY WHITTLE MOODY.

CHORUS.

Moment by moment I'm kept in His love,　Moment by moment I've life from a-bove;

rit.

Looking to Je-sus till glo-ry doth shine; Moment by moment, O Lord, I am Thine.

By permission. From Sankey's *Sacred Songs and Solos.*

392

Because I live, ye shall live also.—JOHN xiv. 19.

1.
DYING with Jesus, by death reckoned mine;
Living with Jesus a new life divine;
Looking to Jesus till glory doth shine;
Moment by moment, O Lord, I am Thine.
　Moment by moment, etc.

2.
Never a battle with wrong for the right,
Never a contest that He doth not fight;
Lifting above us His banner so white—
Moment by moment I'm kept in His sight.

3.
Never a trial that He is not there,
Never a burden that He doth not bear,
Never a sorrow that He doth not share—
Moment by moment I'm under His care.

4.
Never a heart-ache, and never a groan,
Never a tear-drop, and never a moan,
Never a danger but there on the throne
Moment by moment He thinks of His own

5.
Never a weakness that He doth not feel,
Never a sickness that He cannot heal;
Moment by moment, in woe or in weal,
Jesus my Saviour abides with me still.
　　　　　　　　D. W. Whittle.

St. Peter.   C.M.   A. R. REINAGLE.

393
A Name which is above every name.—PHIL. ii. 9.

1 How sweet the Name of Jesus sounds
   In a believer's ear !
   It soothes his sorrows, heals his wounds,
   And drives away his fear.

2 It makes the wounded spirit whole,
   And calms the troubled breast ;
   'Tis manna to the hungry soul,
   And to the weary rest.

3 Dear Name, the rock on which I build,
   My shield and hiding-place,
   My never-failing treasury, filled
   With boundless stores of grace !

4 Jesus ! my Shepherd, Saviour, Friend ;
   My Prophet, Priest, and King ;
   My Lord, my Life, my Way, my End ;
   Accept the praise I bring.

5 Weak is the effort of my heart,
   And cold my warmest thought ;
   But when I see Thee as Thou art,
   I'll praise Thee as I ought.

6 Till then, I would Thy love proclaim
   With every fleeting breath ;
   And may the music of Thy Name
   Refresh my soul in death.

John Newton.

St. Michael.   S.M.   Geneva, 1551.

Alternative Tune, ST. ANDREW, *No.* 424.

394
My tongue shall speak of Thy Word.—PSALM cxix. 172.

1 HELP me, my God, to speak
   True words to Thee each day ;
   Real let my voice be when I praise,
   And trustful when I pray.

2 Thy words are true to me,
   Let mine to Thee be true,—
   The speech of my whole heart and soul,
   However low and few.

3 True words of grief for sin,
   Of longing to be free,
   Of yearning for deliverance,
   And likeness, Lord, to Thee.

4 True words of faith, and hope,
   Of godly joy and grief ;
   Lord, I believe !—oh, hear my cry—
   Help Thou my unbelief !

H. Bonar.

St. Hugh.   C.M   E. J. HOPKINS.

Alternative Tune, ALBANO, *No. 669.*

395

One is your Master, even Christ.—MATT. xxiii. 8.

1 IMMORTAL Love, for ever full,
  For ever flowing free,
  For ever shared, for ever whole,
  A never-ebbing sea!

2 Our outward lips confess the Name
  All other names above;
  Love only knoweth whence it came,
  And comprehendeth love.

3 We may not climb the heavenly steeps
  To bring the Lord Christ down:
  In vain we search the lowest deeps,
  For Him no depths can drown.

4 But warm, sweet, tender, even yet
  A present help is He;
  And faith has still its Olivet,
  And love its Galilee.

5 The healing of His seamless dress
  Is by our beds of pain;
  We touch Him in life's throng and press,
  And we are whole again.

6 Through Him the first fond prayers are said
  Our lips of childhood frame,   [said
  The last low whispers of our dead
  Are burdened with His Name.

7 O Lord and Master of us all!
  Whate'er our name or sign,
  We own Thy sway, we hear Thy call,
  We test our lives by Thine.

8 We faintly hear, we dimly see,
  In differing phrase we pray;
  But, dim or clear, we own ın Thee
  The Light, the Truth, the Way!
                                J. G. Whittier.

396 Mine.   6.6.6.6., with Chorus.   R. FRANK LEHMAN.

CHORUS.

Mine! mine! mine! I know Thou art mine;

Sa - viour, dear Sa - viour, I know Thou art mine.

Alternative Tune, ST. CECILIA, *No.* 80.

396

My Beloved is mine and I am His.—SONG OF SOLOMON ii. 16.

1 DEAR Saviour, Thou art mine,
How sweet the thought to me!
Let me repeat Thy Name,
And lift my heart to Thee.
　Mine! mine! mine! etc.

2 Thou art the sinner's Friend,
So I Thy friendship claim,
A sinner saved by grace,
When Thy sweet message came.

3 My hardened heart was touched;
Thy pardoning voice I heard;
And joy and peace came in,
While listening to Thy Word.

4 So, let me sing Thy praise,
So, let me call Thee mine.
I cannot doubt Thy word,
I know that I am Thine.
　　　　　Anna Hudson.

Abney.　　　　　　　C.M.　　　　　　ASA HULL.

Slow.

Alternative Tune, ST. FLAVIAN, *No.* 356.

397

I the Lord search the heart.—JER. xvii. 10.

1 SEARCH me, O God! my actions try,
And let my life appear
As seen by Thine all-searching eye—
To mine my ways make clear.

2 Search all my sense, and know my heart,
Who only canst make known,
And let the deep, the hidden part
To me be fully shown.

3 Throw light into the darkened cells,
Where passion reigns within:
Quicken my conscience till it feels
The loathsomeness of sin.

4 Search all my thoughts, the secret springs,
The motives that control;
The chambers where polluted things
Hold empire o'er the soul.

5 Search, till Thy fiery glance has cast
Its holy light through all,
And I by grace am brought at last
Before Thy face to fall.

6 Thus prostrate I shall learn of Thee,
What now I feebly prove,
That God alone in Christ can be
Unutterable love!　　*F. Bottome.*

St. Margaret.   8.8.8.8.6.   A. L. Peace.

398   *How shall I give thee up?*—Hos. **xi. 8.**

1.

O LOVE, that wilt not let me go,
  I rest my weary soul in Thee;
I give Thee back the life I owe,
That in Thine ocean depths, its flow
  May richer, fuller be.

2.

O Light, that followest all my way,
  I yield my flickering torch to Thee;
My heart restores its borrowed ray,
That in Thy sunshine's blaze, its day
  May brighter, fairer be.

3.

O Joy, that seekest me through pain,
  I cannot close my heart to Thee;
I trace the rainbow through the rain
And feel the promise is not vain,
  That morn shall tearless be.

4.

O Cross, that liftest up my head,
  I dare not ask to fly from thee;
I lay in dust life's glory dead,
And from the ground, there blossoms red,
  Life that shall endless be.

George Matheson.

399 Memorial.   8.8.8.4.   H. Ross Phillips.

Alternative Tune, ALMSGIVING, *No.* 89.

399 *As the Father hath loved Me, so have I loved you.—JOHN xv. 9.*

1 LOVED! then the way will not be drear;
   For One we know is ever near,
   Proving it to our hearts so clear
      That we are loved.

2 Loved with an everlasting love
   By Him who left His home above,
   To bring us life, and light, and love,
      Because He loved.

3 Loved, when our sky is clouded o'er
   And days of sorrow press us sore;
   Still will we trust Him evermore,
      For we are loved.

4 Loved, when we leave our native soil,
   In heathen lands to live and toil;

   Under His shadow naught can foil—
      Still we are loved.

5 Time, that affects all things below,
   Can never change the love He'll show;
   The heart of Christ with love will flow,
      And we are loved.

6 Loved in the past of yesterday,
   And all along our future way,
   And in the present of to-day—
      For ever loved.

7 Loved when we sing the glad new song
   To Christ, for whom we've waited long;
   With all the happy, ransomed throng—
      For ever loved.   *Grace Pennell.*

Samuel.   6.6.6.6.8.8.   Sir ARTHUR SULLIVAN.

By permission of Novello and Company, Limited.

400 *Then the Lord called Samuel: and he answered, Here am I.—1 SAM. iii. 4.*

1 HUSHED was the evening hymn,
     The temple courts were dark,
   The lamp was burning dim
     Before the sacred ark:
   When suddenly a voice divine
   Rang through the silence of the shrine.

2 The old man, meek and mild,
     The priest of Israel, slept;
   His watch the temple-child,
     The little Levite, kept;
   And what from Eli's sense was sealed
   The Lord to Hannah's son revealed.

3 Oh, give me Samuel's ear!
     The open ear, O Lord,
   Alive and quick to hear
     Each whisper of Thy word;
   Like him to answer at Thy call,
   And to obey Thee first of all.

4 Oh, give me Samuel's heart!
     A lowly heart that waits
   Where in Thy house Thou art,
     Or watches at Thy gates,
   By day and night, a heart that still
   Moves at the breathing of Thy will.

5 Oh, give me Samuel's mind!
     A sweet unmurmuring faith,
   Obedient and resigned
     To Thee in life and death;
   That I may read with child-like eyes
   Truths that are hidden from the wise.   *J. D. Burns.*

Let the Master In!

P.M.

R. LOWRY.

CHORUS.

Then o - pen! o - pen! o - pen, let the Master in!
Then o - pen to.. Him! o - pen to.. Him! in! let Him in!

For the heart will be bright with a heav'nly light When you let the Mas-ter in.

401.

Come in, thou blessed of the Lord; wherefore standest thou without ?—
GEN. xxiv. 31.

1 ONCE I heard a sound at my heart's dark door,
    And was roused from the slumber of sin:
  It was Jesus knocked, He had knocked before;
    Now I said, "Blessèd Master, come in!"
      Then open! open! etc.

2 Then He spread a feast of redeeming love,
    And He made me His own happy guest;
  In my joy I thought that the saints above
    Could be hardly more favoured or blest.

3 In the holy war with the foes of truth,
    He's my shield; He my table prepares.
  He restores my soul, He renews my youth,
    And gives triumph in answer to prayers.

4 He will feast me still with His presence dear,
    And the love He so freely hath given;
  While His promise tells, as I serve Him here,
    Of the banquet of glory in heaven.

S. D. Phelps.

Rest.

8.6.8.8.6.

F. C. Maker.

402

And after the fire a still small voice.—1 Kings xix. 12.

1 Dear Lord and Father of mankind,
   Forgive our foolish ways!
Re-clothe us in our rightful mind;
In purer lives Thy service find,
   In deeper reverence, praise.

2 In simple trust like theirs who heard,
   Beside the Syrian sea,
The gracious calling of the Lord,
Let us, like them, without a word
   Rise up and follow Thee.

3 Oh, Sabbath rest by Galilee!
   Oh, calm of hills above,
Where Jesus knelt to share with Thee
The silence of eternity,
   Interpreted by love.

4 With that deep hush subduing all
   Our words and works that drown
The tender whisper of Thy call,
As noiseless let Thy blessing fall
   As fell Thy manna down.

5 Drop Thy still dews of quietness,
   Till all our strivings cease:
Take from our souls the strain and stress:
And let our ordered lives confess
   The beauty of Thy peace.

6 Breathe through the heats of our desire
   Thy coolness and Thy balm;
Let sense be dumb—let flesh retire;
Speak through the earthquake, wind, and fire,
   O still small voice of calm!

J. G. Whittier.

St. Bees. 7.7.7.7. J. B. DYKES.

403 *Lovest thou Me ?—*JOHN xxi. 17.

1 HARK, my soul! it is the Lord;
'Tis thy Saviour, hear His word;
Jesus speaks, and speaks to thee,
"Say, poor sinner, lov'st thou Me?"

2 "I delivered thee when bound,
And, when bleeding, healed thy wound;
Sought thee wandering, set thee right,
Turned thy darkness into light.

3 "Mine is an unchanging love,
Higher than the heights above;

Deeper than the depths beneath:
Free and faithful, strong as death.

4 "Thou shalt see My glory soon,
When the work of grace is done;
Partner of My throne shalt be;
Say, poor sinner, lov'st thou Me?"

5 Lord! it is my chief complaint
That my love is weak and faint;
Yet I love Thee, and adore:
Oh, for grace to love Thee more!

W. Cowper.

Martyrdom. C.M. H. WILSON.

Alternative Tune, DALEHURST, *No.* 415.

404 *Walk humbly with thy God.—*MICAH vi. 8.

1 OH, for a closer walk with God,
A calm and heavenly frame,
A light to shine upon the road
That leads me to the Lamb!

2 Where is the blessedness I knew
When first I saw the Lord?
Where is the soul-refreshing view
Of Jesus and His Word?

3 What peaceful hours I once enjoyed!
How sweet their memory still!

But they have left an aching void
The world can never fill.

4 The dearest idol I have known,
Whate'er that idol be,
Help me to tear it from Thy throne,
And worship only Thee.

5 So shall my walk be close with God,
Calm and serene my frame:
So purer light shall mark the road
That leads me to the Lamb.

W. Cowper.

Trust.   8.8 8.6.   G. W. TORRANCE.

Alternative Tune, SILVERSTONE, *No.* 411.

405   *His great love wherewith He loved us.*—EPH. ii. 4.

1 O SAVIOUR, I have naught to plead,
On earth beneath, or heaven above,
But just my own exceeding need,
And Thy exceeding love.

2 The need will soon be past and gone,
Exceeding great, but quickly o'er;
Thy love unbought is all Thine own,
And lasts for evermore.

Jane Crewdson.

Sacrifice.   7.6.7.6.   H. LAHEE.

406   *These are they which follow the Lamb whithersoever He goeth.*—REV. xiv. 4.

1 O LAMB of God, still keep me
Close to Thy wounded side;
'Tis only there in safety
And peace I can abide.

2 What foes and snares surround me,
What lusts and fears within!
The grace that sought and found me,
Alone can keep me clean.

3 'Tis only in Thee hiding
I feel myself secure;
Only in Thee abiding,
The conflict can endure;

4 Thine arm the victory gaineth
O'er every hateful foe;
Thy love my heart sustaineth
In all its care and woe.

5 Soon shall my eyes behold Thee,
With rapture face to face;
One half hath not been told me
Of all Thy power and grace;

6 Thy beauty, Lord, and glory,
The wonders of Thy love,
Shall be the endless story
Of all Thy saints above.

J. G. Deck.

St. Agnes. 10.10.10.10. J. LANGRAN.

By permission of Novello and Company, Limited.

Alternative Tunes, MORECAMBE, *No.* 366, *and* TOULON, *No.* 315.

407 *Jesus . . . stood in the midst.*—JOHN xx. 19.

1 HERE, O my Lord, I see Thee face to face;
  Here faith can touch and handle things unseen;
  Here would I grasp with firmer hand Thy grace,
  And all my weariness upon Thee lean.

2 Here would I feed upon the bread of God;
  Here drink with Thee the royal wine of heaven;
  Here would I lay aside each earthly load;
  Here taste afresh the calm of sin forgiven.

3 This is the hour of banquet and of song;
  This is the heavenly table spread for me;
  Here let me feast, and, feasting, still prolong
  The brief bright hour of fellowship with Thee.

4 Too soon we rise; the symbols disappear;
  The feast, though not the love, is past and gone;
  The bread and wine remove, but Thou art here,
  Nearer than ever, still our Shield and Sun.

5 Feast after feast thus comes and passes by,
  Yet passing, points to the great feast above;
  Giving sweet foretastes of the festal joy,
  The Lamb's great bridal-feast of bliss and love.

H. Bonar.

408

Hereby we know that He abideth in us, by the Spirit which He hath given
us.—1 John iii. 24.

1 Not what I am, O Lord, but what Thou art!
   That, that alone, can be my soul's true rest;
   Thy love, not mine, bids fear and doubt depart,
   And stills the tempest of my tossing breast.

2 It is Thy perfect love that casts out fear;
   I know the voice that speaks the "It is I,"
   And in these well-known words of heavenly cheer
   I hear the joy that bids each sorrow fly.

3 Thy Name is Love! I hear it from yon cross;
   Thy Name is Love! I read it in yon tomb;
   All meaner love is perishable dross,
   But this shall light me through time's thickest gloom.

4 It blesses now, and shall for ever bless;
   It saves me now, and shall for ever save;
   It holds me up in days of helplessness,
   It bears me safely o'er each swelling wave.

5 'Tis what I know of Thee, my Lord and God,
   That fills my soul with peace, my lips with song;
   Thou art my health, my joy, my staff, my rod;
   Leaning on Thee, in weakness I am strong.

6 More of Thyself, oh, show me, hour by hour;
   More of Thy glory, O my God and Lord;
   More of Thyself, in all Thy grace and power;
   More of Thy love and truth, Incarnate Word.

                                        H. Bonar.

Quietude.   6.5.6.5.   H. Green.
Slow.

409   *Be still, and know that I am God.*—Psalm xlvi. 10.

1 Speak, Lord, in the stillness,
   While I wait on Thee;
   Hushed my heart to listen
   In expectancy.

2 Speak, O blessèd Master,
   In this quiet hour;
   Let me see Thy face, Lord,
   Feel Thy touch of power.

3 For the words Thou speakest,
   "They are life" indeed;
   Living Bread from heaven,
   Now my spirit feed!

4 All to Thee is yielded,
   I am not my own;

Blissful, glad surrender—
   I am Thine alone.

5 Speak, Thy servant heareth!
   Be not silent, Lord;
   Waits my soul upon Thee
   For the quickening word!

6 Fill me with the knowledge
   Of Thy glorious will;
   All Thine own good pleasure
   In Thy child fulfil.

7 Like "a watered garden,"
   Full of fragrance rare,
   Lingering in Thy presence,
   Let my life appear.
                         E. May Grimes.

St. Anselm.   7.6.7.6., D.   Sir J. Barnby.

410   *Come unto Me, . . . and I will give you rest.*—Matt. xi. 28.

1 On Thee my heart is resting!
    Ah, this is rest indeed!
What else, almighty Saviour,
    Can a poor sinner need?
Thy light is all my wisdom,
    Thy love is all my stay;
Our Father's home in glory
    Draws nearer every day.

2 My guilt is great, but greater
    The mercy Thou dost give;
Thyself, a spotless Offering,
    Hast died that I should live.
With Thee, my soul unfettered
    Has risen from the dust;
Thy blood is all my treasure,
    Thy Word is all my trust.

3 Through me, Thou gentle Master,
    Thy purposes fulfil!
I yield myself for ever
    To Thy most holy will.
What though I be but weakness?
    My strength is not in me;
The poorest of Thy people
    Has all things, having Thee.

T. Monod.

Silverstone. 8.8 8.6. T. M. MUDIE.

411
*Continue ye in My love.—*JOHN xv. 9.

1 O HOLY Saviour, Friend unseen,
  The faint, the weak, on Thee may lean;
  Help me throughout life's varying scene,
  By faith to cling to Thee!

2 Blest with communion so divine,
  Take what Thou wilt, shall I repine
  When, as the branches to the vine,
  My soul may cling to Thee?

3 What though the world deceitful prove,
  And earthly friends and joys remove?

With patient, uncomplaining love,
  Still would I cling to Thee!

4 Though faith and hope awhile be tried,
  I ask not, need not, aught beside:
  How safe, how calm, how satisfied
  The soul that clings to Thee!

5 Blest is my lot, whate'er befall!
  What can disturb me, who appal;
  While as my Strength, my Rock, my All,
  Saviour, I cling to Thee?
                    C. Elliott.

Lucerne. 8.7.8.7. T. A. WILLIS.

412
By permission of the Proprietors of the *Bristol Tune Book.*
*Lord, Thou knowest that I love Thee.—*JOHN xxi. 15.

1 SOMETHING every heart is loving;
  If not Jesus, none can rest:
  Lord, my heart to Thee is given;
  Take it, for it loves Thee best.

2 Thus I cast the world behind me;
  Jesus most beloved shall be;
  Beauteous more than all things beauteous,
  He alone is joy to me.

3 Bright with all eternal radiance
  Is the glory of Thy face;

Thou art loving, sweet, and tender,
  Full of pity, full of grace.

4 When I hated, Thou didst love me,
  Shedd'st for me Thy precious blood;
  Still Thou lovest, lovest ever,
  Shall I not love Thee, my God?

5 Keep my heart still faithful to Thee,
  That my earthly life may be
  But a shadow to that glory
  Of my hidden life in Thee.
            Tersteegen (tr. *Mrs. Bevan*).

Satisfaction.　　　　　　　P.M.　　　　　　　H. GREEN.

And the more I long that oth-ers should be led to know Him too.

413　　　*My soul shall be satisfied.*—PSALM lxiii. 5.

1 HE will never disappoint you! Jesus is far more to me
　Than in all my glowing day-dreams I had fancied He could be;
　And the more I get to know Him, so the more I find Him true,
　And the more I long that others should be led to know Him too.

2 He will never disappoint you! He has saved my soul from sin:
　All the guilt, and all the anguish, which oppressed my heart within,
　He has banished by His presence, and His blessèd kiss of peace
　Has assured my heart for ever that His love will never cease.

3 He will never disappoint you! He is coming by-and-by,
　In my heart I have the witness that His coming draweth nigh.
　All the scoffers may despise me, and no change around may see,
　But He tells me He is coming, and that's quite enough for me.

4 He will never disappoint you! He is All in all to me—
　Blessèd Saviour, Sanctifier; the unchanging Christ is He!
　He has won my heart's affections, and He meets my every need;
　He will never disappoint you, for He satisfies indeed.

Anon. (alt.).

Wiltshire.   **C.M.**   Sir George T. Smart.

414   *I will fear no evil: for Thou art with me.*—Psalm xxiii. 4.

1 The Lord's my Shepherd, I'll not want:
   He makes me down to lie
In pastures green; He leadeth me
   The quiet waters by.

2 My soul He doth restore again;
   And me to walk doth make
Within the paths of righteousness,
   E'en for His own Name's sake.

3 Yea, though I walk in death's dark vale,
   Yet will I fear none ill:

For Thou art with me; and Thy rod
   And staff me comfort still.

4 My table Thou hast furnished
   In presence of my foes;
My head Thou dost with oil anoint,
   And my cup overflows.

5 Goodness and mercy all my life
   Shall surely follow me;
And in God's house for evermore
   My dwelling-place shall be.

        F. Rous.

Daleburst.   **C.M.**   Arthur Cottman.

Alternative Tune, Sawley, No. 370.

415   *A Name which is above every name.*—Phil. ii. 9.

1 There is a Name I love to hear,
   I love to speak its worth;
It sounds like music in my ear,
   The sweetest Name on earth.

2 It tells me of a Saviour's love,
   Who died to set me free;
It tells me of His precious blood,
   The sinner's perfect plea.

3 It tells of One whose loving heart
   Can feel my deepest woe,

Who in my sorrow bears a part
   That none can bear below.

4 It bids my trembling heart rejoice,
   It dries each rising tear;
It tells me in a "still, small voice,"
   To trust and never fear.

5 Jesus, the Name I love so well,
   The Name I love to hear!
No saint on earth its worth can tell,
   No heart conceive how dear!

        F. Whitfield

Exaltation. P.M. C H. FORREST.

CHORUS.

Oh, to be saved from my-self, dear Lord, Oh, to be lost in Thee;

Oh, that it may be no more I, But Christ that lives in me.

Alternative Tune (without Chorus), RAYNOLDS, *No.* 384.

416 *That in all things He might have the pre-eminence.*—COL. i. 18.

1 NOT I, but Christ, be honoured, loved, exalted;
  Not I, but Christ, be seen, be known, be heard;
 Not I, but Christ, in every look and action;
  Not I, but Christ, in every thought and word.
   Oh, to be saved from myself, etc.

2 Not I, but Christ, to gently soothe in sorrow;
  Not I, but Christ, to wipe the falling tear;
 Not I, but Christ, to lift the weary burden;
  Not I, but Christ, to hush away all fear.

3 Not I, but Christ, in lowly, silent labour;
  Not I, but Christ, in humble, earnest toil;
 Christ, only Christ! no show, no ostentation;
  Christ, none but Christ, the gatherer of the spoil.

4 Christ, only Christ, ere long will fill my vision;
  Glory excelling, soon, full soon, I'll see—
 Christ, only Christ, my every wish fulfilling—
  Christ, only Christ, my All in all to be.

Mrs. A. A. Whiddington.

Bullinger.   8.5.8.3.   E. W. Bullinger.

417   *In Thee, O Lord, do I put my trust.*—Psalm lxxi. 1.

1 I am trusting Thee, Lord Jesus,
   Trusting only Thee!
Trusting Thee for full salvation,
   Great and free.

2 I am trusting Thee for pardon,
   At Thy feet I bow;
For Thy grace and tender mercy,
   Trusting now.

3 I am trusting Thee for cleansing,
   In the crimson flood;
Trusting Thee to make me holy,
   By Thy blood.

4 I am trusting Thee to guide me,
   Thou alone shalt lead;
Every day and hour supplying
   All my need.

5 I am trusting Thee, Lord Jesus;
   Never let me fall;
I am trusting Thee for ever,
   And for all.   *Frances R. Havergal.*

Augustine.   S.M.   J. S. Bach (arr.)

Alternative Tune, Doncaster, *No.* 650.

418   *Blessed are the pure in heart: for they shall see God.*—Matt. v. 8.

1 Blest are the pure in heart,
   For they shall see their God,
The secret of the Lord is theirs,
   Their soul is Christ's abode.

2 The Lord, who left the heavens
   Our life and peace to bring,
To dwell in lowliness with men,
   Their Pattern and their King;

3 Still to the lowly soul
   He doth Himself impart,
And for His dwelling and His throne
   Chooseth the pure in heart.

4 Lord, we Thy presence seek:
   May ours this blessing be;
Give us a pure and lowly heart,
   A temple meet for Thee.
       J. Keble and others.

Munich. 7.6.7.6., D. German.

Alternative Tune, Ewing, *No. 567.*

419 *O worship the Lord in the beauty of holiness.*—PSALM xcvi. 9.

1 O SAVIOUR, we adore Thee !
    We bless Thy precious Name,
That Thou abidest faithful,
    That Thou art still the same
As when Thy children saw Thee,
    And heard Thy loving voice,
"Behold My hands, and touch Me,
    O fear not, but rejoice !"

2 We cried to Thee for succour,
    We looked for light to Thee ;
Thy smile our souls has gladdened
    With holy radiancy !
And now with quickened footsteps
    We'll run our heavenly way,
Until the shadows vanish,
    Until the break of day !

3 We've sat beside the river,
    And tasted of Thy grace ;
We long to drink the fountain,
    And see Thee face to face !

Sweet, sweet have been the moments
    That we have spent in prayer ;
But, oh, the holy worship
    Wherewith we'll praise Thee there !

4 Come, let us blend our voices
    With yonder choirs above ;
Swell, swell the mighty anthem
    Which tells that "God is love !"
Soon shall the fainting warrior,
    Soon shall the pilgrim band,
Have fought the last great battle,
    Have reached the promised land.

5 Almighty Lord, we bless Thee !
    Eternal Father, Son,
And Holy, Holy Spirit—
    Mysterious Three in One !
Thou hast done mighty marvels
    Before our wondering gaze :
We've learnt that Thou art faithful,
    In all Thy words and ways !

W. Pennefather.

SECTION VII.—The Christian Life.
(4.) Service.

Swanwick. 6.5.6.5., D., with Chorus. Wm. T. Meyer.

Work for Je - sus, day by day, Serve Him ev-er, fal-ter nev-er, Christ o - bey.

Yield Him ser - vice, loy - al, true : There's a work for Jesus none but you can do.

International Copyright by Hall-Mack Co.

Alternative Tune (without Chorus), VESPERS, *No.* 13.

*Ye serve the Lord Christ.—*COL. iii. 24.

420

1 THERE's a work for Jesus
    Ready at your hand,
  'Tis a task the Master
    Just for you has planned.
  Haste to do His bidding,
    Yield Him service true ;
  There's a work for Jesus,
    None but you can do.
        Work for Jesus, day by day, etc.

2 There's a work for Jesus,
    Humble though it be,
  'Tis the very service
    He would ask of thee.

Go where fields are whitened,
    And the labourers few ;
  There's a work for Jesus,
    None but you can do.

3 There's a work for Jesus,
    Precious souls to bring,
  Tell them of His mercies,
    Tell them of your King.
  Faint not, grow not weary,
    He will strength renew ;
  There's a work for Jesus,
    None but you can do.

                Elsie Duncan Yale.

THE CHRISTIAN LIFE:

Channels Only. 8.7.8.7., with Chorus.

ADA ROSE

Chorus.

Channels on - ly, bless-èd Mas - ter, But with all Thy won-drous power

Flow-ing through us, Thou canst use us Ev -'ry day and ev -'ry hour.

421

Workers together with Him.—2 COR. vi. 1.

1 How I praise Thee, precious Saviour,
   That Thy love laid hold of me;
   Thou hast saved and cleansed and filled
   That I might Thy channel be. [me,
   Channels only, blessèd Master, etc.

2 Just a channel, full of blessing,
   To the thirsty hearts around;
   To tell out Thy full salvation,
   All Thy loving message sound.

3 Emptied that Thou shouldest fill me,
   A clean vessel in Thine hand;
   With no power but as Thou givest,
   Graciously with each command.

4 Witnessing Thy power to save me,
   Setting free from self and sin;
   Thou hast bought me to possess me,
   In Thy fulness, Lord, come in.

5 Jesus, fill now with Thy Spirit
   Hearts that full surrender know;
   That the streams of living water
   From our inner man may flow.

Mary E. Maxwell.

Lymington. 7.6.7.6., D. R. Jackson.

423 *Look on the fields, for they are white already to harvest.*—John iv. 35.

1 Lord of the living harvest
   That whitens o'er the plain,
 Where angels soon shall gather
   Their sheaves of golden grain;
 Accept these hands to labour,
   These hearts to trust and love,
 And deign with them to hasten
   Thy kingdom from above.

2 As labourers in Thy vineyard,
   Still faithful may we be,
 Content to bear the burden
   Of weary days for Thee;
 We ask no other wages,
   When Thou shalt call us home,
 But to have shared the travail
   Which makes Thy kingdom come.

3 Come down, Thou Holy Spirit,
   And fill our souls with light,
 Clothe us in spotless raiment,
   In vesture clean and white;
 Within Thy sacred temple
   Be with us, where we stand,
 And sanctify Thy people,
   Throughout this happy land.

4 Be with us, God the Father!
   Be with us, God the Son!
 And God the Holy Spirit!
   O Blessèd Three in One!
 Make us a royal priesthood,
   Thee rightly to adore,
 And fill us with Thy fulness,
   Both now and evermore.

J. S. B. Monsell

The Quest. 7.6.7.6., D., with Chorus. R. Lowry.

Oh, come! let us go and find them: In the paths of death they roam; At the close of the day, 'twill be sweet to say, " I have brought some lost one home."

422 *When he hath found it, he layeth it on his shoulders, rejoicing.*—LUKE xv. 5.

1 How many sheep are straying,
  Lost from the Saviour's fold!
Upon the lonely mountain
  They shiver with the cold;
Within the tangled thickets,
  Where poison-vines do creep,
And over rocky ledges
  Wander the poor, lost sheep.
    Oh, come! let us go, etc.

2 Oh, who will go to find them?
  Who, for the Saviour's sake,
Will search with tireless patience
  Through brier and through brake?
Unheeding thirst or hunger,
  Who still, from day to day,
Will seek, as for a treasure,
  The sheep that go astray?

3 Say, will you seek to find them?
  From pleasant bowers of ease,
Will you go forth determined
  To find the "least of these"?
For still the Saviour calls them,
  And looks across the wold,
And still He holds wide open
  The door into His fold.

4 How sweet 'twould be at evening,
  If you and I could say,
"Good Shepherd, we've been seeking
  The sheep that went astray!
Heart-sore and faint with hunger,
  We heard them making moan,
And, lo! we come at nightfall,
  And bear them safely home."

Mrs. E. M. H. Gates.

St. Andrew.   S.M.   Sir J. Barnby.

Alternative Tune, Narenza, *No. 41.*

424
All things come of Thee, and of Thine own have we given Thee.—
1 Chron. xxix. 14.

1 We give Thee but Thine own,
    Whate'er the gift may be,
For all we have is Thine alone,
    A trust, O Lord, from Thee.

2 And hearts are bruised and dead,
    And homes are bare and cold;
And lambs, for whom the Shepherd bled,
    Are straying from the fold.

3 To comfort and to bless,
    To find a balm for woe,

To tend the lone and fatherless,
    Is angels' work below.

4 The captive to release,
    To God the lost to bring,
To teach the way of life and peace,
    Is a most Christ-like thing.

5 And we believe Thy word,
    Though dim our faith may be;
Whate'er for Thine we do, O Lord,
    We do it unto Thee.   *W. W. How.*

St. George.   S.M.   H. J. Gauntlett.

Alternative Tune, St. Michael, *No. 275.*

425
*In the morning sow thy seed, and in the evening withhold not thine
hand.—*Eccles. xi. 6.

1 Sow in the morn thy seed,
    At eve hold not thine hand;
To doubt and fear give thou no heed,
    Broadcast it o'er the land.

2 Thou know'st not which may thrive,
    The late or early sown;
Grace keeps the chosen germ alive,
    When and wherever strown.

3 And duly shall appear
    In verdure, beauty, strength,

The tender blade, the stalk, the ear,
    And the full corn at length.

4 Thou canst not toil in vain;
    Cold, heat, and moist, and dry
Shall foster and mature the grain
    For garners in the sky.

5 Thence, when the glorious end,
    The day of God, is come,
The angel-reapers shall descend,
    And heaven cry, Harvest-home!

              J. Montgomery.

M*

Lancashire.　　　　　7.6.7.6., D.　　　　　HENRY SMART.

Alternative Tunes, DIES DOMINICA, *No.* 484, *and* AURELIA, *No.* 503.

He saith unto them, follow Me.—MATT. iv. 19

426

1 O MASTER! when Thou callest,
　　No voice may say Thee nay,
For blest are they that follow
　　Where Thou dost lead the way;
In freshest prime of morning,
　　Or fullest glow of noon,
The note of heavenly warning
　　Can never come too soon.

2 O Master! where Thou callest,
　　No foot may shrink in fear,
For they who trust Thee wholly
　　Shall find Thee ever near;
And quiet room and lonely,
　　Or busy harvest field,
Where Thou, Lord, rulest only,
　　Shall precious produce yield.

3 O Master! whom Thou callest,
　　No heart may dare refuse;
'Tis honour, highest honour,
　　When Thou dost deign to use
Our brighest and our fairest,
　　Our dearest—all are Thine;
Thou who for each one carest,
　　We hail Thy love's design.

4 They who go forth to serve Thee,
　　We, too, who serve at home,
May watch and pray together
　　Until Thy kingdom come;
In Thee for aye united,
　　Our song of hope we raise,
Till that blest shore is sighted,
　　Where all shall turn to praise!

Sarah G. Stock

Harvesters.
Moderato.

P.M.

G. F. Root.

Chorus.

Where are the reapers? Oh, who will come And share in the glo-ry of the "har-vest home"? Oh, who will help us to garn-er in The sheaves of good from the fields of sin?

427 *I will say to the reapers: . . . Gather the wheat into my barn.*—MATT. xiii. 30.

1 OH, where are the reapers that garner in
The sheaves of the good from the fields of sin?
With sickles of truth must the work be done,
And no one may rest till the "harvest home."
Where are the reapers? etc.

2 Go out in the bye-ways and search them all:
The wheat may be there, though the weeds are tall;
Then search in the highway, and pass none by,
But gather from all for the home on high.

3 The fields are all ripening, and far and wide
The world now is waiting the harvest-tide;
But reapers are few, and the work is great,
And much will be lost should the harvest wait.

4 So come with your sickles, ye sons of men,
And gather together the golden grain:
Toil on till the Lord of the harvest come,
Then share in the joy of the "harvest home."

E. E. Rexford.

St. Benet.　　　　7.7.7.7.7.7.　　　　W. H. WILLIAMSON.

Alternative Tune, DIX, *No.* 116.

428　　　*Whatsoever ye do, do it heartily, as to the Lord.*—COL. iii. 23.

1 HEARTILY thy life should be
Spent for Him who died for thee,
All thy being's ransomed powers,
His each day throughout its hours,
　"Till He come," when thou wilt be
　All for Him eternally.

2 Heartily thy tongue should tell
Of His grace, that saved from hell,
Singing forth in joyous lays
Thy Redeemer's worthy praise,
　"Till He come," when thou wilt be
　Praising Him eternally.

3 Heartily thy hands should move,
In the service of His love,
With unceasing labour true,
Both to saint and sinner too,
　"Till He come," when thou wilt be
　Serving Him eternally.

4 Heartily, thy feet should run,
Heartily, His will be done,
Heartily, thy zeal be shown,
Heartily, His smile be won,
　"Till He come," when thou wilt be
　Pleasing Him eternally.
　　　　　　　　　　　Anon.

429 Love Never Faileth.　　　P.M.　　　Arr. from Koschat, by I. H. MEREDITH.

"Love nev - er fail - eth," love is the way.

429　　*Love never faileth.*—1 Cor. xiii. 8. (r.v.)

1.
Out in the darkness, shadowed by sin,
Souls are in bondage, souls we would win;
How can we win them? How show the way?
"Love never faileth," love is the way.

2.
Think how the Master came from above,
Suffered on Calvary, breathing out love;
Think how He loves us, e'en when we stray:
We must love others, love is His way.

3.
See, they are waiting, looking at you,
Silently. watching all that you do;
Seeming so careless, hardened and lost:
"Love never faileth," count not the cost.

4.
"Love never faileth," love is pure gold;
Love is what Jesus came to unfold;
Make us more loving, Master, we pray,
Help us remember, love is Thy way.

Flora Kirkland.

Heber.　　　　8.7.8.7.4.7.　　　　E. J. Hopkins.

430　　*Lo, I am with you alway, even unto the end of the world.*—Matt. xxviii. 20.

1 Speed Thy servants, Saviour, speed them;
　Thou art Lord of winds and waves;
They were bound, but Thou hast freed
Now they go to free the slaves; [them;
　Be Thou with them,
　'Tis Thine arm alone that saves.

2 Friends and home and all forsaking,
　Lord, they go at Thy command;
As their stay Thy promise taking,
While they traverse sea and land:
　Oh, be with them:
　Lead them safely by the hand.

3 When no fruit appears to cheer them,
　And they seem to toil in vain,
Then in mercy, Lord, draw near them,
Then their sinking hopes sustain:
　Thus supported,
　Let their zeal revive again.

4 In the midst of opposition,
　Let them trust, O Lord, in Thee:
When success attends their mission,
Let Thy servants humble be:
　Never leave them,
　Till Thy face in heaven they see;

5 There to reap in joy for ever,
　Fruit that grows from seed here sown;
There to be with Him, who never
Ceases to preserve His own,
　And with triumph
Sing a Saviour's grace alone.

T. Kelly.

Broomsgrove.

UNISON.

6.4.6.4.6.6.6.4.

HARMONY.

UNISON.

F. C. MAKER.

HARMONY.

Alternative Tune, VIGIL, *No. 512.*

Put on the whole armour of God.—EPH. vi. 11.

431

1 "LET not thy hands be slack,"
  Live not in vain;
Out on life's lonely track
  Men toil in pain.
Play thou a brother's part,
Strength, love, and hope impart,
Bid thou the fainting heart
  Look up again!

2 "Let not thy hands be slack,"
  Grip thou thy sword!
Why should'st thou courage lack?
  Think of thy Lord.
Did He not fight for thee?
Stronger than all is He,
And He thy strength will be,
  Rest on His word.

3 "Let not thy hands be slack,"
  Haste to the fray!
Dream not of turning back:
  Life is not play!
Gird thou thy armour on,
Fight till the battle's won,
Then shall thy Lord's "Well done,"
  More than repay!

4 "Let not thy hands be slack,"
  "Fear not! Be strong!"
Cease not to make attack
  On every wrong.
Press on for truth and right—
Hold high the Gospel light—
Expel the dirge of night
  With heaven's song!

5 "Let not thy hands be slack,"
    The days fly fast.
Lost moments come not back
    From the dark past.
Then be not slack of hand!
Help thou the weak to stand!
To God and Fatherland
    Give all thou hast!

S. E. Burrow.

To the Work! P.M. W. H. DOANE.

CHORUS.

Toiling on, toiling on, toiling on, toiling on;
Toil-ing on, toil-ing on, toil-ing on, toil-ing on

Let us hope, Let us watch, And labour till the Master comes.
and trust, and pray,

432 *Son, go work to-day in my vineyard.*—MATT. xxi. 28.

1 To the work! to the work! we are servants of God,
Let us follow the path that our Master has trod;
With the balm of His counsel our strength to renew,
Let us do with our might what our hands find to do.
Toiling on, etc.

2 To the work! to the work! let the hungry be fed,
To the fountain of life let the weary be led!
In the cross and its banner our glory shall be,
While we herald the tidings, "Salvation is free!"

3 To the work! to the work! there is labour for all,
For the kingdom of darkness and error shall fall:
And the name of Jehovah exalted shall be,
In the loud-swelling chorus, "Salvation is free!"

4 To the work! to the work! in the strength of the Lord,
And a robe and a crown shall our labour reward.
When the home of the faithful our dwelling shall be,
And we shout with the ransomed, "Salvation is free!"

Fanny J. Crosby.

Rescue the Perishing. P.M. W. H. DOANE.

Res-cue the per-ish-ing, Care for the dy-ing; Je-sus is merci-ful, Je-sus will save.

433 *Go out into the highways and hedges, and compel them to come in, that My house may be filled.—LUKE xiv. 23.*

1 RESCUE the perishing, care for the dying,
   Snatch them in pity from sin and the grave;
   Weep o'er the erring one, lift up the fallen,
   Tell them of Jesus, the Mighty to save.
      Rescue the perishing, etc.

2 Though they are slighting Him, still He is waiting,
   Waiting the penitent child to receive:
   Plead with them earnestly, plead with them gently;
   He will forgive, if they only believe.

3 Down in the human heart, crushed by the tempter,
   Feelings lie buried that grace can restore;
   Touched by a loving heart, wakened by kindness,
   Chords that were broken will vibrate once more.

4 Rescue the perishing, duty demands it;
   Strength for thy labour the Lord will provide:
   Back to the narrow way patiently win them;
   Tell the poor wanderers a Saviour has died.

                                    Fanny J. Crosby.

434 Stuttgart. 8.7.8.7. *Psalmodia Sacra.*

434

They which live should not henceforth live unto themselves, but unto Him which died for them.—2 COR. v. 15.

1 LIFE is real, life is earnest,
  And the grave is not its goal;
  "Dust thou art, to dust returnest,"
  Was not spoken of the soul.

2 Not enjoyment, and not sorrow,
  Is our destined end or way;
  But to act that each to-morrow
  Finds us farther than to-day.

3 Lives of good men all remind us
  We can make our lives sublime;

And departing, leave behind us
  Footprints on the sands of time;

4 Footprints that perhaps another,
  Sailing o'er life's solemn main,
  Some forlorn and shipwrecked brother,
  Seeing, shall take heart again.

5 Let us then be up and doing,
  Nor our onward course abate;
  Still achieving, still pursuing,
  Learn to labour and to wait.

H. W. Longfellow.

St. Helen's. 8.5.8.3. Sir ROBERT P. STEWART.

Alternative Tunes, STEPHANOS, *No. 235, and* CAIRNBROOK, *No. 255.*

435 *From henceforth expecting till His enemies be made His footstool.*—HEB. x. 13.

1 HE expecteth, He expecteth!
  Down the stream of time,
  Still the words come softly ringing
  Like a chime.

2 Oft-times faint, now waxing louder
  As the hour draws near,
  When the King, in all His glory,
  Shall appear.

3 He is waiting with long patience
  For His crowning day,
  For that kingdom which shall never
  Pass away.

4 And till every tribe and nation
  Bow before His throne,
  He expecteth loyal service
  From His own.

5 He expecteth—but He heareth
  Still the bitter cry
  From earth's millions, "Come and help
  For we die."   [us,

6 He expecteth—doth He see us
  Busy here and there,
  Heedless of those pleading accents
  Of despair?

7 Shall we—dare we disappoint Him?
  Brethren, let us rise!
  He who died for us is watching
  From the skies—

8 Watching till His royal banner
  Floateth far and wide,
  Till He seeth of His travail—
  Satisfied!

Alice J. Janvrin.

Golden Sheaves.   8.7.8.7., D.   Sir Arthur S. Sullivan.

436   *A word spoken in due season, how good is it!*—Prov. xv. 23.

1 If any little word of mine
   May make a life the brighter,
If any little song of mine
   May make a heart the lighter,
God help me speak the little word,
   And take my bit of singing,
And drop it in some lonely vale,
   To set the echoes ringing.

2 If any little love of mine
   May make a life the sweeter,
If any little care of mine
   May make a friend's the fleeter,
If any lift of mine may ease
   The burden of another,
God give me love, and care, and strength
   To help my toiling brother.

3 If any little word of mine
   Can make the pathway clearer,
If any little thought of mine
   Can bring a soul the nearer,
If any little deed of mine
   Can clear away a sorrow,
God help me speak, and think, and do,
   And wait not for the morrow.

4 Then many a burden shall be eased,
   Because I help to bear it,
And many a care be lighter made,
   Because I try to share it;
And many a grief shall fly away
   When my bright song shall bid it;
And Christ, the Lord of love, will say,
   "'Twas unto Me ye did it."

Anon. and F. S. T.

St. Beatrice.   P.M.   Sir J. F. Bridge.

437   *Behold a sower went forth to sow.*—Matt. xiii. 3.

1 The sower went forth sowing,
  The seed in secret slept
Through weeks of faith and patience,
  Till out the green blade crept;
And warmed by golden sunshine
  And fed by silver rain,
At last the fields were whitened
  To harvest once again.
Oh, praise the heavenly Sower
  Who gave the fruitful seed,
And watched and watered duly,
  And ripened for our need.

2 Behold, the heavenly Sower
  Goes forth with better seed,
The word of sure salvation,
  With feet and hands that bleed;
Here in His church 'tis scattered,
  Our spirits are the soil;
Then let an ample fruitage
  Repay His pain and toil.
Oh, beauteous is the harvest
  Wherein all goodness thrives,
And this the true thanksgiving,
  The first-fruits of our lives.

3 Within a hallowed acre
  He sows yet other grain,
When peaceful earth receiveth
  The dead He died to gain:
For though the growth be hidden,
  We know that they shall rise;
Yea, even now they ripen
  In sunny Paradise.
Oh, summer land of harvest,
  Oh, fields for ever white
With souls that wear Christ's raiment,
  With crowns of golden light!

4 One day the heavenly Sower
  Shall reap where He hath sown,
And come again rejoicing,
  And with Him bring His own;
And then the fan of judgment
  Shall winnow from His floor
The chaff into the furnace
  That flameth evermore.
O holy, awful Reaper,
  Have mercy in the day
Thou puttest in Thy sickle,
  And cast us not away.

W. St. Hill Bourne.

Harvest Home. P.M. Geo. A. Miner (arr.).

Refrain. *Repeat pp*

Bringing in the sheaves! Bringing in the sheaves!

1st time. 2nd time.

We shall come re-joi-cing, Bring-ing in the sheaves! Bring-ing in the sheaves!

438 *He that goeth forth and weepeth, bearing precious seed, shall doubtless come
again with rejoicing, bringing his sheaves with him.*—PSALM cxxvi. 6.

1 SOWING in the morning, sowing seeds of kindness,
  Sowing in the noontide and the dewy eves;
  Waiting for the harvest, and the time of reaping:
    We shall come rejoicing, bringing in the sheaves!
      Bringing in the sheaves! etc.

2 Sowing in the sunshine, sowing in the shadows,
  Fearing neither clouds nor winter's chilling breeze;
  By and by the harvest, and the labour ended,
    We shall come rejoicing, bringing in the sheaves!
                              Knowles Shaw.

439 **Spohr.** 8.6.8 6.8.6. L. SPOHR.

Alternative Tune, St. Silas, *No.* 368.

439 *The glory which Thou gavest me I have given them.*—John xvii. 22.

1 Dismiss me not Thy service, Lord,
　But train me for Thy will;
For even I, in fields so broad,
　Some duties may fulfil;
And I will ask for no reward,
　Except to serve Thee still.

2 How many serve, how many more
　May to the service come:
To tend the vines, the grapes to store,
　Thou dost appoint for some;
Thou hast Thy young men at the war,
　Thy little ones at home.

3 All works are good, and each is best
　As most it pleases Thee.
Each worker pleases when the rest
　He serves in charity;
And neither man nor work unblest
　Wilt Thou permit to be.

4 Our Master all the work hath done
　He asks of us to-day;
Sharing His service, every one
　Share too His Sonship may:
Lord, I would serve and be a son;
　Dismiss me not, I pray.
　　　　　　　　　T. T. Lynch.

Work, for the Night is Coming.　　P.M.　　　　　L. Mason.

440　　*The night cometh when no man can work.*—John ix. 4.

1 Work, for the night is coming,
　Work through the morning hours,
Work, while the dew is sparkling,
　Work 'mid springing flowers:
Work, when the day grows brighter,
　Work in the glowing sun;
Work, for the night is coming,
　When man's work is done.

2 Work, for the night is coming,
　Work through the sunny noon;
Fill brightest hours with labour,
　Rest comes sure and soon.

Give every flying minute
　Something to keep in store:
Work, for the night is coming,
　When man works no more.

3 Work, for the night is coming,
　Under the sunset skies;
While their bright tints are glowing,
　Work, for daylight flies.
Work, till the last beam fadeth,
　Fadeth to shine no more:
Work, while the night is darkening,
　When man's work is o'er.
　　　　　　　　　A. L. Walker.

Midlane. *Spirited.*   S.M., with Chorus.   W. H. Doane

CHORUS.

Re - vive Thy work, O Lord! While here to Thee we bow; De-scend, O gracious Lord, descend! Oh, come, and bless us now!

Alternative Tune (without Chorus), MORAVIA, *No.* 130.

441

O Lord, revive Thy work.—HAB. iii. 2.

1 REVIVE Thy work, O Lord!
Thy mighty arm make bare;
Speak with the voice that wakes the dead,
And make Thy people hear!
Revive Thy work, O Lord! etc.

2 Revive Thy work, O Lord!
Exalt Thy precious Name!
And may Thy love in every heart
Be kindled to a flame!

3 Revive Thy work, O Lord!
And bless to all Thy Word!
And may its pure and sacred truth
In living faith be heard!

4 Revive Thy work, O Lord!
Give Pentecostal showers!
Be Thine the glory, Thine alone!
The blessing, Lord, be ours!
Albert Midlane.
(Arr. by *Fanny J. Crosby.*)

442 Sunset.   8.8.8.4.   Sir J. BARNBY.

442
Bear ye one another's burdens, and so fulfil the law of Christ.—GAL. vi. 2.

1 DEAR Master, what can children do?
  The angels came from heaven above
  To comfort Thee; may children too
      Give Thee their love?

2 No more, as on that night of shame,
  Art Thou in dark Gethsemane,
  Where worshipping, an angel came
      To strengthen Thee.

3 But Thou hast taught us that Thou art
  Still present in the crowded street,
  In every lonely, suffering heart
      That there we meet.

4 And not one simple, loving deed,
  That lessens gloom, or lightens pain,
  Or answers some unspoken need,
      Is done in vain—

5 Since every passing joy we make
  For men and women that we see,
  If it is offered for Thy sake,
      Is given to Thee.

6 O God, our Master, help us then
  To bless the weary and the sad,
  And, comforting the hearts of men,
      To make Thee glad.

Annie Matheson

Whitburn. L.M. H. BAKER.

Alternative Tune, HOLLEY, *No.* 378.

443
Speak, for Thy servant heareth.—1 SAM. iii. 10.

1 LORD, speak to me, that I may speak
  In living echoes of Thy tone;
  As Thou hast sought, so let me seek
  Thy erring children, lost and lone.

2 Oh, lead me, Lord, that I may lead
  The wandering and the wavering feet;
  Oh, feed me, Lord, that I may feed
  Thy hungering ones with manna sweet.

3 Oh, strengthen me, that while I stand
  Firm on the rock, and strong in Thee,
  I may stretch out a loving hand
  To wrestlers with the troubled sea!

4 Oh, teach me, Lord, that I may teach
  The precious things Thou dost impart;
  And wing my words, that they may reach
  The hidden depths of many a heart!

5 Oh, give Thine own sweet rest to me,
  That I may speak, with soothing power,
  A word in season, as from Thee,
  To weary ones in needful hour.

6 Oh, fill me with Thy fulness, Lord,
  Until my very heart o'erflow
  In kindling thought and glowing word,
  Thy love to tell, Thy praise to show.

7 Oh, use me, Lord, use even me,
      Just as Thou wilt, and when, and where,
  Until Thy blessèd face I see,
  Thy rest, Thy joy, Thy glory share.
                          Frances R. Havergal.

Eaton Square.   7.6.7.6., D., with Chorus.   W. G. FISCHER

CHORUS.

I love to tell the Sto-ry,'Twill be my theme in glo-ry, To tell the old, old Sto-ry Of Je-sus and His love.

Alternative Tune (without Chorus), ANGELS' STORY, *No. 627.*

444   *How beautiful upon the mountains are the feet of Him that bringeth good tidings.*—ISA. lii. 7.

1 I LOVE to tell the Story
    Of unseen things above,
Of Jesus and His glory,
    Of Jesus and His love :
I love to tell the Story,
    Because I know it's true ;
It satisfies my longings,
    As nothing else would do.
        I love to tell the Story, etc.

2 I love to tell the Story :
    More wonderful it seems
Than all the golden fancies
    Of all our golden dreams :
I love to tell the Story ;
    It did so much for me ;
And that is just the reason
    I tell it now to thee.

3 I love to tell the Story :
    'Tis pleasant to repeat
What seems, each time I tell it,
    More wonderfully sweet :
I love to tell the Story :
    For some have never heard
The message of salvation
    From God's own holy Word.

4 I love to tell the Story :
    For those who know it best
Seem hungering and thirsting
    To hear it like the rest :
And when in scenes of glory
    I sing the new, new song,
'Twill be the old, old Story
    That I have loved so long.
                Kate Hankey.

Sarby. L.M. T. R. MATTHEWS.

445

Let us not be weary in well-doing.—GAL. vi. 9.

1 Go, labour on; spend, and be spent,
  Thy joy to do the Father's will;
  It is the way the Master went;
  Should not the servant tread it still?

2 Go, labour on; 'tis not for naught;
  Thy earthly loss is heavenly gain;
  Men heed thee, love thee, praise thee not;
  The Master praises—what are men?

3 Go, labour on; your hands are weak,
  Your knees are faint, your soul cast down;
  Yet falter not; the prize you seek
  Is near—a kingdom and a crown.

4 Go, labour on while it is day:
  The world's dark night is hastening on;
  Speed, speed thy work; cast sloth away:
  It is not thus that souls are won.

5 Toil on, faint not, keep watch, and pray;
  Be wise, the erring soul to win;
  Go forth into the world's highway,
  Compel the wanderer to come in.

6 Toil on, and in thy toil rejoice;
  For toil comes rest, for exile home;
  Soon shalt thou hear the Bridegroom's voice,
  The midnight cry, "Behold, I come!"

H. Bonar.

Huddersfield. S.M. WILLIAMS' Psalmody.

Alternative Tune, DAY OF PRAISE, *No.* 500.

446

*Blessed is that servant, whom his Lord when He cometh shall find so
doing.—MATT. xxiv. 46.*

1 YE servants of the Lord,
  Each in his office wait,
  Observant of His heavenly word,
  And watchful at His gate.

2 Let all your lamps be bright,
  And trim the golden flame;
  Gird up your loins, as in His sight,
  For holy is His Name.

3 Watch: 'tis your Lord's command,
  And while we speak He's near;

  Mark the first signal of His hand,
  And ready all appear.

4 Oh, happy servant he,
  In such a posture found!
  He shall his Lord with rapture see,
  And be with honour crowned.

5 Christ shall the banquet spread
  With His own royal hand,
  And raise that favoured servant's head
  Amidst the angelic band.

P. Doddridge.

SECTION VII.—The Christian Life.
(5.) Consecration and Love to Christ.

St. Catherine. 7.6.7.6., D. R. F. DALE.

447 *If any man hear My voice, and open the door, I will come in to him.—*
REV. iii. 20.

1 O JESUS, Thou art standing
  Outside the fast-closed door,
In lowly patience waiting
  To pass the threshold o'er:
Shame on us, Christian brethren,
  His Name and sign who bear;
Oh, shame, thrice shame upon us,
  To keep Him standing there!

2 O Jesus, Thou art knocking,
  And lo! that hand is scarred,
And thorns Thy brow encircle,
  And tears Thy face have marred:
Oh, love that passeth knowledge,
  So patiently to wait!
Oh, sin that hath no equal,
  So fast to bar the gate!

3 O Jesus, Thou art pleading
  In accents meek and low;
"I died for you, My children,
  And will ye treat Me so?"
O Lord, with shame and sorrow
  We open now the door:
Dear Saviour, enter, enter,
  And leave us nevermore.
            W. W. How.

St. Christopher. 7.6.8.6.8.6.8.6. F. C. MAKER.

448 *God forbid that I should glory, save in the cross.*—GAL. vi. 14.

1 BENEATH the cross of Jesus
  I fain would take my stand,
The shadow of a mighty rock,
  Within a weary land;
A home within the wilderness,
  A rest upon the way,
From the burning of the noontide heat,
  And the burden of the day.

2 O safe and happy shelter!
  O refuge tried and sweet!
O trysting-place where heaven's love
  And heaven's justice meet!
As to the holy patriarch
  That wondrous dream was given,
So seems my Saviour's cross to me,
  A ladder up to heaven.

3 There lies, beneath its shadow,
  But on the farther side,
The darkness of an awful grave
  That gapes both deep and wide:

And there between us stands the cross,
  Two arms outstretched to save;
Like a watchman set to guard the way
  From that eternal grave.

4 Upon that cross of Jesus
  Mine eye at times can see
The very dying form of One
  Who suffered there for me;
And from my smitten heart, with tears,
  Two wonders I confess—
The wonders of His glorious love,
  And my own worthlessness.

5 I take, O cross, thy shadow,
  For my abiding place;
I ask no other sunshine than
  The sunshine of His face;
Content to let the world go by,
  To know no gain nor loss—
My sinful self my only shame,
  My glory all the cross.

E. C. Clephane.

449 Constance. [FIRST TUNE.]   8.7.8.7., D.   Sir ARTHUR S. SULLIVAN.

Amicus Divinus. [SECOND TUNE.]   8.7.8.7., D.   GEO. C. STEBBINS.

449

Alternative Tune, GOLDEN SHEAVES, *No.* 436.

This is my Beloved, and this is my Friend.—SONG OF SOLOMON v. 16.

1 I'VE found a Friend, oh, such a Friend!
    He loved me ere I knew Him;
He drew me with the cords of love,
    And thus He bound me to Him:
And round my heart still closely twine
    Those ties which nought can sever;
For I am His, and He is mine,
    For ever and for ever.

2 I've found a Friend, oh, such a Friend!
    He bled, He died to save me;
And not alone the gift of life,
    But His own self He gave me:
Naught that I have my own I call,
    I hold it for the Giver:
My heart, my strength, my life, my all,
    Are His, and His for ever.

3 I've found a Friend, oh, such a Friend!
    All power to Him is given,
To guard me on my onward course,
    And bring me safe to heaven.
Th' eternal glories gleam afar,
    To nerve my faint endeavour:
So now to watch! to work! to war!
    And then—to rest for ever!

4 I've found a Friend, oh, such a Friend!
    So kind and true and tender,
So wise a Counsellor and Guide,
    So mighty a Defender:
From Him, who loves me now so well,
    What power my soul can sever?
Shall life, or death, or earth, or hell?
    No; I am His for ever!

J. G. Small.

Sursum Corda.   6.4.6.4.10.10.   GEORGE LOMAS.

Copyright by W. Garrett Horder.

450

Unto Thee, O Lord, do I lift up my soul.—PSALM xxv. 1.

1 I LIFT my heart to Thee,
    Saviour Divine;
For Thou art all to me,
    And I am Thine.
Is there on earth a closer bond than this,
That "my Belovèd's mine, and I am His"?

2 Thine am I by all ties;
    But chiefly Thine,
That through Thy sacrifice
    Thou, Lord, art mine.
By Thine own cords of love, so sweetly wound
Around me, I to Thee am closely bound.

3 How can I, Lord, withhold
    Life's brightest hour
From Thee; or gathered gold
    Or any power?
Why should I keep one precious thing from
    Thee,   [for me?
When Thou has given Thine own dear Self

4 I pray Thee, Saviour, keep
    Me in Thy love,
Until death's holy sleep
    Shall me remove
To that fair realm where, sin and sorrow o'er,
Thou and Thine own are one for evermore.

C. E. Mudie.

The Burden=Bearer.   P.M.   M. R. BOYD.

Affetuoso.

Lord, it is I who need Thy love, Need Thy strength and need Thy power;

Oh, keep me, use me, and hold me fast, Each moment, each day, each hour.

451 *Come unto Me, all ye that labour and are heavy laden.*—Matt. xi. 28.

1 Is there a heart that is willing to lay
 Burdens on Jesus' breast?
 He is so loving, and gentle, and true—
 Come unto Him and rest.
  Lord, it is I who need Thy love, etc.

2 Is there a heart that is lonely to-day,
 Needing a faithful friend?
 Jesus will always keep close by your side,
 Loving you to the end.

3 Is there a heart that has failed to o'ercome
 Sin with its mighty power?
 Jesus is stronger than Satan and sin,
 Trust Him this very hour.

4 Is there a heart that is longing to bring
 Blessing to some lost soul?
 Jesus is willing the weakest to use,
 Let Him thy life control.

                    M. R. B. and F. P. W.

The Pilgrim Way. C.M., with Chorus. R. Hudson Pope.

Chorus.

Like Je-sus, like Je-sus, I want to be like Je-sus; I

love Him so, I.. want to grow Like Je-sus, day by day.

Alternative Tune (without Chorus), Abridge, *No.* 472.

452 *Grow in grace, and in the knowledge of our Lord.*—2 Peter iii. 18.

1 In truth and grace I want to grow
 Like Jesus, day by day;
 And scatter sunshine where I go,
 Along my pilgrim way.
  Like Jesus, like Jesus, etc.

2 I want to live a life of love
 Like Jesus, day by day;
 And point some soul to heaven above,
 Along my pilgrim way.

3 I want to do some kindly deed
 Like Jesus, day by day;
 And for His kingdom sow the seed
 Along my pilgrim way *Ida S. Taylor.*

St. Edmund. [FIRST TUNE.] 6.4.6.4.6.6.6.4. Sir Arthur S. Sullivan.

By permission of Novello and Company, Limited.

Phelps. [SECOND TUNE.] 6.4.6.4.6.6.6.4. R. Lowry.

453 *What shall I render unto the Lord for all His benefits toward me?—*
PSALM cxvi. 12.

1 SAVIOUR! Thy dying love
    Thou gavest me,
Nor should I aught withhold,
    My Lord, from Thee;
In love my soul would bow,
My heart fulfil its vow,
Some offering bring Thee now,
    Something for Thee.

2 At the blest mercy-seat,
    Pleading for me,
My feeble faith looks up,
    Jesus, to Thee:
Help me the cross to bear,
Thy wondrous love declare,
Some song to raise, or prayer—
    Something for Thee.

3 Give me a faithful heart—
    Likeness to Thee—
That each departing day
    Henceforth may see
Some work of love begun,
Some deed of kindness done,
Some wanderer sought and won,
    Something for Thee.

4 All that I am and have—
    Thy gifts so free—
In joy, in grief, through life,
    O Lord, for Thee!
And when Thy face I see,
My ransomed soul shall be,
Through all eternity,
    Something for Thee.

S. D. Phelps.

Lowry. P.M. R. LOWRY.

REFRAIN.

Fol-low! fol-low! I would follow Je-sus; Anywhere, everywhere, I would follow on!

Fol-low! fol-low! I would follow Je-sus! Everywhere He leads me I would fol-low on!

454   *If any man serve Me, let him follow Me.*—JOHN xii. 26.

1 Down in the valley with my Saviour I would go,
   Where the flowers are blooming and the sweet waters flow;
   Everywhere He leads me I would follow, follow on;
   Walking in His footsteps till the crown be won.
       Follow! follow! I would follow Jesus; etc.

2 Down in the valley with my Saviour I would go,
   Where the storms are sweeping and the dark waters flow;
   With His hand to lead me I will never, never fear;
   Danger cannot harm me if my Lord is near.

3 Down in the valley or upon the mountain steep,
   Close beside my Saviour would my soul ever keep;
   He will lead me safely in the path that He has trod,
   Up to where they gather on the hills of God.

W. O. Cushing.

N

Margate. 7.6.7.6., D. E. J. BELLERBY.

455 *Christ shall give thee light.*—EPH. v. 14.

1 SHINE on me, O Lord Jesus,
    And let me ever know
The grace that shone from Calvary,
    Where Thou didst love me so.
"My child, I am thy Saviour,
    'Tis not what thou dost feel,
But Mine own gracious promise
    Which does thy pardon seal."

2 Shine in me, O Lord Jesus,
    And let Thy searching light
Reveal each hidden purpose,
    Each thought as in Thy sight.
"My child, I am thy Searcher,
    I try each loving heart,
For I would have most holy
    All who in Me have part."

3 Shine through me then, Lord Jesus,
    That all the world may see
The life I live is Thy life,
    And thus be drawn to Thee.

"My child, I am thy Power;
    With those who hear My voice
I ever dwell, and use them,
    Thus making them rejoice."

4 Shine out, shine out, Lord Jesus,
    Thou Light of all the world;
Oh, let Thy Gospel banner
    Be everywhere unfurled!
"My child, hast thou forgotten
    That name is also thine?
My fruit is borne on branches,
    Not by the parent Vine."

5 Arise and shine, Lord Jesus,
    Thou Bright and Morning Star;
I long for Thine appearing,
    When peace shall follow war.
"My child, before I gather
    My family in one,
Its number needs completing;
    T'wards this, what hast thou done?"

E. J. Bellerby (abridged).

456 **Aspiration.** P.M. P. P. BLISS

Alternative Tune, LONGSTAFF, *No.* 474.

456 *Covet earnestly the best gifts.*—1 COR. xii. 31.

1 MORE holiness give me,
    More strivings within ;
More patience in suffering,
    More sorrow for sin ;
More faith in my Saviour,
    More sense of His care ;
More joy in His service,
    More purpose in prayer.

2 More gratitude give me,
    More trust in the Lord ;
More zeal for His glory,
    More hope in His Word ;

More tears for His sorrows,
    More pain at His grief ;
More meekness in trial,
    More praise for relief.

3 More purity give me,
    More strength to o'ercome ;
More freedom from earth-stains,
    More longings for home ;
More fit for the kingdom,
    More used would I be,
More blessed and holy,
    More, Saviour, like Thee !

P. P. Bliss.

Gounod.
    8.7.8.7.7.7.
    C. GOUNOD.

By permission of Novello and Company, Limited.

Alternative Tune, IRBY, *No.* 120.

457 *I have called you friends.*—JOHN xv. 15.

1 ONE there is above all others,
    Well deserves the name of Friend ;
His is love beyond a brother's—
    Costly, free, and knows no end :
    They who once His kindness prove,
    Find it everlasting love.

2 Which of all our friends, to save us,
    Could, or would, have shed his blood ?
Christ, the Saviour, died to have us
    Reconciled in Him to God :
    This was boundless love indeed !
    Jesus is a Friend in need.

3 When He lived on earth abasèd,
    "Friend of sinners" was His Name ;
Now above all glory raisèd,
    He rejoices in the same :
    Still He calls them brethren, friends,
    And to all their wants attends.

4 Oh, for grace our hearts to soften !
    Teach us, Lord, at length to love ;
We, alas ! forget too often
    What a Friend we have above ;
    But when home our souls are brought,
    We will love Thee as we ought.

John Newton.

St. Chrysostom.   8.8.8.8.8.8.   Sir J. Barnby.

By permission of Novello and Company, Limited.

Alternative Tune, St. Catherine, *No.* 290.

458   *Lord, Thou knowest that I love Thee.*—John xxi. 15.

1 Jesus, my Lord, my God, my All,
  Hear me, blest Saviour, when I call;
  Hear me, and from Thy dwelling-place
  Pour down the riches of Thy grace;
    Jesus, my Lord, I Thee adore,
    Oh, make me love Thee more and more.

2 Jesus, too late I Thee have sought,
  How can I love Thee as I ought?
  And how extol Thy matchless fame,
  The glorious beauty of Thy Name?
    Jesus, my Lord, I Thee adore,
    Oh, make me love Thee more and more.

3 Jesus, what didst Thou find in me,
  That Thou hast dealt so lovingly?
  How great the joy that Thou hast brought
  So far exceeding hope or thought!
    Jesus, my Lord, I Thee adore,
    Oh, make me love Thee more and more.

4 Jesus, of Thee shall be my song,
  To Thee my heart and soul belong;
  All that I have or am is Thine,
  And Thou, blest Saviour, Thou art mine.
    Jesus, my Lord, I Thee adore,
    Oh, make me love Thee more and more.
                                    H. Collins.

459 St. Alphege.   7.6.7.6.   H. J. Gauntlett.

Alternative Tunes, BARTON, *No. 535, and* SACRIFICE, *No. 406.*

459

O Lord, truly I am Thy servant.—PSALM cxvi. 16.

1 IN full and glad surrender,
I give myself to Thee,
Thine utterly and only
And evermore to be.

2 O Son of God, who lov'st me,
I will be Thine alone;
And all I have and am, Lord,
Shall henceforth be Thine own!

3 Reign over me, Lord Jesus;
Oh, make my heart Thy throne:
It shall be Thine, dear Saviour,
It shall be Thine alone.

4 Oh, come and reign, Lord Jesus;
Rule over everything!
And keep me always loyal,
And true to Thee, my King.

Frances R. Havergal.

Haven of Rest.　　　　　P.M.　　　　　MRS. C. H. MORRIS.

Shel·ter me safe in that "Ha-ven of Rest."

460

I will trust in the covert of Thy wings.—PSALM lxi. 4.

1 NEARER, still nearer, close to Thy heart,
Draw me, my Saviour, so precious Thou art;
Fold me, oh, fold me close to Thy breast,
Shelter me safe in that "Haven of Rest."

2 Nearer, still nearer, nothing I bring,
Naught as an offering to Jesus my King;
Only my sinful, now contrite heart,
Grant me the cleansing Thy blood doth impart.

3 Nearer, still nearer, Lord, to be Thine,
Sin, with its follies, I gladly resign;
All of its pleasures, pomp and its pride,
Give me but Jesus, my Lord crucified.

4 Nearer, still nearer, while life shall last,
Till all its struggles and trials are past;
Then through eternity, ever I'll be
Nearer, my Saviour, still nearer to Thee. *C. H. Morris.*

11.11.11.11.

461 Clarendon Street. [FIRST TUNE.]

A. J. GORDON.

Featherston. [SECOND TUNE.] 11.11.11.11.

W. O. GIBB.

If ev-er I lov'd Thee, if ev-er I lov'd Thee, if ev-er I lov'd Thee, my Saviour,'tis now.

461

1 My Saviour, I love Thee, I know Thou art mine;
For Thee all the pleasures of sin I resign;
My gracious Redeemer, my Saviour, art Thou;
If ever I loved Thee, my Saviour, 'tis now.

2 I love Thee because Thou hast first lovèd me,
And purchased my pardon on Calvary's tree;
I love Thee for wearing the thorns on Thy brow;
If ever I loved Thee, my Saviour, 'tis now.

3 In mansions of glory and endless delight,
I'll ever adore Thee in heaven so bright;
I'll sing, with the glittering crown on my brow,
"If ever I loved Thee, my Saviour, 'tis now."

W. R. Featherston.

Everybody should know.   P.M.   Verse original. Chorus E. O. Excell, arr.

Words and Music by permission of Mrs. H. C. Dixon.

462 *Tell thy friends how great things the Lord hath done for thee.*—MARK v. 19.

1 I HAVE such a wonderful Saviour,
Who helps me wherever I go;
That I must be telling His goodness,
That everybody should know.
Everybody should know, etc.

2 His mercy and love are unbounded,
He makes me with gladness o'erflow;
Oh, He is "the Chief of ten thousand:"
That everybody should know!

3 He helps me when trials surround me,
His grace and His goodness to show;
Oh, how can I help but adore Him,
That everybody should know!

4 My life and my love I will give Him,
And faithfully serve Him below,
Who brought me His wondrous salvation
That everybody should know.

Mrs. Frank A. Breck.

Trust and Obey. P.M. D. B. TOWNER

CHORUS.

Trust and o - bey! For there's no other way To be happy in Jesus, But to trust and o - bey.

463 *The obedience of faith.*—ROM. xvi. 26.

1 WHEN we walk with the Lord,
   In the light of His Word,
 What a glory He sheds on our way!
   While we do His good will,
   He abides with us still,
 And with all who will trust and obey!
   Trust and obey, etc.

2 Not a shadow can rise,
   Not a cloud in the skies,
 But His smile quickly drives it away;
   Not a doubt nor a fear,
   Not a sigh nor a tear,
 Can abide while we trust and obey!

3 Not a burden we bear,
   Not a sorrow we share,
 But our toil He doth richly repay:
   Not a grief nor a loss,
   Not a frown nor a cross,
 But is blest if we trust and obey.

4 But we never can prove
   The delights of His love,
 Until all on the altar we lay;
   For the favour He shows,
   And the joy He bestows,
 Are for them who will trust and obey.

5 Then in fellowship sweet
   We will sit at His feet,
 Or we'll walk by His side in the way;
   What He says we will do,
   Where He sends we will go—
 Never fear, only trust and obey!

J. H. Sammis.

464 Resurrection Life. P.M. T. RYDER
Moderato.

CHORUS.

Glo-ry be to God.

4.64   *Buried with Him . . . walk in newness of life.*—ROM. vi. 4.

1 "BURIED with Christ," and raised with
    Him too;
  What is there left for me to do?
  Simply to cease from struggling and strife,
  Simply to "walk in newness of life."
    Glory be to God.

2 "Risen with Christ," my glorious Head;
  Holiness, now, the pathway I tread,
  Beautiful thought, while walking therein :
  "He that is dead is freed from sin."
    Glory be to God.

3 "Living with Christ," who "dieth no more,"
  Following Christ, who goeth before,

I am from bondage utterly freed,
Reckoning self as "dead indeed."
    Glory be to God.

4 Living for Christ, my members I yield,
Servants to God, for evermore sealed,
"Not under law," I'm now "under grace,"
Sin is dethroned, and Christ takes its place.
    Glory be to God.

5 Growing in Christ; no more shall be named
Things of which now I'm truly ashamed,
"Fruit unto holiness" will I bear,
Life evermore, the end I shall share.
    Glory be to God.

                          T. Ryder.

Heathlands.   7.7.7.7.7.7.   HENRY SMART.

Alternative Tune, WELLS, *No.* 486.

465   *Ye are not your own . . . ye are bought with a price.*—1 COR. vi. 19, 20.

1 JESUS, Master, whose I am,
    Purchased Thine alone to be,
  By Thy blood, O spotless Lamb,
    Shed so willingly for me,
  Let my heart be all Thine own,
  Let me live to Thee alone.

2 Other lords have long held sway;
    Now, Thy Name alone to bear,
  Thy dear voice alone obey,
    Is my daily, hourly prayer :
  Whom have I in heaven but Thee?
  Nothing else my joy can be.

3 Jesus, Master, whom I serve,
    Though so feebly and so ill,
  Strengthen hand and heart and nerve
    All Thy bidding to fulfil ;
  Open Thou mine eyes to see
  All the work Thou hast for me.

4 Jesus, Master, wilt Thou use
    One who owes Thee more than all?
  As Thou wilt! I would not choose ;
    Only let me hear Thy call.
  Jesus, let me always be,
  In Thy service, glad and free
              Frances R. Havergal.

Raleigh. 6.6.6.6.8.8. E. Prout.

466

I thought on my ways, and turned my feet unto Thy testimonies.—
PSALM cxix. 59.

1 I BRING my sins to Thee,
The sins I cannot count,
That all may cleansèd be
In Thy once-opened fount.
I bring them, Saviour, all to Thee:
The burden is too great for me.

2 My heart to Thee I bring,
The heart I cannot read,
A faithless, wandering thing,
An evil heart indeed.
I bring it, Saviour, now to Thee,
That fixed and faithful it may be.

3 My joys to Thee I bring—
The joys Thy love hath given,
That each may be a wing
To lift me nearer heaven.
I bring them, Saviour, all to Thee,
For Thou hast purchased all for me.

4 My life I bring to Thee,
I would not be my own;
O Saviour, let me be
Thine ever, Thine alone!
My heart, my life, my all, I bring
To Thee, my Saviour, and my King.
Frances R. Havergal.

St. Andrew. 8.7.8.7. E. H. Thorne.

Alternative Tune, St. Oswald, *No. 276.*

467

He saith unto them, Follow Me.—MATT. iv. 19.

1 JESUS calls us; o'er the tumult
Of our life's wild, restless sea,
Day by day His sweet voice soundeth,
Saying, "Christian, follow Me."

2 As of old apostles heard it
By the Galilean lake,
Turned from home and toil and kindred,
Leaving all for His dear sake.

3 Jesus calls us from the worship
Of the vain world's golden store:

From each idol that would keep us,
Saying, "Christian, love Me more."

4 In our joys, and in our sorrows,
Days of toil, and hours of ease,
Still He calls, in cares and pleasures,
"Christian, love Me more than these."

5 Jesus calls us—by Thy mercies,
Saviour, may we hear Thy call;
Give our hearts to Thy obedience,
Serve and love Thee best of all.
Mrs. C. F. Alexander.

Baca. 6.6.6.6.6.6. W. H. HAVERGAL.

468

They . . . gave their own selves to the Lord.—2 COR. viii. 5.

1 I GAVE My life for thee,
   My precious blood I shed,
That thou might'st ransomed be,
   And quickened from the dead:
I gave My life for thee;
What hast thou given for Me?

2 I spent long years for thee
   In weariness and woe,
That an eternity
   Of joy thou mightest know:
I spent long years for thee;
Hast thou spent *one* for Me?

3 My Father's home of light,
   My rainbow-circled throne,
I left for earthly night,

For wanderings sad and lone:
   I left it all for thee;
Hast thou left aught for Me?

4 I suffered much for thee—
   More than thy tongue can tell
Of bitter agony,
   To rescue thee from hell:
I suffered much for thee;
What canst thou bear for Me?

5 Lord, let my life be given,
   And every moment spent,
For God, for souls, for heaven,
   And all earth's ties be rent.
Thou gavest Thyself for me,
Now I give all for Thee.

Frances R. Havergal.

Rockingham. L.M. E. MILLER.

469

*God forbid that I should glory, save in the cross of our Lord Jesus
Christ.*—GAL. vi. 14.

1 WHEN I survey the wondrous cross
   On which the Prince of glory died,
My richest gain I count but loss,
   And pour contempt on all my pride.

2 Forbid it, Lord, that I should boast,
   Save in the cross of Christ my God:
All the vain things that charm me most,
   I sacrifice them to His blood.

3 See from His head, His hands, His feet,
   Sorrow and love flow mingled down:
Did e'er such love and sorrow meet,
   Or thorns compose so rich a crown?

4 Were the whole realm of nature mine,
   That were an offering far too small;
Love so amazing, so divine,
   Demands my soul, my life, my all!

Isaac Watts.

Sicilian Mariners. 8.7.8.7. MERRICK and TATTERSALL'S Psalms.

Alternative Tune, LUCERNE, *No.* 412.

Hitherto hath the Lord helped us.—1 SAM. vii. 12.

470

1 COME, Thou Fount of every blessing,
  Tune my heart to sing Thy grace,
Streams of mercy, never ceasing,
  Call for songs of loudest praise.

2 Jesus sought me, when a stranger,
  Wandering from the fold of God;
He, to rescue me from danger,
  Interposed His precious blood.

3 Oh, to grace how great a debtor
  Daily I'm constrained to be!
Let that grace, Lord, like a fetter,
  Bind my wandering heart to Thee.

4 Prone to wander, Lord, I feel it,
  Prone to leave the God I love:
Here's my heart; Lord, take and seal it,
  Seal it from Thy courts above.
                                R. Robinson.

Ewburst. 8.8.8.7. CECIL J. ALLEN.

My Refuge, my Saviour.—2 SAM. xxii. 3.

471

1 I AM not skilled to understand
  What God hath willed, what God hath
I only know at His right hand [planned;
  Stands One who is my Saviour!

2 I take Him at His word indeed:
  "Christ died for sinners," this I read;
And in my heart I find a need
  Of Him to be my Saviour!

3 That He should leave His place on high,
  And come for sinful man to die,

You count it strange?—so once did I,
  Before I knew my Saviour!

4 And oh, that He fulfilled may see
  The travail of His soul in me,
And with His work contented be,
  As I with my dear Saviour!

5 Yea, living, dying, let me bring
  My strength, my solace from this spring,
That He who lives to be my King
  Once died to be my Saviour.
                                Dora Greenwell.

Abridge. C.M. ISAAC SMITH.

472 *King of kings, and Lord of lords.*—REV. xix. 16.

1 O JESUS, King most wonderful,
  Thou Conqueror renowned;
  Thou Sweetness most ineffable,
  In whom all joys are found;

2 When once Thou visitest the heart,
  Then truth begins to shine;
  Then earthly vanities depart,
  Then kindles love divine.

3 Jesus! Thy mercies are untold,
  Through each returning day;
  Thy love exceeds a thousand-fold
  Whatever we can say.

4 May every heart confess Thy Name,
  And ever Thee adore;
  And, seeking Thee, itself inflame
  To seek Thee more and more.

5 Thee may our tongues for ever bless;
  Thee may we love alone:
  And ever in our lives express
  The image of Thine own.

6 Grant us, while here on earth we stay,
  Thy love to feel and know;
  And when from hence we pass away,
  To us Thy glory show.
  Bernard of Clairvaux, trans. *E. Caswall.*

North Coates. 6.5.6.5. T. R. MATTHEWS.

By permission of Novello and Company, Limited.

473 *I, if I be lifted up . . . will draw all men unto Me.*—JOHN xii. 32.

1 O MY Saviour, lifted
  From the earth for me,
  Draw me, in Thy mercy,
  Nearer unto Thee.

2 Lift my earth-bound longings,
  Fix them, Lord, above;
  Draw me with the magnet
  Of Thy mighty love.

3 And I come, Lord Jesus;
  Dare I turn away?
  No! Thy love hath conquered,
  And I come to-day.

4 Bringing all my burdens,
  Sorrow, sin and care;
  At Thy feet I lay them,
  And I leave them there.
  W. W. How.

Longstaff.   11.11.11.11.   GEO. C. STEBBINS.

By permission. From Sankey's "Sacred Songs and Solos."
Alternative Tune, ST. ASAPH, *No.* 491.

474   *Be ye holy: for I am the Lord your God.*—LEV. xx. 7.

1 TAKE time to be holy, speak oft with thy Lord,
Abide in Him always, and feed on His Word.
Make friends of God's children, help those who are weak;
Forgetting in nothing His blessing to seek.

2 Take time to be holy, the world rushes on;
Spend much time in secret with Jesus alone.
By looking to Jesus like Him thou shalt be;
Thy friends, in thy conduct, His likeness shall see.

3 Take time to be holy, let Him be thy Guide;
And run not before Him whatever betide:
In joy or in sorrow still follow thy Lord,
And, looking to Jesus, still trust in His Word.

4 Take time to be holy, be calm in thy soul;
Each thought and each temper beneath His control.
Thus led by His Spirit to fountains of love,
Thou soon shalt be fitted for service above.
W. D. Longstaff.

475 Littlehampton.   P.M.   J. S. TYLER.

CHORUS.

1, 2, 3. Hast Thou not a blessing for me, A blessing for me,
4. Oh, yes! Thou hast a blessing for me, A blessing for me,

a blessing for me? Hast Thou not a blessing for me? A bless-ing even for me!
a blessing for me! Oh, yes! Thou hast a blessing for me! A bless-ing even for me!

475   *Hast Thou not . . . a blessing for me?*—Gen. xxvii. 36.

1 HAST Thou not a blessing for me,
   For me, Thy sinful child?
   Although I've wandered far from Thee,
   O'er deserts waste and wild.
   Hast Thou not a blessing for me, etc.

2 My heart is all defiled with sin,
   But Jesus, He has died:
   Oh! cleanse me in the precious blood
   That flowed from His dear side.

3 My Saviour intercedes for me
   Before Thy throne on high:
   Oh, look upon His precious blood,
   And save me, or I die.

4 My Father, bless Thy feeble child,
   And fill me with Thy love:
   And may Thy Holy Spirit fit
   Me for Thy fold above.
   Oh, yes! Thou hast a blessing for me, etc.

                                   J. S. Tyler.

St. Aubin.   8.8.8.5.

476   *They sung a new song, saying, Thou art worthy.*—Rev. v. 9.

1 PRAISE the Saviour, ye who know Him:
   Who can tell how much we owe Him?
   Gladly let us render to Him
   All we have and are!

2 Jesus is the Name that charms us,
   He for conflict fits and arms us;
   Nothing moves and nothing harms us
   When we trust in Him.

3 Trust in Him, ye saints, for ever;
   He is faithful, changing never;

   Neither fear nor guile can sever
   Those He loves from Him.

4 Keep us, Lord, oh, keep us cleaving
   To Thyself, and still believing,
   Till the hour of our receiving
   Promised joys in heaven!

5 Then we shall be where we would be,
   Then we shall be what we should be,
   Things which are not now, nor could be,
   Then shall be our own.   *T. Kelly.*

Shrewsbury. 6.5.6.5., D. C. H. FORREST.

477 *As the Father hath loved Me, so have I loved you.*—JOHN XV. 9.

1 IN the heart of Jesus
    There is love for you,
Love most pure and tender,
    Love most deep and true;
Why should you be lonely,
    Why for friendship sigh,
When the heart of Jesus
    Has a full supply?

2 In the mind of Jesus
    There is thought for you,
Warm as summer sunshine,
    Sweet as morning dew;
Why should you be fearful,
    Why take anxious thought,
Since the mind of Jesus
    Cares for those He bought?

3 In the field of Jesus
    There is work for you;
Such as even angels
    Might rejoice to do:
Why stand idly sighing
    For some life-work grand,
While the field of Jesus
    Seeks your reaping hand?

4 In the home of Jesus
    There's a place for you;
Glorious, bright, and joyous,
    Calm and peaceful too:
Why then, like a wanderer,
    Roam with weary pace,
If the home of Jesus
    Holds for you a place?

Alice M. Pugh.

478 Ellers. 10.10.10.10. E. J. HOPKINS.

Alternative Tune, DALKEITH, *No. 256.*

478

Glorify God in your body, and in your spirit, which are God's.—
1 Cor. vi. 20.

1 GOD made me for Himself, to serve Him here,
  With love's pure service and in filial fear;
  To show His praise, for Him to labour now;
  Then see His glory where the angels bow.

2 All needful grace was mine through His dear Son,
  Whose life and death my full salvation won;
  The grace that would have strengthened me, and taught;
  Grace that would crown me when my work was wrought.

3 And I, poor sinner, cast it all away;
  Lived for the toil or pleasure of each day;
  As if no Christ had shed His precious blood,
  As if I owed no homage to my God

4 O Holy Spirit, with Thy fire divine,
  Melt into tears this thankless heart of mine;
  Teach me to love what once I seemed to hate,
  And live to God, before it be too late.

Sir H. W. Baker.

479 Rozel.   10.10.10.10., with Chorus.   Mrs. P. P. BLISS

1. { I will love Je-sus and serve Him; for see How the dear Saviour has watch'd o-ver me!
   { How He has guarded and guid-ed my way! How He has kept me by night and by day!

CHORUS.

Him will I love, and His will I be, All because He has first loved me.

Him will I love, and His will I be, All because He loves me...

I will love Thee, O Lord, my strength.—PSALM xviii. 1.

2 I will love Jesus and learn of His will,
  Trusting Him ever, through good and through ill;
  Seeking His blessing, where'er I may be,
  Knowing He loveth and careth for me.

3 I will love Jesus! and, sure of His love,
  I shall be safe as the blessèd above;
  Oh, when He calls to the glory on high,
  How we will praise Him—the angels and I !   *Paulina.*

Innsbruck. [FIRST TUNE.] 8.8.6.8.8.6. H. IZAAK.

Ravendale. [SECOND TUNE.] 8.8.6.8.8.6. W. STOKES.

480

The love of God, which is in Christ Jesus our Lord.—ROM. viii. 39.

1 O LOVE Divine, how sweet Thou art!
  When shall I find my willing heart
    All taken up by Thee?
  I thirst, I faint, I die to prove
  The greatness of redeeming love,
    The love of Christ to me.

2 Stronger His love than death or hell;
  Its riches are unsearchable:
    The first-born sons of light
  Desire in vain its depths to see;
  They cannot reach the mystery,
    The length, and breadth, and height.

3 God only knows the love of God:
  Oh, that it now were shed abroad
    In this poor stony heart!
  For love I sigh, for love I pine:
  This only portion, Lord, be mine—
    Be mine this better part!

3 Oh, that I could for ever sit
  With Mary at the Master's feet!
    Be this my happy choice:
  My only care, delight, and bliss,
  My joy, my heaven on earth, be this,
    To hear the Bridegroom's voice.

                              C. Wesley.

St. Bees.　　　　　　　　7.7.7.7.　　　　　　　　J. B. DYKES.

481　　　*Bless me, even me also.*—GEN. xxvii. 38.

1 HEAVENLY Father, bless me now;
　At the cross of Christ I bow;
　Take my guilt and grief away,
　Hear and heal me now, I pray.

2 Now, O Lord, this very hour
　Send Thy grace and show Thy power;
　While I rest upon Thy Word,
　Come and bless me now, O Lord.

3 Now, just now, for Jesus' sake,
　Lift the clouds, the fetters break:
　While I look, and as I cry,
　Touch and cleanse me, or I die.

4 Never did I so adore
　Jesus Christ, Thy Son, before;
　Now the time! and this the place!
　Gracious Father, show Thy grace.
　　　　　　　　　　　　Alexander Clark.

Mozart.　　　　　　　　7.7.7.7.　　　　　　　From MOZART.

Alternative Tune, CONSECRATION, *No.* 78.

482　　*Ye are not your own. For ye are bought with a price.*—1 COR. vi. 19, 20.

1 TAKE my life, and let it be
　Consecrated, Lord, to Thee;
　Take my moments and my days,
　Let them flow in ceaseless praise.

2 Take my hands, and let them move
　At the impulse of Thy love;
　Take my feet, and let them be
　Swift and beautiful for Thee.

3 Take my voice, and let me sing
　Always, only, for my King;
　Take my lips, and let them be
　Filled with messages from Thee.

4 Take my silver and my gold,
　Not a mite would I withhold;
　Take my intellect, and use
　Every power as Thou shalt choose.

5 Take my will, and make it Thine;
　It shall be no longer mine:
　Take my heart, it is Thine own;
　It shall be Thy royal throne.

6 Take my love; my Lord, I pour
　At Thy feet its treasure store:
　Take myself, and I will be
　Ever, only, all, for Thee.
　　　　　　　　　　　　Frances R. Havergal.

Grace Divine. P.M. W. H. DOANE.

REFRAIN.

Draw me near - er, near-er, bless-ed Lord, To the cross where Thou hast

near - er, near - er,

died; Draw me near-er, near-er, nearer, blessed Lord, To Thy precious wounded side.

483 *Draw me, we will run after Thee.*—SONG OF SOLOMON i. 4.

1 I AM Thine, O Lord; I have heard Thy
    As it told Thy love to me;   [voice,
  But I long to rise in the arms of faith,
    And be closer drawn to Thee.
        Draw me near- . . . er, etc.

2 Consecrate me now to Thy service, Lord,
    By the power of grace divine;
  Let my soul look up with a steadfast hope,
    And my will be lost in Thine.

3 Oh, the pure delight of a single hour
    That before Thy throne I spend,
  When I kneel in prayer, and with Thee, my
    I commune as friend with friend. [God,

4 There are depths of love that I cannot
    Till I cross the narrow sea;   [know,
  There are heights of joy that I may not
    Till I rest in peace with Thee.   [reach,
        Fanny J. Crosby.

484 Dies Dominica. 7.6.7.6., D. J. B. DYKES.

By permission of Novello and Company, Limited.
Alternative Tune, LYMINGTON, *No.* 423.

484

I love my Master . . . I will not go out free.—EXODUS xxi. 5.

1 I LOVE, I love my Master,
    I will not go out free!
For He is my Redeemer;
    He paid the price for me.
I would not leave His service,
    It is so sweet and blest;
And in the weariest moments
    He gives the truest rest.

2 My Master shed His life-blood
    My vassal life to win,
And save me from the bondage
    Of tyrant self and sin.

He choose me for His service,
    And gave me power to choose
That blessèd, perfect freedom,
    Which I shall never lose.

3 I would not halve my service,
    His only it must be!
His *only*—Who so loved me,
    And gave Himself for me.
Rejoicing and adoring,
    Henceforth my song shall be—
"I love, I love my Master,
    I will not go out free!"

                          Frances R. Havergal.

St. Jude.   8.7.8.8.7.   CHARLES VINCENT.

485   *For to me to live is Christ.*—PHIL. i. 21.

1 OH, the bitter shame and sorrow,
    That a time could ever be,
When I let the Saviour's pity
Plead in vain, and proudly answered,
    "All of self, and none of Thee!"

2 Yet He found me; I beheld Him
    Bleeding on the accursèd tree,
Heard Him pray, "Forgive them, Father!"
And my wistful heart said faintly—
    "Some of self, and some of Thee."

3 Day by day His tender mercy,
    Healing, helping, full, and free,
Sweet and strong, and, ah! so patient,
Brought me lower, while I whispered,
    "Less of self, and more of Thee."

4 Higher than the highest heavens,
    Deeper than the deepest sea,
Lord, Thy love at last hath conquered;
Grant me now my supplication—
    "None of self, and all of Thee."

                          Theo. Monod.

Wells.   7.7.7.7.7.7.   D. BORTNIANSKI

Alternative Tune, REDHEAD, *No.* 252.

486   *Then shall I know even as also I am known.*—1 COR. xiii. 12.

1 WHEN this passing world is done,
When has sunk yon radiant sun,
When I stand with Christ on high,
Looking o'er life's history:
Then, Lord, shall I fully know,
Not till then, how much I owe.

2 When I stand before the throne,
Dressed in beauty not my own;
When I see Thee as Thou art,
Love Thee with unsinning heart:
Then, Lord, shall I fully know,
Not till then, how much I owe.

3 When the praise of heaven I hear,
Loud as thunder to the ear,
Loud as many waters' noise,
Sweet as harp's melodious voice:
Then, Lord, shall I fully know,
Not till then, how much I owe.

4 E'en on earth, as through a glass,
Darkly let Thy glory pass:
Make forgiveness feel so sweet,
Make Thy Spirit's help so meet;
E'en on earth, Lord, let me know
Something of the debt I owe.

5 Chosen not for good in me,
Wakened up from wrath to flee:
Hidden in the Saviour's side,
By the Spirit sanctified;
Teach me, Lord, on earth to show,
By my love, how much I owe.

R. M. McCheyne.

487 Darwall's 148th.   6.6.6.6.8.8.   J. DARWALL.

487   *Far above . . . every name that is named.*—Eph. i. 21.

1   Join all the glorious names
      Of wisdom, love, and power,
    That ever mortals knew,
      That angels ever bore :
    All are too mean to speak His worth,
    Too mean to set my Saviour forth.

2   Great Prophet of my God,
      My tongue would bless Thy Name :
    By Thee the joyful news
      Of our salvation came.
    The joyful news of sins forgiven,
    Of hell subdued and peace with heaven.

3   Jesus, my great High Priest,
      Offered His blood, and died ;
    My guilty conscience seeks

    No sacrifice beside :
    His powerful blood did once atone,
    And now it pleads before the throne.

4   I love my Shepherd's voice ;
      His watchful eye shall keep
    My wandering soul among
      The thousands of His sheep :
    He feeds His flock, He calls their names,
    His bosom bears the tender lambs.

5   My Saviour and my Lord,
      My Conqueror and my King,
    Thy sceptre and Thy sword,
      Thy reigning grace I sing :
    Thine is the power ; behold, I sit
    In willing bonds beneath Thy feet.
                                Isaac Watts.

Glory to Jesus.   10.10.10.10.   From Batiste, har. by C. W. & E. M.

Chorus. Glo-ry to Je-sus—wonderful Sa-viour ! Glory to Je-sus, the One I a-dore ; . . .

D.C. for Chorus.

Glo-ry to Je-sus—wonderful Sa-viour ! Glo-ry to Jesus, and praise ev-er-more.

488   *Who gave Himself for us, that He might redeem us from all iniquity.*—
                              Titus ii. 14.

1.
Jesus has loved me—wonderful Saviour !
  Jesus has loved me, I cannot tell why ;
Came He to rescue sinners all worthless,
  My heart He conquered—for Him I would
    Glory to Jesus, etc.   [die.

2.
Jesus has saved me—wonderful Saviour !
  Jesus has saved me, I cannot tell how ;
All that I know is, He was my ransom,
  Dying on Calvary with thorns on His brow.

3.
Jesus will lead me—wonderful Saviour !
  Jesus will lead me, I cannot tell where ;
But I will follow, through joy or sorrow,
  Sunshine or tempest, sweet peace or despair.

4.
Jesus will crown me—wonderful Saviour !
  Jesus will crown me, I cannot tell when ;
White throne of splendour hail I with glad-
                                    ness,
Crowned in the presence of angels and men.
                            J. W. MacGill.

Cambridge. 8.8.8.6. CHARLES FISHWICK.

489   *Lord, I will follow Thee whithersoever Thou goest.*—LUKE ix. 57.

1 JUST as I am, Thine own to be,
Friend of the young, who lovest me,
To consecrate myself to Thee,
    O Jesus Christ—I come.

2 In the glad morning of my day,
My life to give, my vows to pay,
With no reserve, and no delay—
    With all my heart, I come.

3 I would live ever in the light,
I would work ever for the right,

I would serve Thee with all my might—
    Therefore to Thee I come.

4 Just as I am, young, strong, and free,
To be the best that I can be,
For truth, and righteousness, and Thee,
    Lord of my life—I come.

5 And for Thy sake to win renown,
And then to take the victor's crown,
And at Thy feet to lay it down,
    O Master, Lord—I come.
        Marianne Farningham.

Escendune. 8.8.8.3. HUGH BLAIR.

490   *Seek ye first the kingdom of God, and His righteousness.*—MATT. vi. 33.

1 SEEK ye first, not earthly pleasure,
Fading joy and failing treasure;
But the love that knows no measure
    Seek ye first.

2 Seek ye first, not earth's aspirings,
Ceaseless longings, vain desirings;
But your precious soul's requirings
    Seek ye first.

3 Seek ye first God's peace and blessing—
Ye have all if this possessing;
Come, your need and sin confessing:
    Seek Him first.

4 Seek Him first; then, when forgiven,
Pardoned, made an heir of heaven,

Let your life to Him be given:
    Seek this first.

5 Seek this first: be pure and holy;
Like the Master, meek and lowly;
Yielded to His service wholly:
    Seek this first.

6 Seek the coming of His kingdom;
Seek the souls around to win them;
Seek to Jesus Christ to bring them:
    Seek this first.

7 Seek this first. His promise trying—
It is sure, all need supplying.
Heavenly things—on Him relying—
    Seek ye first.
        G. M. Taylor.

St. Asaph.   11.11.11.11.   A. H. MANN.

Copyright. By permission of the Composer.

491   *Who gave Himself for us.*—TITUS ii. 14.

1 How loving is Jesus who came from the sky,
In tenderest pity for sinners to die!
His hands and His feet, they were nailed to the tree,
And all this He suffered for sinners like me!

2 How gladly does Jesus free pardon impart
To all who receive Him by faith in their heart!
No evil befalls them, their home is above,
And Jesus throws round them the arms of His love.

3 How precious is Jesus to all who believe!
And out of His fulness what grace they receive!
When weak He supports them, when erring He guides,
And everything needful He kindly provides.

4 Oh, give then to Jesus your earliest days:
They only are blessèd who walk in His ways:
In life and in death He will still be your Friend,
For those whom He loves He will love to the end.

Mrs. R. H. Ballantyne.

St. Fulbert.   C.M.   H. J. GAUNTLETT.

Alternative Tune, LYNTON, *No.* 578.

492   *Now is the accepted time; behold, now is the day of salvation.*—2 COR. vi. 2.

1 O GOD, I thank Thee for Thy Word,
Which bids me choose the right;
And now I kneel before Thee, Lord,
To make my choice to-night.

2 Although of very little worth,
And stained by sin beside,
I place my life at Thy command,
For ever on Thy side.

3 Not blindly, with unthinking haste,
Or mere emotion stirred;
I choose the life with Christ in God,
And rest upon Thy Word.

4 Gladly with heart and hand and soul,
Accept Thy service free,
And find my joy and strength in this
That Thou hast chosen me.

R. Hudson Pope.

Section VII.—The Christian Life.
(6.) Pilgrimage and Conflict.

The Golden Chain.   8.7.8.7.8.8.7.   Sir J. Barnby.

By permission of Novello and Company, Limited.

493   *He is . . . my father's God, and I will exalt Him.—*Exod. xv. 2.

1 We come unto our fathers' God:
  Their Rock is our salvation:
The Eternal Arms, their dear abode,
  We make our habitation: [brought;
We bring Thee, Lord, the praise they
We seek Thee as Thy saints have sought
  In every generation.

2 The fire divine, their steps that led,
  Still goeth bright before us;
The heavenly shield, around them spread,
  Is still high holden o'er us:
The grace those sinners that subdued,
The strength those weaklings that renewed,
  Doth vanquish, doth restore us.

3 The cleaving sins that brought them low
  Are still our souls oppressing;
The tears that from their eyes did flow
  Fall fast, our shame confessing;

As with Thee, Lord, prevailed their cry,
So our strong prayer ascends on high,
  And bringeth down Thy blessing.

4 Their joy unto their Lord we bring;
  Their song to us descendeth:
The Spirit who in them did sing
  To us His music lendeth.
His song in them, in us, is one;
We raise it high, we send it on—
  The song that never endeth!

5 Ye saints to come, take up the strain,
  The same sweet theme endeavour!
Unbroken be the golden chain!
  Keep on the song for ever!
Safe in the same dear dwelling-place,
Rich with the same eternal grace,
  Bless the same boundless Giver!
                              T. H. Gill.

494 Daybreak.   8.7.8.7., with Chorus.   W. F. Sherwin.

CHORUS.

Hear the call! Oh, gird your armour on, Grasp the Spi-rit's

migh-ty sword, Take the helmet of sal-va-tion, Pressing on to bat-tle for the Lord!

494

Wherefore take unto you the whole armour of God.—EPH. vi. 13.

1 Lo! the day of God is breaking;
   See the gleaming from afar!
Sons of earth, from slumber waking,
   Hail the Bright and Morning Star!
   Hear the call, etc.

2 Trust in Him who is your Captain,
   Let no heart in terror quail;
Jesus leads the gathering legions;
   In His Name we shall prevail.

3 Onward marching, firm and steady,
   Faint not, fear not Satan's frown,
For the Lord is with you alway,
   Till you wear the victor's crown.

4 Conquering hosts with banners waving,
   Sweeping on o'er hill and plain,
Ne'er shall halt till swells the anthem,
   "Christ o'er all the world doth reign!"
                           W. F. Sherwin.

St. John's, Horton.   6.6 6.6.   E. H. G. SARGENT.

495

Ye serve the Lord Christ.—COL. iii. 24.

1 LORD, we have come to Thee
   In answer to Thy call,
And now, from sin set free,
   We gladly yield Thee all.

2 Lord, keep us strong for Thee,
   Uphold us by Thy might,
Lest we should ever grow
   Discouraged in the fight.

3 Lord, keep us unashamed
   In standing up for Thee,
Help us to bear the cross,
   And witness manfully.

4 Lord, may we serve Thee well,
   And help some other soul

To run the heavenly race,
   And with us reach the goal.

5 Lord, teach us how to pray,
   And show us what we need;
We know that Thou dost hear
   When Jesus' Name we plead.

6 Lord, may we love Thy Word,
   And read it every day;
Teach us Thy holy will,
   Then help us to obey.

7 Lord, teach us how to praise!
   May life with tongue unite
To sing Thy praise with joy,
   And serve Thee with delight.
                           E. H. G. Sargent.

Victor Divine.   P.M.   JNO. R. SWEENEY.

CHORUS.

"Not to the strong is the bat-tle, Not to the swift is the race; Yet to the true and the faith-ful Vic-t'ry is pro-mised thro' grace."

496   *The Lamb shall overcome them: for He is Lord of lords, and King of kings.*—REV. xvii. 14.

1 CONQUERING now and still to conquer,
  Rideth a King in His might,
Leading the host of all the faithful
  Into the midst of the fight:
See them with courage advancing!
  Clad in their brilliant array,
Shouting the Name of their Leader.
  Hear them exultingly say:
    "Not to the strong," etc.

2 Conquering now and still to conquer:
  Who is this wonderful King?
Whence all the armies which He leadeth,
  While of His glory they sing?

He is our Lord and Redeemer,
  Saviour and Monarch divine;
They are the stars that for ever
  Bright in His kingdom will shine.

3 Conquering now and still to conquer:
  Jesus, Thou Ruler of all,
Thrones and their sceptres all shall perish,
  Crowns and their splendour shall fall;
Yet shall the armies Thou leadest,
  Faithful and true to the last,
Find in Thy mansions eternal
  Rest, when their warfare is past.
                    S. Martin.

Pilgrims. 11.10.11.10., with Refrain. HENRY SMART.

REFRAIN.

An - gels of Je - sus, an - gels of light, Sing - ing to wel - come the pil - grims of the night.

497 *The night is far spent, the day is at hand.*—ROM. xiii. 12

1 HARK! hark, my soul; angelic songs are swelling
  O'er earth's green fields and ocean's wave-beat shore:
  How sweet the truth those blessèd strains are telling
  Of that new life when sin shall be no more!
  Angels of Jesus, angels of light, etc.

2 Onward we go, for still we hear them singing,
  "Come, weary souls, for Jesus bids you come."
  And through the dark, its echoes sweetly ringing,
  The music of the Gospel leads us home.

3 Far, far away, like bells at evening pealing,
  The voice of Jesus sounds o'er land and sea;
  And laden souls, by thousands meekly stealing,
  Kind Shepherd, turn their weary steps to Thee.

4 Rest comes at length, though life be long and dreary,
  The day must dawn, and darksome night be past;
  Faith's journey ends in welcome to the weary,
  And Heaven, the heart's true home, will come at last.

5 Angels! sing on: your faithful watches keeping,
  Sing us sweet fragments of the songs above;
  Till morning's joy shall end the night of weeping,
  And life's long shadows break in cloudless love.
                                        F. W Faber.

Yield Not to Temptation. 11.11.11.11., with Chorus.
H. R. PALMER

CHORUS.

Ask the Saviour to help you, Comfort, strengthen, and keep you; He is will-ing to aid you, He will car-ry you through.

498 *God . . . will not suffer you to be tempted above that ye are able.—*
1 COR. x. 13.

1 YIELD not to temptation, for yielding is sin;
Each victory will help you some other to win;
Fight manfully onward, dark passions subdue,
Look ever to Jesus, He'll carry you through.
    Ask the Saviour to help you, etc.

2 Shun evil companions, bad language disdain,
God's Name hold in reverence, nor take it in vain;
Be thoughtful and earnest, kind-hearted and true,
Look ever to Jesus, He'll carry you through.

3 To him that o'ercometh God giveth a crown,
Through faith we shall conquer, though often cast down;
He, who is our Saviour, our strength will renew;
Look ever to Jesus, He'll carry you through.
                                    H. R. Palmer

Vigilate.   7.7.7.3.   W. H. Monk.

499   *Watch and pray.*—Matt. xxvi. 41.

1 "Christian, seek not yet repose,"
  Hear thy gracious Saviour say;
  Thou art in the midst of foes:
  "Watch and pray."

2 Principalities and powers,
  Mustering their unseen array,
  Wait for thy unguarded hours:
  "Watch and pray."

3 Gird thy heavenly armour on,
  Wear it ever night and day;
  Ambushed lies the evil one:
  "Watch and pray."

4 Hear the victors who o'ercame,
  Still they mark each warrior's way;
  All with one sweet voice exclaim,
  "Watch and pray."

5 Hear, above all, hear thy Lord,
  Him thou lovest to obey;
  Hide within thy heart His word:
  "Watch and pray."

6 Watch, as if on that alone
  Hung the issue of the day;
  Pray, that help may be sent down:
  "Watch and pray."

Charlotte Elliott.

Day of Praise.   S.M.   C. Steggall.

500   *Wherefore take unto you the whole armour of God.*—Eph. vi. 13.

1 Arm, soldiers of the Lord!
  The fight is set with wrong;
  Take shield and breastplate, helm and sword.
  And sing your battle-song.

2 Stand fast for Love, your Lord;
  Faith be your mighty shield;
  And let the Spirit's burning sword
  Flash foremost in the field.

3 Truth be your girdle strong;
  And hope your helmet shine,
  Whene'er the battle seemeth long
  And wearied hearts repine.

4 With news of gospel peace
  Let your swift feet be shod;
  Your breastplate be the righteousness
  That keeps the soul for God.

5 And for the weary day,
  And for the slothful arm,
  For wounds, defeat, distress, dismay,
  Take prayer, the heavenly charm.

6 "From strength to strength" your cry,
  Your battlefield the world;
  Strike home, and press where Christ on high
  His banner hath unfurled.

Stopford A. Brooke.

Armageddon. 6.5.6.5., 12 lines. REICHARDT, adapted by SIR JOHN GOSS.

Alternative Tune, SUMUS TIBI, *No.* 531.

Who is on the Lord's side?—EXOD. xxxii. 26.

501

1 WHO is on the Lord's side?
　Who will serve the King?
Who will be His helper
　Other lives to bring?
Who will leave the world's side?
　Who will face the foe?
Who is on the Lord's side?
　Who for Him will go?
　　By Thy grand redemption,
　　By Thy grace divine,
　　We are on the Lord's side:
　　Saviour, we are Thine!

2 Not for weight of glory,
　Not for crown and palm,
Enter we the army,
　Raise the warrior-psalm;
But for love that claimeth
　Lives for whom He died:
He whom Jesus nameth
　Must be on His side!
　　By Thy love constraining,
　　By Thy grace divine,
　　We are on the Lord's side:
　　Saviour, we are Thine!

3 Jesus, Thou hast bought us,
　Not with gold or gem,
But with Thine own life-blood,
　For Thy diadem.
With Thy blessing filling
　All who come to Thee,

Thou hast made us willing,
　Thou hast made us free.
　　By Thy grand redemption,
　　By Thy grace divine,
　　We are on the Lord's side:
　　Saviour, we are Thine!

4 Fierce may be the conflict,
　Strong may be the foe;
But the King's own army
　None can overthrow;
Round His standard ranging,
　Victory is secure,
For His truth unchanging
　Makes the triumph sure.
　　Joyfully enlisting,
　　By Thy grace divine,
　　We are on the Lord's side:
　　Saviour, we are Thine!

5 Chosen to be soldiers
　In an alien land,
"Chosen, called, and faithful,"
　For our Captain's band,
In His service royal,
　Let us not grow cold;
Let us be right loyal,
　Noble, true, and bold.
　　Master, Thou wilt keep us,
　　By Thy grace divine,
　　Always on the Lord's side:
　　Saviour, always Thine!

Frances R. Havergal.

Be Prepared!   P.M.   R. Hudson Pope.

Be prepared, "Watch and pray That ye en-ter not in-to temp-ta - - tion."

502   *Your feet shod with the preparation of the Gospel.*—Eph. vi. 15.

1 Hark to the call that resounds from
    Be prepared!   [heaven,
Rise in the strength that in Christ is given,
    Be prepared!
    Laying every weight aside,
    Looking only to our Guide,
    Sure of the path, though all untried,
While we watch and we pray and trust in
    Be prepared, etc.   [Him,

2 When our Captain bids us follow,
    Be prepared!
Should He lead to joy or sorrow,
    Be prepared!
    Forward march with footsteps sure,
    Or if He shall say " Endure,"
    Under His command secure,
We are sure of a glorious victory.

3 When the tempter seeks to harm us,
    Be prepared!
Wiles of his need not alarm us
    If prepared.   [shield,
    Christ our strength, and Christ our
    Taught by Him the sword to wield,
    Satan cannot hold the field,
While we're strong in the might of Christ
    our Lord.

4 And for the last great heavenly roll-call
    Be prepared!
When thy King shall take His kingdom,
    Be prepared!
    Having His salvation claimed,
    And the Name of Jesus named,
    At His coming not ashamed,
We receive at His hand the crown of life.

                       R. Hudson Pope.

o

Aurelia. 7.6.7.6., D. S. S. WESLEY.

503
He is the Head of the body, the Church.—COL. i. 18.

1 THE church's one foundation
  Is Jesus Christ her Lord;
She is His new creation
  By water and the Word:
From heaven He came and sought her
  To be His holy Bride,
With His own blood He bought her,
  And for her life He died.

2 Elect from every nation,
  Yet one o'er all the earth,
Her charter of salvation
  One Lord, one faith, one birth;
One holy Name she blesses,
  Partakes one holy food,
And to one hope she presses
  With every grace endued.

3 Though with a scornful wonder
  Men see her sore opprest,
By schisms rent asunder,
  By heresies distrest;

Yet saints their watch are keeping,
  Their cry goes up, "How long?"
And soon the night of weeping
  Shall be the morn of song.

4 'Mid toil and tribulation,
  And tumult of her war,
She waits the consummation
  Of peace for evermore;
Till with the vision glorious
  Her longing eyes are blest,
And the great church victorious
  Shall be the church at rest.

5 Yet she on earth hath union
  With God the Three in One,
And mystic sweet communion
  With those whose rest is won.
Oh, happy ones and holy!
  Lord, give us grace that we
Like them, the meek and lowly,
  On high may dwell with Thee!
  S. J. Stone.

504 All Things through Christ. P.M.
R. HUDSON POPE.

504   *I can do all things through Christ, which strengtheneth me.*—PHIL. iv. 13.

1 SOLDIER, soldier, fighting in the world's
      great strife,
On thyself relying, battling for thy life;
    Trust thyself no longer,
    Trust to Christ—He's stronger:
"I can all things, all things do
Through Christ, which strengtheneth me."

2 In your daily duty, standing up for right,
Are you sometimes weary—heart not always
    Doubt your Saviour never,   [light?
    This your motto ever:
"I can all things, all things do
Through Christ, which strengtheneth me."

3 If your way be weary He will help you
      through—   [too:
Help you in your troubles and your pleasures

     Say, when Satan's by you;
     Say, when all things try you:
"I can all things, all things do
Through Christ, which strengtheneth me."

4 In a world of trouble, tempted oft to stray,
You need never stumble; Satan cannot
    Will but tempt you vainly,   [stay—
    If you tell him plainly
"I can all things, all things do
Through Christ, which strengtheneth me."

5 Jesus' power is boundless—boundless as the
He is always able, able to keep me—   [sea;
    Power bring from my weakness,
    Glory from my meekness:
"I can all things, all things do
Through Christ, which strengtheneth me."

                         R. Hudson Pope.

Cloisters.   11.11.11.5.   Sir J. BARNBY.

505   *I also will keep thee from the hour of temptation, which shall come upon*
                    all the world.—REV. iii. 10.

1 LORD of our life, and God of our salvation,
Star of our night, and Hope of every nation,
Hear and receive Thy church's supplication,
     Lord God Almighty!

2 Lord, Thou canst help when earthly armour
      faileth,   [assaileth,
Lord, Thou canst save when sin itself
Lord, o'er Thy church nor death nor hell
      prevaileth;
     Grant us Thy peace, Lord.

3 Peace in our hearts our evil thoughts
      assuaging,   [engaging,
Peace in Thy church where brothers are
Peace when the world its busy war is waging,
     Calm Thy foes raging.

4 Grant us Thy help till backward they are
      driven,   [forgiven,
Grant them Thy truth, that they may be
Grant peace on earth, and after we have
     Peace in Thy heaven.   [striven,

              M. A. Lowenstern and P. Pusey.

Stand up for Jesus.   7.6.7.6., D.   ADAM GEIBEL.

UNISON.

Stand up   for Je - sus! Ye sol-diers of the   cross; . . Lift
Stand up, stand up for Je - sus!

high His roy-al ban-ner, It must not,   it must not   suf-fer ..   loss.

Alternative Tune, NEW YORK, No. 517.
Stand fast in the faith.—1 COR. xvi. 13.

506

1 STAND up! stand up for Jesus!
    Ye soldiers of the cross;
Lift high His royal banner,
    It must not suffer loss:
From victory unto victory
    His army shall He lead,
Till every foe is vanquished,
    And Christ is Lord indeed.

2 Stand up! stand up for Jesus!
    The trumpet call obey;
Forth to the mighty conflict
    In this His glorious day!
Ye that are men, now serve Him
    Against unnumbered foes;
Let courage rise with danger,
    And strength to strength oppose.

3 Stand up! stand up for Jesus!
    Stand in His strength alone;
The arm of flesh will fail you;
    Ye dare not trust your own.
Put on the Gospel armour,
    And, watching unto prayer,
Where duty calls, or danger,
    Be never wanting there.

4 Stand up! stand up for Jesus!
    The strife will not be long;
This day the noise of battle—
    The next the victor's song;
To him that overcometh
    A crown of life shall be;
He, with the King of glory,
    Shall reign eternally.

G. Duffield.

Only an Armour=Bearer. P.M.

P. P. BLISS.

CHORUS.

Hear ye the battle cry, "Forward!" the call, See, see the falt'ring ones, backward they fall:

Repeat.

1.   2.

Surely my Captain may depend on me, Tho' but an armour-bearer I may be.   I may be.

507 *His armour-bearer said unto him, Do all that is in thine heart: turn thee;*
behold, I am with thee according to thy heart.—1 SAM. xiv. 7.

1 ONLY an armour-bearer, firmly I stand,
    Waiting to follow at the King's command;
    Marching if "onward" shall the order be;
    Standing by my Captain, serving faithfully.
      Hear ye the battle-cry, etc.

2 Only an armour-bearer, now in the field,
    Guarding a shining helmet, sword, and shield;
    Waiting to hear the thrilling battle-cry,
    Ready then to answer, "Master, here am I."

3 Only an armour-bearer, yet may I share
    Glory immortal, and a bright crown wear;
    If in the battle to my trust I'm true,
    Mine shall be the honours in the Grand Review.

P. P. Bliss.

Sunningdale. P.M. NORMAN BENNET.
Har. by A. T. GEORGE.

Brisk march time.

CHORUS.

Then forward all, for the Captain's nigh Then fight full well, For He stands hard by, With a vic-tor's crown.

508 *Be strong and of good courage.—JOSHUA i. 9.*

1 WE are soldiers every one,
   And the fight is just begun;
And the Captain ever stands hard by,
   For He sees our every need,
   And our inmost thoughts doth read,
      As we Satan's host defy.
         Then forward all, etc.

2 When the foes are thick around,
   And we try to stand our ground,
And each heart is ever beating high;
   Then the soldiers of the Lord
   Use the Spirit's mighty sword,
      And assure the victory.

3 When our sins about us lower,
   And we feel their mighty power,
When our hearts are nearly faint with fear,
   Then we look to Him above,
   Whom we honour and we love,
      And He says, "Be of good cheer."

4 When the battle-clouds are past
   And we find our home at last,
Then the joy of every heart shall be.
   The song of living praise,
   To the Father of all days,
      That shall sound from sea to sea.
         Norman Bennet.

509 St. Helier. L.M., with Chorus. ASA HULL.

CHORUS.

Stand up for Jesus, nobly stand! Firm as a rock on o-cean's

strand! Stand up, His right-eous cause de-fend; Stand up for Je-sus, your best Friend.

Alternative Tune, MAINZER, No. 60.

509
Stand fast in the Lord.—PHIL. iv. 1.

1 STAND up for Jesus, Christian, stand!
Firm as a rock on ocean's strand!
Beat back the waves of sin that roll
Like raging floods around thy soul!
    Stand up for Jesus, nobly stand! etc.

2 Stand up for Jesus, Christian, stand!
Sound forth His Name o'er sea and land!
Spread ye His glorious Word abroad,
Till all the world shall own Him Lord!

3 Stand up for Jesus, Christian, stand!
Lift high the cross with steadfast hand!
Till heathen lands, with wondering eye,
Its rising glory shall descry.

4 Stand up for Jesus, Christian, stand!
Soon with the blest, immortal band
We'll dwell for aye, life's journey o'er,
In realms of light on heaven's bright shore
                        Anon.

Dare to be a Daniel!   P.M.   P. P. BLISS.

CHORUS.

Dare to be a Dan-iel! Dare to stand a-lone! Dare to have a pur-pose firm! Dare to make it known.

510
But Daniel purposed in his heart that he would not defile himself with the portion of the king's meat, nor with the wine which he drank.—DAN. i. 8.

1 STANDING by a purpose true,
  Heeding God's command,
Honour them, the faithful few!
  All hail to Daniel's band!
    Dare to be a Daniel! etc.

2 Many mighty men are lost,
  Daring not to stand,
Who for God had been a host
  By joining Daniel's band.

3 Many giants, great and tall,
  Stalking through the land,
Headlong to the earth would fall,
  If met by Daniel's band.

4 Hold the Gospel banner high!
  On to victory grand!
Satan and his host defy,
  And shout for Daniel's band!
               P. P. Bliss.

Valour.
UNISON.

P.M.

E. H. G. SARGENT.

Be strong in the Lord, ye sol - diers, Be strong in His pow'r and might; Gird on you His per-fect ar - mour—Be strong, be strong and fight!

511   *Be strong in the Lord.*—EPH. vi. 10.

1 BE strong in the Lord, ye soldiers,
    Be strong in His power and might;
Gird on you His perfect armour,
    And stand up for truth and right.
His armour will never fail you,
    Victorious you shall be
'Gainst all the wiles of Satan,
    From sin's dominion free.
        Be strong in the Lord. etc.

2 The hosts of Satan's army
    Are ranged against the Lord,
And, while we're standing idle,
    Make havoc with the sword.
Come, join the King's own army,
    And fight for all that's true,
The voice of sin resisting,
    Through Christ, who strengtheneth you.

3 Not human foes we're fighting,
  But evil powers of sin,
'Gainst rulers of this world's darkness,
  Around us and within.
Then take Salvation's helmet,
  Hold fast the shield of Faith,
And, trusting Him who gave it,
  Be faithful unto death.

The Captain of our salvation
  Is standing ever near;
Take courage, then, ye soldiers,
  What cause have ye to fear?
Though Satan's host should number
  A thousand 'gainst a score,
Count Christ your heavenly Captain,
  For thrice ten thousand more.

E. H. G. Sargent.

Vigil. P.M. A. PATTON.

512 *What I say unto you, I say unto all, Watch !*—MARK xiii. 37.

1 HARK, 'tis the watchman's cry,
  "Wake, brethren, wake!"
Jesus, our Lord, is nigh,
  Wake, brethren, wake!
Sleep is for sons of night,
Ye are children of the light,
Yours is the glory bright:
  Wake, brethren, wake!

2 Call to each waking band,
  "Watch, brethren, watch!"
Clear is our Lord's command,
  Watch, brethren, watch!
Be ye as men that wait
Ready at their Master's gate,
E'en though He tarry late:
  Watch, brethren, watch!

3 Heed we the steward's call,
  "Work, brethren, work!"
There's room enough for all,
  Work, brethren, work!
This vineyard of our Lord
Constant labour will afford;
Yours is a sure reward:
  Work, brethren, work!

4 Hear we the Shepherd's voice,
  "Pray, brethren, pray!"
Would ye His heart rejoice,
  Pray, brethren, pray!
Sin calls for constant fear,
Weakness needs the strong One near:
Long as ye tarry here,
  Pray, brethren, pray!

5 Now sound the final chord,
  "Praise, brethren, praise!"
Thrice holy is the Lord,
  Praise, brethren, praise!
What more befits the tongues,
Soon to lead the angels' songs,
While heaven the note prolongs?
  Praise, brethren, praise!

Anon., in The Revival.

o*

Dresden.   7.6.7.6., D., with Refrain.   J. A. P. Schultze.

REFRAIN.

Marching to the con-flict

In heav'n-ly armour clad, We're singing as we're marching, For Je-sus makes us glad.

513

Quit you like men, be strong.—1 Cor. xvi. 13.

1 WE'RE marching to the conflict
    In heavenly armour clad,
We're singing as we're marching,
    For Jesus makes us glad:
We know we shall be victors
    When ends this mortal strife,
For Jesus leads His army,
    The "Children of the Light."
      Marching to the conflict, etc.

2 We're marching to the conflict,
    And guarding every part:
The shield of Faith is turned to stay
    And quench each fiery dart;
Stronger than bands of iron,
    Truth girds us for the strife;
King Jesus is the Way, the Truth,
    And our eternal Life.

3 We're marching to the conflict,
    And, till the tumult cease,
Our feet are always carrying
    Sweet messages of Peace
To those who, faint and weary,
    Steel their proud hearts no more,
But wide to Christ, their Saviour-King,
    Open the long-closed door.

4 Bright on each head there glitters
    Salvation for a crest,
Earnest to every warrior child
    Of God's eternal rest:
Each heart is safely shelter'd
    'Neath Christ's own Righteousness,
More lasting covering by far
    Than our poor soiled dress.

5 We're marching to the conflict,
    Grasping our two-edged sword,
Which never yet returnèd void
    For 'tis God's holy Word:
Its point is sharp for ever,
    Both hilt and blade are proof,
For forged it was by God's own hand,
    His blessèd Word of truth.

6 We're marching on to conquest,
    And soon we all shall stand,
Waving the palm of victory,
    On heaven's golden strand;
Blessing the day when Jesus' voice
    Called us from shades of night
To join His victor army,
    The "Children of the Light."
               G. Banaster.

Soldiers of the Master. P.M. H. ERNEST NICHOL.

CHORUS. UNISON.

Soldiers of the Master, onward tread, Telling out the grand old

HARMONY.

sto-ry! Rea-dy day by day Jesus to o-bey, Soldiers of the King of Glo-ry.

Words and Music Copyright of the National Sunday School Union.

514

A good soldier of Jesus Christ.—2 TIM. ii. 3.

1.

WHERE the flag is flying, where the fight is
  Where the trumpet-call is ringing, [keen,
There you find the soldiers, steady and serene,
  There you hear the sound of singing:
Servants of the Master, scorning fear or
  flight, [Light!
  Fighting for the Truth, the Life, the
    Soldiers of the Master, etc.

2.

Where the darkness reigneth, where the
  power of sin,
Binds the heart of man in sadness, [win,
There you find the soldiers, waiting souls to
  Bringing them to light and gladness.
Servants of the Master, strong in love and
  might, [Light!
  Fighting for the Truth, the Life, the

3.

Where the doubts are thickest, where the
  strength of youth
Falls beneath the chains of error, [truth,
There you find the soldiers, with the lamp of
  Freeing men from thoughts of terror.
Servants of the Master, strong in faith and
  sight, [Light!
  Fighting for the Truth, the Life, the

4.

Where from angel chorus through the heavenly
  Rings a song of triumph splendid, [dome,
There you find the soldiers entering their
  By the heavenly hosts attended. [home,
Servants of the Master, clad in spotless
  white,
  One with Him in Truth, in Life, in Light!
                                    Colin Sterne.

Jesus—Author and Finisher. 6.5.6.5., D., with Chorus.

A. F. GIBSON and M. W.

Looking un-to Je-sus,

Pa-tient-ly we run; Trusting Thee to fin-ish What Thou hast be-gun.

Alternative Tune, ST. GERTRUDE, No. 525.

515 *Looking unto Jesus, the Author and Finisher of our faith.—HEB. xii. 2.*

1 JESUS, Prince and Saviour,
　　As we look to Thee:
Thou of faith the Author,
　　Finisher wilt be.
Every weight and hindrance,
　　Each besetting sin,
Lay we gladly from us,
　　In the race to win.
　　　　Looking unto Jesus, etc.

2 Thou, with joy before Thee,
　　Didst endure the cross,
All the shame despising,
　　Counting not the loss.

From the grave triumphant,
　　Victor Thou didst stand,
Now in grace art seated,
　　At Thy God's right hand.

3 Give us grace, dear Saviour,
　　To consider Thee,
Lest we faint in battle,
　　Lest we weary be.
So that, sin resisting,
　　Striving unto blood.
We, too, may be victors,
　　Through Thy dying love.
　　　　　　Geo. Goodman.

516 Patient to Bear.　　　P.M.

A. F. MORDAUNT SMITH.

CHORUS.

Deep in the heart let Je-sus a-bide,

rall.

Lifting the soul to song; Safe in His love what-ev-er be-tide, Quit you like men—be strong!

516

Run with patience the race.—HEB. xii. 1.

1 PATIENT to bear;
   Ready to dare,
Ever against the wrong;
   Trusting the Lord;
   Waiting His word;
Serving with joyful song.
   Deep in the heart, etc.

2 Fearing no foe,
   Forward still go,
Bearing His banner high;

Through praise or blame,
Strong in His Name,
Daring to do, or die!

3 Dark though the day,
   Rough though the way,
Trust, and be ever brave;
   Light He will send,
   Ways He will mend—
Mighty His arm to save.

Alec Rae.

New York.   7.6.7.6., D.   'S'   G. J. WEBB.

1. Ashamed to be a Christian! Afraid the world should know   I'm on the way to Zi-on,

D.S.—For-bid it, O my Sa-viour,

FINE.   D.S.

Where joys e-ter-nal flow!   A-fraid to wear Thy co-lours, Or blush to follow   Thee!

That I should ev-er be.

517   *Be not thou therefore ashamed of the testimony of our Lord.*—2 TIM. i. 8.

2 Ashamed to be a Christian!
   To love my God and King!
The fire of zeal is burning,
   My soul is on the wing:
I want a faith made perfect,
   That all the world may see
I stand a living witness
   Of mercy rich and free.

3 Ashamed to be a Christian!
   My guilty fear, depart!
I will not heed the tempter
   That whispers to my heart.
Dear Saviour, though unworthy,
   Yet this my only plea—
Thy all-atoning merit:
   For Thou hast died for me.   *Anon.*

Count Your Blessings.

P.M.

E. O. Excell.

CHORUS.

Count your blessings, name them one by one, Count your
Count your ma-ny bless-ings, name them one by one, Count your ma-ny

bless-ings, see what God hath done; Count your bless-ings,
bless-ings, see what God hath done; Count your ma-ny bless-ings,

name them one by one, And it will sur-prise you what the Lord hath done.

518 *Blessed be God . . . who hath blessed us with all spiritual blessings.*—Eph. i. 3.

1 When upon life's billows you are tempest-
tost, [lost,
When you are discouraged, thinking all is
Count your many blessings, name them
one by one, [hath done.
And it will surprise you what the Lord
Count . . . your blessings, etc.

2 Are you ever burdened with a load of care?
Does the cross seem heavy you are called
to bear? [will fly,
Count your many blessings, every doubt
And you will be singing as the days go by.

3 When you look at others with their lands
and gold, [wealth untold;
Think that Christ has promised you His
Count your many blessings; wealth can
never buy [high.
Your reward in heaven, nor your home on

4 So, amid the conflict, whether great or small,
Do not be discouraged, God is over all;
Count your many blessings, angels will
attend, [end.
Help and comfort give you to your journey's
J. Oatman, Jun.

From "Salvation Army Music."

Volunteers. P.M.

1. Oh, we are vol-unteers in the ar-my of the Lord, Forming in-to line at our
under marching or-ders to take the battle-field,

Captain's word; We are And we'll ne'er give o'er the fight till the foe shall yield.

Chorus.

Come and join the ar-my, the ar-my of the Lord; Je-sus is our

Cap-tain; we ral-ly at His word; Sharp will be the con-flict

with the pow'rs of sin, But with such a Lead-er we are sure to win.

519 *For we wrestle not against flesh and blood, but against principalities, against*
powers, . . . against spiritual wickedness in high places.—Eph. vi. 12.

2 The glory of our flag is the emblem of the
   dove,   [love;
Gleaming are our swords from the forge of
We go forth, but not to battle for earthly
   honours vain;   [to gain.
'Tis a bright immortal crown that we seek

3 Our foes are in the field, pressing hard on
   every side:
Envy, anger, hatred, with self and pride;

They are cruel, fierce, and strong, ever ready
   to attack: [drive them back.
We must watch, and fight, and pray, if we'd

4 Oh, glorious is the struggle in which we
   draw the sword!
Glorious is the kingdom of Christ our Lord!
It shall spread from sea to sea, it shall reach
   from shore to shore,   [more.
And His people shall be blessèd for ever.
Anon.

Cheltenham.　　11.11.11.11., with Chorus.　　Arr. by LIVESEY CARROTT.

CHORUS.

Press for-ward, look up-ward, be strong in the Lord, Our hope in His mer-cy, our trust in His Word; Press for-ward, look up-ward, march homeward and sing, "All glo-ry to Je-sus, to Je-sus our King."

520　*I press toward the mark for the prize of the high calling of God in Christ Jesus.*—PHIL. iii. 14.

1 MARCH onward, march onward! our banner of light
Is waving before us majestic and bright;
March onward through trial, temptation, and strife,
No rest from the conflict—the battle of life.
　　Press forward, look upward, etc.

2 March onward, undaunted, whate'er may oppose;　　　　[foes;
The sword of the Spirit will vanquish our
Though legions of darkness our pathway assail,　　　　[prevail.
If prayer be our watchword, they cannot

3 The shaft of the tempter will strike, but in vain,
Our buckler of faith in Immanuel's Name;
The storm-cloud may gather, the thunder may roll,
Yet God is the Refuge and Rock of the soul.

4 March onward, oh, vision of rapture untold!
The victors for Jesus ere long shall behold
The land of our promise, the home of our rest,
And dwell with our Captain eternally blest.
　　　　　　　　　　　　　　　Anon.

Harrogate. P.M. R. HUDSON POPE.

CHORUS.

Thro' Jesus Christ, the

cres. *rall.*

same yes-ter-day, and to-day, and for ev-er and ev-er.

521 *Jesus Christ the same yesterday, and to-day, and for ever.*—HEB. xiii. 8.

1 O GOD, by whose almighty grace
Unworthy sinners have a place
 In Christ, our Saviour-King,
Whose life hath brought us from the dead,
Whose power hath safely kept and led,
 Thy praise we sing!
Oh, guard our hearts and tune our song,
And give us victory all along!
 Through Jesus Christ, the same, etc.

2 To Thy great Word, the Word of truth,
Oh, help us to take heed in youth,
 And by it cleanse our way!
And as we walk this sin-stained shore,
Oh, let our path shine more and more
 To perfect day!
Oh, light the way and guide our feet
Until the journey be complete!

3 From selfishness our hearts defend;
And, since we know Thee as our Friend,
 Some others may we bring.
Our work and witness richly bless,
And help us boldly to confess
 Our Lord and King!
Teach us Thy great salvation's plan,
And guard us from the fear of man:

4 Teach us to look to Christ alone,
To trust His strength, and not our own,
 And thus to conquer sin;
To live the life that God hath planned,
And take the victory from His hand,
 And so to win!
Our hearts, our all, we yield to Thee,
That more than conquerors we may be.
     R. Hudson Pope.

Monks Gate.   6.5.6.5.6.6.6.5.   Adapted from an English Traditional Melody.
Brightly.

Hymn and Tune from *The English Hymnal.* By permission of the Oxford University Press.

They that say such things declare plainly that they seek a country.—
HEB. xi. 14.

522

1 HE who would valiant be
  'Gainst all disaster,
Let him in constancy
  Follow the Master.
There's no discouragement
Shall make him once relent
His first avowed intent
  To be a pilgrim.

2 Who so beset him round
  With dismal stories,
Do but themselves confound—
  His strength the more is.
No foes shall stay his might,
Though he with giants fight:
He will make good his right
  To be a pilgrim.

3 Since, Lord, thou dost defend
  Us with Thy Spirit,
We know we at the end
  Shall life inherit.
Then fancies flee away!
I'll fear not what men say,
I'll labour night and day
  To be a pilgrim.

J. Bunyan (altd.).

523 Crusader Hymn.   P.M.   R. HUDSON POPE.
UNISON.

Alternative Tune, St. Philip, *No. 568.*

523   *More than conquerors through Him that loved us.*—Rom. viii. 37.

1 O God and Saviour of the sons of men,
  We, Thy crusaders, would Thy love ac-
    claim;   [Thy Name,
  In our fresh manhood make us, through
    More than conquerors, more than con-
    querors.

2 The battle rages cruel, fierce, and long;
  We hold no parley with the powers of
    wrong;   [strong,
  In Christ, our Saviour, stronger than the
    More than conquerors, more than con-
    querors.

3 Help us, Lord Jesus, in the hour of strife;
  Cover our heads in battle, guard our life;
  Lest we should lose our crown, the victor's
    prize—   [querors.
    More than conquerors, more than con-

4 Bright in the east behold the Morning
    Star,
  The Saviour coming in the clouds afar;
  Soon is the triumph, soon the end of war,
    More than conquerors, more than con-
    querors.

     5 Jesus, we hail Thee, Lord of earth and heaven,
      For Thou wast slain, and from the grave art risen;
        To Thee the glory and the power be given,
          Thou, more than Conqueror, more than Conqueror.
                              Geo. Goodman.

St. Ethelwald.   **S.M.**   **W. H. Monk.**

Alternative Tune, St. Michael, *No. 394.*

524   *Put on the whole armour of God, that ye may be able to stand against the*
                              wiles of the devil.—Eph. vi. 11.

1 Soldiers of Christ, arise,
    And put your armour on,
  Strong in the strength which God supplies
    Through His eternal Son:

2 Strong in the Lord of hosts,
    And in His mighty power;
  Who in the strength of Jesus trusts
    Is more than conqueror.

3 Stand then in His great might,
    With all His strength endued;
  And take, to arm you for the fight,
    The panoply of God.

4 From strength to strength go on,
    Wrestle, and fight, and pray;
  Tread all the powers of darkness down,
    And win the well-fought day:

     5 That, having all things done,
       And all your conflicts past,
     Ye may o'ercome through Christ alone,
       And stand complete at last.   *C. Wesley.*

St. Gertrude. [FIRST TUNE.] 6.5.6.5., D., with Refrain. Sir ARTHUR S. SULLIVAN.

REFRAIN.

Onward, Christian sol - diers,

Marching as to war, Looking un - to Je - sus, Who is gone be - fore.

By permission of Novello and Company, Limited.

525 *Be strong and of a good courage: . . . for the Lord thy God, He it is that doth go with thee.*—DEUT. xxxi. 6.

1 ONWARD, Christian soldiers,
    Marching as to war,
Looking unto Jesus,
    Who is gone before:
Christ, the royal Master,
    Leads against the foe;
Forward into battle,
    See, His banners go.
        Onward, Christian soldiers, etc.

2 At the Name of Jesus,
    Satan's host doth flee;
On then, Christian soldiers,
    On to victory!
Hell's foundations quiver
    At the shout of praise:
Brothers, lift your voices:
    Loud your anthems raise.

525 Geibel. [SECOND TUNE.]

UNISON.   6.5.6.5., D., with Refrain.   ADAM GEIBEL.

REFRAIN. HARMONY.

On - ward, Christian soldiers,

Onward, onward, Christian

Marching as to war, . . . Looking un-to Je - sus, Who is gone be-fore.

3 Like a mighty army,
   Moves the church of God :
Brothers, we are treading
   Where the saints have trod :
We are not divided,
   All one body we,
One in hope and doctrine,
   One in charity.

4 Crowns and thrones may perish,
   Kingdoms rise and wane ;
But the church of Jesus
   Constant will remain :
Gates of hell can never
   'Gainst that church prevail ;
We have Christ's own promise,
   And that cannot fail.

5 Onward, then, ye people,
   Join our happy throng ;
Blend with ours your voices
   In the triumph-song ;
Glory, praise, and honour,
   Unto Christ the King ;
This through countless ages
   Men and angels sing.

               S. Baring-Gould.

Radiancy.   P.M.   CHAS. H. GABRIEL.

CHORUS.

Let the blessed sunshine in, . .   Let the blessed sunshine in : . .
the sun-shine in,   the sunshine in :

Clear the dark-ened win-dows, o - pen wide the door, Let the blessed sunshine in.

526   *Light is sweet, and a pleasant thing it is . . . to behold the sun.*—ECCLES. xi. 7.

1 Do you fear the foe will in the conflict win?
Is it dark without you—darker still within?
Clear the darkened windows, open wide the door,
   Let the blessèd sunshine in.
     Let the blessèd sunshine in, etc.

2 Does your faith grow fainter in the cause you love?
Are your prayers unanswered from the throne above?
Clear the darkened windows, open wide the door,
   Let the blessèd sunshine in.

3 Would you go rejoicing on the upward way,
Knowing naught of darkness—dwelling in the day?
Clear the darkened windows, open wide the door,
   Let the blessèd sunshine in.

                   Ada Blenkhorn.

Sound the Battle Cry!

Vigorously.

P.M.

W. F. SHERWIN.

CHORUS.

Rouse then, soldiers! Ral-ly round the banner! Ready, steady, Pass the word along;

Onward! forward! Shout a-loud Hosan-na! Christ is Captain Of the mighty throng!

527 *Be thou faithful unto death, and I will give thee a crown of life.*—REV. ii. 10.

1 SOUND the battle-cry,
　See! the foe is nigh;
　Raise the standard high
　　For the Lord!
Gird your armour on,
Stand firm every one,
Rest your cause upon
　His holy Word!
　　Rouse then, soldiers, etc.

2 Strong to meet the foe,
　Marching on we go,
　While our cause we know
　　Must prevail;
Shield and banner bright
Gleaming in the light,
Battling for the right,
　We ne'er can fail!

3 O Thou God of all,
　Hear us when we call!
　Help us, one and all,
　　By Thy grace:
When the battle's done,
And the victory won,
May we wear the crown
　Before Thy face!

W. F. Sherwin.

Gleaming. 6.5.6.5., D., with Chorus. J. HARDY.

CHORUS.

Gleaming in the sunshine, Floating in the air, See the banner waving, Beautiful and fair.

Gleaming in the sunshine, Floating in the air, See the banner waving, Beautiful and fair.

528 *Thou hast given a banner to them that fear Thee, that it may be displayed.*—PSALM lx. 4.

1 GLEAMING in the sunshine,
    Floating in the air,
See the banner waving,
    Beautiful and fair:
In the Saviour's army
    It shall lead us on,
Till the battle's over,
    Till the victory's won.
       Gleaming in the sunshine, etc.

2 Jesus is our Captain,
    Jesus is our King; ·
Joyfully for Jesus
    We will fight and sing:

He supplies our armour—
    Truth and faith and love;
He will bring us safely
    To our home above.

3 In the Saviour's army,
    Ripe for heaven, are seen
Those who bore the banner
    When the strife was keen:
Men and maidens gather,
    In the flush of youth,
Round the blessèd standard,
    Round the flag of truth.

4 And the smiling faces
    And the beaming eyes
Of the little children
    He will not despise;
Thousands in His army
    Mighty deeds have done:
With the love of Jesus
    They have fought and won.

5 "Come, ye heavy-laden"—
    'Tis the Saviour's voice:
Hear His invitation,
    Make Him now your choice!
Join His glorious army,
    Join without delay;
'List beneath His banner,
    While it is to-day.

                    J. Hardy.

Merleswood Melody.   P.M.   R. Hudson Pope.

529   *Flee also youthful lusts: follow righteousness.*—2 Tim. ii. 22.

1 WE praise Thee, Lord, whose wondrous
    Has turned our wandering feet, [grace
And led us into heavenly ways
    That we Thy Son should meet.
And now we tread the narrow road
    We long to do the right, Lord;
And pray for strength, as men of God,
    To *Flee* and *Follow* and *Fight*, Lord.

2 We'll *flee* from each unholy thing,
    From every evil thought,
From passion's snare, from worldly care,
    From pride, with folly fraught;
And as, awakened by Thy call,
    We fled from wrath to Thee, Lord,
So help us still, from all things ill,
    As men of God, to *flee*, Lord.

3 We'll *follow* on to know the Lord,
    We'll keep along His track;
Forgetting all that lies behind,
    We'll never once look back!
The way grows brighter on before,
    We hope Thy day to see, Lord;
So let us gird our loins the more,
    And gladly follow Thee, Lord.

4 We'll *fight!* for there is many a foe
    From whom we may not run;
As Israel fought with Amalek,
    So fighting must be done!
The fight of Faith our fight shall be,
    Till faith shall end in sight, Lord;
As men of God we'll live for Thee,
    And *Flee* and *Follow* and *Fight*, Lord!
                    M. Goodman.

True-hearted. 11.10.11.10., with Chorus. JOSIAH BOOTH.

CHORUS.

Peal out the watchword, and si-lence it nev - er, Song of our spi-rits, re - joic-ing and free :

"True-hearted, whole-hearted, now and for ev - er, King of our lives, by Thy grace we will be !"

530

Called, and chosen, and faithful.—REV. xvii. 14.

1 TRUE-HEARTED, whole-hearted! faithful and loyal,
   King of our lives, by Thy grace we will be!
Under Thy standard, exalted and royal,
   Strong in Thy strength we will battle for Thee!
   Peal out the watch-word, etc.

2 True-hearted, whole-hearted! fullest allegiance
   Yielding henceforth to our glorious King!
Valiant endeavour and loving obedience
   Freely and joyously now would we bring.

3 True-hearted! Saviour, Thou knowest our story,
   Weak are the hearts that we lay at Thy feet;
Sinful and treacherous! yet, for Thy glory,
   Heal them and cleanse them from sin and deceit.

4 True-hearted, whole-hearted! Saviour, all-glorious,
   Take Thy great power and reign Thou alone,
Over our wills and affections victorious—
   Freely surrendered and wholly Thine own.

Frances R. Havergal.

Sumus Tibi.   6.5.6.5., 12 lines.   H. Elliot Button.

By permission of Novello and Company, Limited.

Alternative Tunes, St. Gertrude, *No.* 525, *and* Armageddon, *No.* 501.

Speak unto the children of Israel, that they go forward.—Exod. xiv. 15.

531

1 Forward be our watchword,
  Steps and voices joined;
Seek the things before us,
  Not a look behind:
Burns the fiery pillar
  At our army's head;
Who shall dream of shrinking,
  By our Captain led?
    Forward through the desert,
      Through the toil and fight;
    Canaan lies before us,
      Zion beams with light

2 Forward, when in childhood
  Buds the infant mind;
All through youth and manhood
  Not a thought behind:
Speed through realms of nature,
  Climb the steps of grace,
Faint not, till in glory
  Gleams our Father's face.
    Forward, all the lifetime,
      Climb from height to height,
    Till the head be hoary,
      Till the eve be light.

3 Glories upon glories
  Hath our God prepared,
By the souls that love Him
  One day to be shared:
Eye hath not beheld them,
  Ear hath never heard,
Nor of these hath uttered
  Thought or speech a word.
    Forward, ever forward,
      Clad in armour bright,
    Till the veil be lifted,
      Till our faith be sight.

4 Far o'er yon horizon
  Rise the city towers,
Where our God abideth,
  That fair home is ours:
Flash the streets with jasper,
  Shine the gates with gold,
Flows the gladdening river,
  Shedding joys untold.
    Thither, onward thither,
      In the Spirit's might;
    Pilgrims, to your country,
      Forward into light! *H. Alford.*

The Fall of Jericho. P.M. J. MOUNTAIN.
Bold and martial.

By permission. From Sankey's *Sacred Songs and Solos.*

532 *It came to pass, when the people heard the sound of the trumpet, and the people shouted with a great shout, that the wall fell down flat.*—JOSHUA vi. 20.

1 THE walls of Jericho were strong;
    But stronger was the mighty Lord:
And He—the Captain of God's host—
    Had given them His faithful word,
That if they would the walls surround,
    And would the trumpets blow;
He then would give them victory,
    And overthrow their foe.

2 The gates of Jericho were strong—
    They could not any stronger be:
But there was One who them defied—
    And with the host of God was He
No work for Him would be too great,
    Too hard to undertake;
For He could burst the gates of brass,
    The bars of iron break.

3 And we, O Lord, are waging war
    Against the mighty hosts of sin:
And neither skill nor strength have we,
    So oft have we defeated been.
But if Thou wilt our Captain be,
    Our weakened ranks command,
Then led by Thee we'll face the foe,
    His fierce assaults withstand.

4 Strong Son of God! we need more faith
    In Thine almighty power to save:
Oh, hear the prayer of contrite hearts,
    As we Thy keeping grace would crave;
Help us to trust in Thee alone,
    To save us every day;
Oh, make us, in the rest of faith,
    Triumphant all the way!

                    J. Mountain.

The Banner of the Cross. P.M. J. McGranahan.

CHORUS.

Marching on! . . Marching on! . . For Christ count ev'rything but loss ; . .

Marching on! on! on! Marching on! on! on! For Christ count ev'rything, ev'rything but loss;

And to crown Him King, toil and sing, 'Neath the ban-ner of the cross!

And to crown Him King, we'll toil and sing, Be-neath the ban-ner of the cross!

Words and Music by permission of Mrs. H. C. Dixon.

533

*Thou hast given a banner to them that fear Thee.—*PSALM lx. 4.

1 THERE'S a royal banner given for display
   To the soldiers of the King;
   As an ensign fair we lift it up to-day,
   While as ransomed ones we sing.
       Marching on, etc.

2 Though the foe may rage and gather as the flood,
   Let the standard be displayed!
   And beneath its folds, as soldiers of the Lord,
   For the truth be not dismayed!

3 Over land and sea, wherever man may dwell,
   Make the glorious tidings known;
   Of the crimson banner now the story tell,
   While the Lord shall claim His own!

4 When the glory dawns—'tis drawing very near;
   It is hastening day by day—
   Then before our King the foe shall disappear,
   And the cross the world shall sway!
                                   El Nathan.

534 Chalvey. [FIRST TUNE.] S.M.D. L. G. HAYNE.

Leominster. [SECOND TUNE.] S.M.D. G. W. MARTIN.

534

When a few years are come, then I shall go the way whence I shall not return.—Job xvi. 22.

1 A FEW more years shall roll,
  A few more seasons come,
And we shall be with those that rest
  Asleep within the tomb.
Then, O my Lord, prepare
  My soul for that great day ;
Oh, wash me in Thy precious blood,
  And take my sins away.

2 A few more suns shall set
  O'er these dark hills of time,
And we shall be where suns are not—
  A far serener clime.
Then, O my Lord, prepare
  My soul for that bright day ;
Oh, wash me in Thy precious blood,
  And take my sins away.

3 A few more storms shall beat
  On this wild rocky shore,
And we shall be where tempests cease,
  And surges swell no more.

Then, O my Lord, prepare
  My soul for that calm day ;
Oh, wash me in Thy precious blood,
  And take my sins away.

4 A few more struggles here,
  A few more partings o'er,
A few more toils, a few more tears,
  And we shall weep no more.
Then, O my Lord, prepare
  My soul for that blest day ;
Oh, wash me in Thy precious blood,
  And take my sins away.

5 'Tis but a little while
  And He shall come again,
Who died that we might live—who lives
  That we with Him may reign :
Then, O my Lord, prepare
  My soul for that glad day ;
Oh, wash me in Thy precious blood,
  And take my sins away.

H. Bonar.

Barton. · 7.6.7.6. · J. H. KNECHT.

Alternative Tune, ST. ANSELM, *No.* 410.

535

As the sufferings of Christ abound in us, so our consolation also aboundeth by Christ.—2 Cor. i. 5.

1 O HAPPY band of pilgrims,
  If onward ye will tread
With Jesus as your Fellow,
  To Jesus as your Head !

2 Oh, happy, if ye labour
  As Jesus did for men :
Oh, happy, if ye hunger
  As Jesus hungered then !

3 The faith by which ye see Him,
  The hope in which ye yearn,
The love that through all troubles
  To Him alone will turn :

4 What are they but His heralds
  To lead you to His sight ?
What are they save the effluence
  Of uncreated light ?

5 The trials that beset you,
  The sorrows ye endure,
The manifold temptations
  That death alone can cure :

6 What are they but His jewels
  Of right celestial worth ?
What are they but the ladder
  Set up to heaven on earth ?

7 The cross that Jesus carried,
  He carried as your due ;
The crown that Jesus weareth,
  He weareth it for you.

8 O happy band of pilgrims,
  Look upward to the skies,
Where such a light affliction
  Shall win you such a prize !

Tr. J. M. Neale.

St. Asaph.　　　　　　　　8.7.8.7., D.　　　　　　W. S. Bambridge.

Alternative Tune, St. Oswald, *No.* 276.

536　　*He led them on safely, so that they feared not.*—Psalm lxxviii. 53.

1 Through the night of doubt and sorrow
　Onward goes the pilgrim band,
Singing songs of expectation,
　Marching to the promised land.
Clear before us through the darkness
　Gleams and burns the guiding light ;
Brother clasps the hand of brother,
　Stepping fearless through the night.

2 One the light of God's own presence,
　O'er His ransomed people shed,
Chasing far the gloom and terror,
　Brightening all the path we tread.
One the object of our journey,
　One the faith which never tires,
One the earnest looking forward,
　One the hope our God inspires.

3 One the strain the lips of thousands
　Lift as from the heart of one ;
One the conflict, one the peril,
　One the march in God begun.
One the gladness of rejoicing
　On the far eternal shore,
Where the One Almighty Father
　Reigns in love for evermore.

4 Onward, therefore, pilgrim brothers,
　Onward with the cross our aid :
Bear its shame, and fight its battle,
　Till we rest beneath its shade.
Soon shall come the great awaking ;
　Soon the rending of the tomb ;
Then the scattering of all shadows,
　And the end of toil and gloom.

　　　　　　B. S. Ingemann, Tr. S. Baring-Gould.

537 Dare to do Right!　　　　P.M.　　　　W. B. Bradbury.

REFRAIN.

Dare, dare, dare to do right!

true! ...

Dare, dare, dare to be true! Dare, dare to be true! dare to be true!

537 *Thou shalt do that which is right and good in the sight of the Lord.—*
DEUT. vi. 18.

1 DARE to do right! dare to be true!
   You have a work that no other can do;
   Do it so bravely, so kindly, so well,
   Angels will hasten the story to tell.
   Dare, dare, dare to do right! etc.

2 Dare to do right! dare to be true!
   God, who created you, cares for you too;
   Treasures the tears that His striving ones shed,
   Counts and protects every hair of your head.

3 Dare to do right! dare to be true!
   Keep the great judgment-seat always in view:
   Look at your work as you'll look at it then,
   Scanned by Jehovah, and angels, and men.

4 Dare to do right! dare to be true!
   Jesus, your Saviour, will carry you through;
   City and mansion, and throne all in sight,
   Can you not dare to be true and do right?
                                    G. L. Taylor.

Pentecost.   L.M.   W. BOYD.

538 *A good soldier of Jesus Christ.—*2 TIM. ii. 3.

1 FIGHT the good fight with all thy might,
   Christ is thy strength, and Christ thy right;
   Lay hold on life, and it shall be
   Thy joy and crown eternally.

2 Run the straight race through God's good grace,
   Lift up thine eyes, and seek His face;
   Life with its way before us lies,
   Christ is the path, and Christ the prize.

3 Cast care aside, lean on thy Guide;
   His boundless mercy will provide;
   Lean, and the trusting soul shall prove,
   Christ is its life, and Christ its love.

4 Faint not, nor fear, His arms are near,
   He changeth not, and thou art dear;
   Only believe, and thou shalt see
   That Christ is all in all to thee.
                                    J. S. B. Monsell.

P

There's a Fight to be Fought. P.M. Naomi Pope.

539

Fight the good fight of faith.—1 Tim. vi. 12.

UNISON.

1. There's a fight to be fought, and a race to be run, There are dangers to meet by the way,

But the Lord is my light and the Lord is my life, And the Lord is my strength and stay.

On His word I depend, He's my Saviour and Friend; And He tells me to trust and o - bey;

For the Lord is my light and the Lord is my life, And the Lord is my strength and stay.

2 In His wonderful love, He came down from above
　To suffer and die on the tree;
Now He's reigning up there, where He's gone to prepare
　A place in His kingdom for me.
Let us sing as we go, for He loveth us so,
　We can never be lost by the way;
For the Lord is our light and the Lord is our life,
　And the Lord is our strength and stay.

3 Then He'll bring us at length, by His infinite strength,
　To the land that is fairer than day;
For the Lord is my light and the Lord is my life,
　And the Lord is my strength and stay.
So we'll sing to His praise, to the end of our days,
　As we travel each dangerous way;
For the Lord is my light and the Lord is my life,
　And the Lord is my strength and stay.

Naomi Pope.

Hereford New. 6.10.10.6.

540 *Blessed be the God and Father of our Lord Jesus Christ.*—EPH. i. 3.

1 BLESSÈD be God, our God!
Who gave for us His well-belovèd Son,
The gift of gifts, all other gifts in one—
Blessèd be God, our God!

2 What will He not bestow,
Who freely gave this mighty gift unbought,
Unmerited, unheeded, and unsought—
What will He not bestow?

3 He sparèd not His Son!
'Tis this that silences each rising fear;
'Tis this that bids the hard thought dis-
He sparèd not His Son! [appear—

4 Who shall condemn us now? [above,
Since Christ has died, and risen, and gone
For us to plead at the right hand of Love,
Who shall condemn us now?

5 'Tis God that justifies!
Who shall recall the pardon or the grace,
Or who the broken chain of guilt replace?
'Tis God that justifies!

6 The victory is ours!
For us in might came forth the Mighty One;
For us He fought the fight, the triumph won—
The victory is ours!

H. Bonar.

University College. 7.7.7.7. H. J. GAUNTLETT.

541 *Speak unto the children of Israel, that they go forward.*—EXOD. xiv. 15.

1 OFT in danger, oft in woe,
Onward, Christians, onward go;
Fight the fight, maintain the strife,
Strengthened with the Bread of life.

2 Onward, Christians, onward go!
Join the war, and face the foe:
Will ye flee in danger's hour?
Know ye not your Captain's power?

3 Let your drooping hearts be glad:
March, in heavenly armour clad;

Fight, nor think the battle long,
Soon shall victory tune your song.

4 Let not sorrow dim your eye,
Soon shall every tear be dry;
Let not fears your course impede,
Great your strength, if great your need.

5 Onward, then, to battle move,
More than conquerors ye shall prove;
Though opposed by many a foe,
Christian soldiers, onward go!

H. K. White, and others.

Lux Eoi. 8.7.8.7., D. Sir Arthur S. Sullivan.

By permission of Novello and Company, Limited.

542 *Abide with us.*—LUKE xxiv. 29.

1 LORD, our meeting now is ended,
  Homeward must our steps be turned ;
So we gather here to thank Thee
  For the lessons we have learned,
Of the Father's love almighty,
  Of the Holy Spirit's power,
Of the Christ who died to save us,
  And will keep us every hour.

2 Let us never, never waver,
  Never compromise nor yield,
Never let our light be hidden,
  Nor our love to Thee concealed;
Never be ashamed to own Thee,
  Though the world may scoff and jeer,
Fill us with the love of Jesus,
  Perfect love that casts out fear.

3 May we find our all in Jesus,
  In our risen, living King,
Strength to suffer, power to conquer,
  Tongue to speak and voice to sing.
Love to win and joy to brighten,
  Grace to keep from every fall—
Yesterday, to-day, for ever,
  Christ Himself our all in all.

4 So with mingled joy and sadness,
  From each other we must part,
Yet in Jesus still united,
  Bound together heart to heart ;
Shining by His light reflected,
  Growing daily in His grace,
Till His glory burst upon us,
  And we "see Him face to face."

R. Hudson Pope.

543 Our Captain. 6.5.6.5., with Chorus. R. B. PHAYRE.

CHORUS.

Jesus is our Captain, Jesus is our Friend; Jesus gives us vic-tory, Victory to the end.

543   *The Captain of their salvation.*—HEB. ii. 10.

1 LIFT your voices, soldiers,
　Raise your hearts on high,
Jesus is our Captain,
　We to Him draw nigh.
　　Jesus is our Captain, etc.

2 When you're tempted, soldiers,
　When your hearts are sad,
Jesus is your safeguard,
　Christ can make you glad.

3 When sin's heavy burden
　Hangs upon your soul,
Jesus' blood can cleanse you,
　Christ can make you whole.

4 Trust your Captain, soldiers,
　Trust Him all the way—
Marching, fighting, dying,
　May we always say :
　　　　　　　E. Phayre.

St. Andrew of Crete.　　6.5.6.5., D.　　J. B. DYKES.

Unison in verses 1, 2, 3.

Harmony.

544   *Whom resist stedfast in the faith.*—1 PETER v. 9.

1 CHRISTIAN, dost thou see them
　On the holy ground,
How the hosts of darkness,
　Compass thee around?
Christian, up and smite them,
　Counting gain but loss ;
Smite them, Christ is with thee,
　Soldier of the Cross.

2 Christian, dost thou feel them,
　How they work within,
Striving, tempting, luring,
　Goading into sin?
Christian, never tremble ;
　Never be downcast ;
Gird thee for the conflict,
　Watch, and pray, and fast.

3 Christian, dost thou hear them,
　How they speak thee fair ?
"Quit thy weary vigil,
　Cease from watch and prayer ;"
Christian, answer boldly,
　"While I breathe I pray :"
Peace shall follow battle,
　Night shall end in day.

4 "Well I know thy trouble,
　O My servant true ;
Thou art very weary—
　I was weary too :
But that toil shall make thee
　Some day all Mine own,
And the end of sorrow
　Shall be near My throne."
　　　　　　Tr. J. M. Neale.

Filius Dei. C.M.D. A. R. GAUL, MUS.BAC.

Alternative Tune, ELLACOMBE, *No. 96.*

545 *If we suffer, we shall also reign with Him.*—2 TIM. ii. 12.

1 THE Son of God goes forth to war,
  A kingly crown to gain;
His blood-red banner streams afar!
  Who follows in His train?
Who best can drink his cup of woe,
  Triumphant over pain,
Who patient bears his cross below,
  He follows in His train.

2 The martyr first, whose eagle eye
  Could pierce beyond the grave;
Who saw his Master in the sky,
  And called on Him to save.
Like him, with pardon on his tongue,
  In midst of mortal pain,
He prayed for them that did the wrong:
  Who follows in his train?

3 A glorious band, the chosen few
  On whom the Spirit came,
Twelve valiant saints, their hope they knew,
  And mocked the cross and flame.
They met the tyrant's brandished steel,
  The lion's gory mane;
They bowed their necks, the death to feel:
  Who follows in their train?

4 A noble army, men and boys,
  The matron and the maid,
Around the Saviour's throne rejoice,
  In robes of light arrayed.
They climbed the steep ascent of heaven
  Through peril, toil, and pain;
O God, to us may grace be given
  To follow in their train.

R. Heber.

546 *Crucis Milites.* 7.7.7.7. MYLES B. FOSTER.

Alternative Tune, UNIVERSITY COLLEGE, *No. 541.*

546 *Take the helmet of salvation, and the sword of the Spirit.*—EPH. vi. 17.

1 SOLDIERS of the Cross, arise !
  Gird you with your armour bright ;
Mighty are your enemies,
  Hard the battle you must fight.

2 O'er a faithless fallen world
  Raise your banner in the sky ;
Let it float there wide unfurled ;
  Bear it onward, lift it high.

3 'Mid the homes of want and woe,
  Strangers to the living Word,
Let the Saviour's heralds go,
  Let the voice of hope be heard.

4 Where the shadows deepest lie,
  Carry truth's unsullied ray ;

Where are crimes of blackest dye,
  There the saving sign display.

5 To the weary and the worn
  Tell of realms where sorrows cease ;
To the outcast and forlorn
  Speak of mercy and of peace.

6 Guard the helpless, seek the strayed ;
  Comfort troubles, banish grief ;
In the might of God arrayed,
  Scatter sin and unbelief.

7 Be the banner still unfurled,
  Still unsheathed the Spirit's sword,
Till the kingdoms of the world
  Are the kingdom of the Lord.

W. W. How.

We Rest on Thee.   11.10.11.10.

Devotionally.   J. MOUNTAIN.

Words and Music by permission of Morgan and Scott, Limited.

547   *Ye shall find rest unto your souls.*—MATT. xi. 29.

1 "WE rest on Thee"—our Shield and our Defender !
  We go not forth alone against the foe ;
Strong in Thy strength, safe in Thy keeping tender,
  "We rest on Thee, and in Thy Name we go."

2 Yea, "in Thy Name," O Captain of salvation !
  In Thy dear Name, all other names above ;
Jesus our Righteousness, our sure Foundation,
  Our Prince of glory and our King of love.

3 "We go" in faith, our own great weakness feeling,
  And needing more each day Thy grace to know :
Yet from our hearts a song of triumph pealing,
  "We rest on Thee, and in Thy Name we go."

4 "We rest on Thee"—our Shield and our Defender !
  Thine is the battle, Thine shall be the praise
When passing through the gates of pearly splendour,
  Victors—we rest *with* Thee, through endless days.

Edith G. Cherry.

Eastham. 7.6.8.6., D. F. A. G. OUSELEY.

Alternative Tune, ALFORD, *No.* 558.

548 *Stand fast in the faith . . . be strong.*—1 COR. xvi. 13.

1 STAND fast for Christ thy Saviour!
  Stand fast whate'er betide!
Keep thou the Faith, unstained, unshamed,
  By keeping at His side;
Be faithful, ever faithful,
  Where'er thy lot be cast,
Stand fast for Christ! Stand fast for
  Stand faithful to the last.   [Christ!

2 Strong-founded like a lighthouse,
  That stands the storm and shock,
So be thy soul as if it shared,
  The granite of the rock:
Then far beyond the breakers,
  Let thy calm light be cast,
Stand fast for Christ! Stand fast for
  Stand faithful to the last.   [Christ!

3 Stout-hearted like a soldier,
  Who never leaves the fight,
But meets the foeman face to face
  And meets him with his might:

So bear thee in thy battles
  Until the war be past—
Stand fast for Christ! Stand fast for
  Stand faithful to the last.   [Christ!

4 Against each fair temptation
  Be swift upon thy guard,
Resist the devil, and his flight
  Shall be thy rich reward,
And God's consoling angels
  Shall come when he has passed—
Stand fast like Christ! Stand fast like
  Stand faithful to the last.   [Christ!

5 Stand fast for Christ thy Saviour!
  He once stood fast for thee,
And standeth still, and still shall stand
  For all eternity—
Be faithful, oh, be faithful,
  To love so true, so vast—
Stand fast for Christ! Stand fast for
  Stand faithful to the last.   [Christ!
                          W. J. Mathams.

549 Southwold. P.M.

549

They saw no man, save Jesus only.—MATT. xvii. 8.

1 BE our joyful song to-day,
  Jesus! only Jesus!
He who takes our sins away,
  Jesus! only Jesus!
Name with every blessing rife,
Be our joy and hope through life,
Be our strength in every strife,
  Jesus! only Jesus!

2 Once we wandered far from God,
  Knowing not of Jesus;
Treading still the downward road
  Leading far from Jesus;

Till the Spirit taught us how
'Neath the Saviour's yoke to bow,
And we fain would follow now,
  Jesus! only Jesus!

3 Be our trust through years to come.
  Jesus! only Jesus!
Password to our heavenly home,
  Jesus! only Jesus!
When from sin and sorrow free,
On through all eternity,
This our theme and song shall be,
  Jesus! only Jesus!   *Anon.*

Sharon.   8.7.8.7.   W. BOYCE.

550   *They that wait upon the Lord shall renew their strength.*—ISA. xl. 31.

1 FATHER, hear the prayer we offer!
  Not for ease that prayer shall be,
But for strength that we may ever
  Live our lives courageously.

2 Not for ever in green pastures
  Do we ask our way to be:
But by steep and rugged pathways
  Would we strive to climb to Thee.

3 Not for ever by still waters
  Would we idly quietly stay;

But would smite the living fountains
  From the rocks along our way.

4 Be our strength in hours of weakness,
  In our wanderings be our Guide;
Through endeavour, failure, danger,
  Father, be Thou at our side.

5 Let our path be bright or dreary,
  Storm or sunshine be our share;
May our souls, in hope unweary,
  Make Thy work our ceaseless prayer.
                          E. M. Willis.

P*

St. Leonards.   8.7.8.5.   A. CYRIL BARHAM GOULD.

Words and Music Copyright.

551   *Let this mind be in you, which was also in Christ Jesus.*—PHIL. ii. 5.

1 MAY the mind of Christ my Saviour
    Live in me from day to day,
  By His love and power controlling
    All I do and say.

2 May the Word of God dwell richly
    In my heart from hour to hour,
  So that all may see I triumph
    Only through His power.

3 May the peace of God my Father
    Rule my life in everything,
  That I may be calm to comfort
    Sick and sorrowing.

4 May the love of Jesus fill me,
    As the waters fill the sea;
  Him exalting, self abasing,
    This is victory.

5 May I run the race before me,
    Strong and brave to face the foe,
  Looking only unto Jesus
    As I onward go.

6 May His beauty rest upon me
    As I seek the lost to win,
  And may they forget the channel,
    Seeing only Him.
                    Katie Barclay Wilkinson.

Breslau.   L.M.   German.

Alternative Tune, MAINZER, *No.* 60.

552   *If any man will come after Me, let him deny himself, and take up his
                    cross, and follow Me.*—MATT. xvi. 24.

1 "TAKE up thy cross," the Saviour said,
    "If thou wouldst My disciple be;
  Deny thyself, the world forsake,
    And humbly follow after Me."

2 Take up thy cross; let not its weight
    Fill thy weak soul with vain alarm:
  His strength shall bear thy spirit up,
    And brace thy heart and nerve thine
        arm.

3 Take up thy cross, nor heed the shame,
    Nor let thy foolish pride rebel;

  Thy Lord for thee the cross endured
    To save thy soul from death and hell.

4 Take up thy cross then in His strength,
    And calmly every danger brave;
  'Twill guide thee to a better home,
    And lead to victory o'er the grave.

5 Take up thy cross and follow Him,
    Nor think till death to lay it down;
  For only he who bears the cross
    May hope to wear the glorious crown.
                    C. W. Everest.

Quit you like Men!   11.10.11.10., with Chorus.   R. HUDSON POPE.

Chorus.

Faith-ful and loy-al, Lord, may we be; .. Liv-ing or

dy-ing, still faithful un-to Thee; Serv-ing the Christ, and in serving Him made free.

553

Quit you like men, be strong.—1 COR. xvi. 13.

1 "QUIT you like men!" Life's battle lies before you;
    Will ye prove traitors to your Prince above?
  Will ye desert His standard floating o'er you,
    The bannered cross of Jesus' dying love?
      Faithful and loyal, etc.

2 "Quit you like men!" Heaven's victor-voices call you;
    Oh, be ashamed of all your coward shame!
  Let not the fear of man or fiend appal you,
    They always win who fight in Jesus' Name.

3 "Quit you like men!" No longer slaves of passion,
    Led by your lusts or mammon's selfish greed;
  No more enthralled by some unholy fashion—
    Freed by God's Son, then are ye free indeed!

4 "Quit you like men!" Be true to your true nature:
    Are not our bodies temples of our God?
  Grow up in Christ to manhood's fullest stature;
    Tread in the steps the Perfect Man hath trod.

5 "Quit you like men!" Behold the Man that liveth
    And once was slain, that ye may live to God;
  Take to your hearts the eternal life He giveth—
    Peace, power and pardon, purchased with His blood.

W. H. M. H. Aitken.

St. Theresa.
554
6.5.6.5., D., with Refrain.

His banner over me was love.—SONG OF SOLOMON ii. 4.

Treble voices in Unison.

Sir ARTHUR S. SULLIVAN.

1. Brightly gleams our ban-ner, Pointing to the sky, .. Waving wand'rers onward

To their home on high. Journeying o'er the des - ert, Glad-ly thus we pray,

And with hearts u - ni - ted, Take our heavenward way,— Bright-ly gleams our ban-ner,

Unison.

Point-ing to the sky, Waving wand'rers on-ward To their home on high!

By permission of Novello and Company, Limited.

2 Jesus, Lord and Master,
   At Thy sacred feet,
Here with hearts rejoicing
   See Thy children meet;
Often have we left Thee,
   Often gone astray;
Keep us, mighty Saviour,
   In the narrow way.

3 Pattern of our childhood,
   Once Thyself a child,
Make our childhood holy,
   Pure, and meek, and mild;
In the hour of danger
   Whither can we flee,
Save to Thee, dear Saviour,
   Only unto Thee?

4 All our days direct us,
   In the way we go,
Lead us on victorious
   Over every foe;
Bid Thine angels shield us
   When the storm-clouds lower;
Pardon Thou and save us
   In the last dread hour.

5 Then with saints and angels
   May we join above,
Offering prayers and praises
   At Thy throne of love.
When the march is over,
   Then come rest and peace,
Jesus in His beauty,
   Songs that never cease.

T. J. Potter.

Pilgrimage. P.M.

555

We are journeying unto the place of which the Lord said, I will give it you.—NUMBERS x. 29.

1. {Whither, pilgrims, are you go-ing, Going each with staff in hand?
    We are go-ing on a journey, Going at our King's command,} Over hills and plains and val-leys, We are go-ing to His pal-ace, We are go-ing to His pal-ace, Go-ing to the better land; We are go-ing to His pal-ace, Go-ing to the bet-ter land.

2 Tell us, pilgrims, what you hope for
   In that far-off, better land?
Spotless robes, and crowns of glory,
   From a Saviour's loving hand.
We shall drink of life's clear river,
We shall dwell with God for ever,
We shall dwell with God for ever,
   In that bright, that better land.

3 Pilgrims, may we travel with you
   To that bright and better land?
Come and welcome, come and welcome,
   Welcome to our pilgrim band.
Come, oh, come! and do not leave us;
Christ is waiting to receive us,
Christ is waiting to receive us,
   In that bright, that better land.

Anon

Marching Beneath the Banner. P.M.

H. ERNEST NICHOL.

556

And the Lord went before . . . to lead them.—EXODUS xiii. 21.

TREBLES AND ALTOS ONLY. *In march time.* 𝅘𝅥 = 132.

* 1. Hark to the sound of voi-ces! Hark to the tramp of feet! Is it a mighty ar-my

FOUR PARTS.

Treading the bu-sy street? Near-er it comes and nearer, Singing a glad re-frain:

CHORUS. UNISON.

List what they say as they haste away To the sound of a martial strain: "Marching beneath the

Well marked in the Bass.

ban - ner, Fighting beneath the cross, Trusting in Him who saves us,

HARMONY.

Ne'er shall we suf fer loss! Singing the songs of home - land, Loud-ly the chorus

rings, We march to the fight in our armour bright At the call of the King of kings."

2 Out of the mist of error,
  Out of the realms of night,
Out of the pride of learning,
  Seeking the home of light;
Out of the strife for power,
  Out of the greed of gold,
Onward they roam to their heavenly home,
  And the treasure that grows not old.

3 Out of the bonds of evil,
  Out of the chains of sin,
Ever they're pressing onward,
  Fighting the fight within;

Holding the passions under,
  Ruling the sense with soul,   [Lord,
Wielding the sword in the name of the
  As they march to their heavenly goal.

4 On then, ye gallant soldiers,
  On to your home above!
Yours is the truth and glory,
  Yours is the power and love.
Here are ye trained for heroes,
  Yonder ye serve the King;   [white,
March to the light 'neath the banner
  With the song that ye love to sing:
                              Colin Sterne.

  * In verses 1, 2, and 3, the effect should be produced of the gradual approach from the distance
of a band of soldiers.   Copyright. By permission of H. E. Nichol, Charlotte Street, Hull.

Deerhurst.   8.7.8.7., D.   J. LANGRAN.

By permission of Novello and Company, Limited.

557   *Having your loins girt about with truth.*—EPH. vi. 14.

1 GIRD thy loins up, Christian soldier,
    Lo! thy Captain calls thee out:
  Let the danger make thee bolder,
    War in weakness, dare in doubt.
  Buckle on thy heavenly armour;
    Patch up no inglorious peace;
  Let thy courage wax the warmer
    As thy foes and fears increase.

2 Bind thy golden girdle round thee,
    Truth to keep thee firm and right:
  Never shall the foe confound thee
    While the truth maintains thy fight.
  Righteousness within thee rooted
    May appear to take thy part;
  But let righteousness imputed
    Be the breastplate of thy heart.

3 Shod with gospel preparation,
    In the paths of promise tread;
  Let the hope of free salvation
    As a helmet guard thy head.

When beset with various evils
    Wield the Spirit's two-edged sword;
  Cut thy way through hosts of devils,
    While they fall before the Word.

4 But, when dangers closer threaten,
    And thy soul draws near to death,
  When assaulted sore by Satan,
    Then upraise the shield of faith;
  Fiery darts of fierce temptations,
    Intercepted by thy God,
  There shall lose their force in patience,
    Sheathed in love, and quenched in blood.

5 Though to speak thou art not able,
    Always pray and never rest.
  Prayer's a weapon for the feeble,
    Weakest souls can wield it best.
  Ever on thy Captain calling,
    Make thy worst condition known;
  He shall hold thee up when falling,
    Or shall lift thee up when down.
                              J. Hart.

Section VIII.—Heaven.

Alford.   7.6.8.6., D.   J. B. Dykes.

558   *We . . . shall be caught up together with them in the clouds, to meet the Lord in the air.*—1 Thess. iv. 17.

1 Ten thousand times ten thousand,
  In sparkling raiment bright;
The armies of the ransomed saints
  Throng up the steeps of light:
'Tis finished, all is finished,
  Their fight with death and sin;
Fling open wide the golden gates,
  And let the victors in.

2 What rush of Hallelujahs
  Fills all the earth and sky!
What ringing of a thousand harps
  Bespeaks the triumph nigh!
Oh, day, for which creation
  And all its tribes were made!
Oh, joy, for all its former woes
  A thousandfold repaid!

3 Oh, then what raptured greetings
  On Canaan's happy shore!
What knitting of severed friendships up,
  Where partings are no more!
Then eyes with joy shall sparkle
  That brimmed with tears of late;
Orphans no longer fatherless,
  Nor widows desolate.

4 Bring near Thy great salvation,
  Thou Lamb for sinners slain;
Fill up the roll of Thine elect,
  Then take Thy power and reign!
Appear, Desire of nations.
  Thine exiles long for home;
Show in the heavens Thy promised sign;
  Thou Prince and Saviour, come!

H. Alford.

Glory. 7.6.7.6.7.6.7.5. Charles Vincent.

Alternative Tune, Rutherford, *No.* 154.

Thy land, O Immanuel.—Isaiah viii. 8.

559

1 The sands of time are sinking,
    The dawn of heaven breaks:
The summer morn I've sighed for,
    The fair sweet morn awakes:
Dark, dark hath been the midnight,
    But day-spring is at hand,
And glory, glory dwelleth
    In Immanuel's land.

2 O Christ, He is the fountain,
    The deep, sweet well of love,
The streams on earth I've tasted
    More deep I'll drink above;
There, to an ocean fulness,
    His mercy doth expand,
And glory, glory dwelleth
    In Immanuel's land.

3 With mercy and with judgment,
    My web of time He wove,
And aye the dews of sorrow,
    Were lustred by His love:
I'll bless the hand that guided,
    I'll bless the heart that planned,
When throned where glory dwelleth
    In Immanuel's land.

4 Oh, I am my Belovèd's,
    And my Belovèd's mine;
He brings a poor vile sinner
    Into His house of wine.
I stand upon His merit;
    I know no other stand,
Not e'en where glory dwelleth
    In Immanuel's land.

5 The bride eyes not her garment:
    But her dear bridegroom's face,
I will not gaze at glory,
    But on my King of grace,
Not at the crown He giveth,
    But on His piercèd hand:
The Lamb is all the glory
    Of Immanuel's land.

6 I've wrestled on towards heaven
    'Gainst storm and wind and tide,
Now like a weary traveller
    That leaneth on his guide,
Amid the shades of evening,
    While sinks life's lingering sand,
I hail the glory dawning
    In Immanuel's land.

Mrs. A. R. Cousin.

Singing Glory. C.M., with Refrain. Anon.

Singing glo - ry, glo - ry, glo - ry, Singing glo - ry, glo - ry, glo - ry!

560 *These are they which . . . have washed their robes, and made them white in the blood of the Lamb.*—Rev. vii. 14.

1 AROUND the throne of God in heaven
    Thousands of children stand,
  Children whose sins are all forgiven,
    A holy, happy band:
      Singing glory, glory, etc.

2 What brought them to that world above,
    That heaven so bright and fair,
  Where all is peace and joy and love?
    How came those children there?

3 Because the Saviour shed His blood
    To wash away their sin;
  Bathed in that pure and precious flood,
    Behold them white and clean!

4 On earth they sought the Saviour's grace,
    On earth they loved His Name;
  So now they see His blessèd face,
    And stand before the Lamb.

Anne Shepherd.

11.11.11.11., with Refrain.

561 Bright Home of our Saviour! Sir H. R. Bishop.

Home! home! sweet, sweet home! Pre-pare me, dear Saviour, for yon-der blest home.

561   *In my Father's house are many mansions.*—JOHN xiv. 2.

1 BRIGHT home of our Saviour, what glories await [pearly gate!
The spirits that pass through thy bright,
What anthems of rapture, unceasing and high, [sky!
Compose the loud chorus that gladdens the
Home! home! sweet, sweet home! etc.

2 The home of the ransomed, the land of the blest;
Where pilgrims shall enter a glorious rest,
Shall wander in gladness through pastures of green, [serene.
And drink the still waters of pleasures

3 The home that our Saviour has gone to prepare— [there;
No heart can conceive of the blessedness
Of raptures unending awaiting the just
When pure in His likeness they rise from the dust.

4 We bless Thee, dear Saviour, who call'st us to share
The beautiful home Thou hast gone to pre- [pare;
We trust in Thy mercy that, washed from our sin,
Through yonder bright gates we may all enter in.   *Anon.*

Ⓗappy Land.   P.M.   Telugu Melody.

562   *And I saw a new heaven and a new earth.*—REV. xxi. 1.

1 THERE is a happy land,
     Far, far away,
Where saints in glory stand,
     Bright, bright as day.
Oh, how they sweetly sing,
Worthy is our Saviour King!
Loud let His praises ring—
     Praise, praise for aye!

2 Come to this happy land,
     Come, come away:
Why will ye doubting stand?
     Why still delay?

Oh, we shall happy be,
When, from sin and sorrow free,
Lord, we shall live with Thee,
     Blest, blest for aye!

3 Bright in that happy land
     Beams every eye;
Kept by a Father's hand,
     Love cannot die:
On then to glory run,
Be a crown, a kingdom won;
And bright above the sun
     Reign, reign for aye.

                        Andrew Young.

563 Castle Rising. [FIRST TUNE.]

C.M.D.

F. A. J. HERVEY.

By permission of Novello and Company, Limited.

St. Paul. [SECOND TUNE.]

C.M.D.

Sir JOHN STAINER.

563

The things which are seen are temporal; but the things which are not seen are eternal.—2 Cor. iv. 18.

1 THE roseate hues of early dawn,
The brightness of the day,
The crimson of the sunset sky,
How fast they fade away!
Oh, for the pearly gates of heaven,
Oh, for the golden floor,
Oh, for the Sun of Righteousness
That setteth nevermore!

2 O'er the dull ocean broods the night,
And all the strand is dark,
Save where a line of broken foam
Lies at low water mark.
Oh, for the land that needs no night,
Where never night shall be;
Oh, for the quiet home in heaven,
Where there is no more sea!

3 The highest hopes we cherish here,
How fast they tire and faint,
How many a spot defiles the robe
That wraps an earthly saint!
Oh, for a heart that never sins,
Oh, for a soul washed white,
Oh, for a voice to praise our King,
Nor weary day or night!

4 Here faith is ours, and heavenly hope,
And grace to lead us higher;
But there are perfectness and peace,
Beyond our best desire.
Oh, by Thy love and anguish, Lord,
Oh, by Thy life laid down,
Grant that we fall not from Thy grace,
Nor cast away our crown!

Mrs. C. F. Alexander.

City Bright.   P.M.   J. S. TYLER.

564

There shall in no wise enter into it any thing that defileth.—Rev. xxi. 27.

1 THERE is a city bright,
Closed are its gates to sin;
Naught that defileth,
Naught that defileth,
Can ever enter in.

2 Saviour, I come to Thee!
O Lamb of God, I pray,
Cleanse me and save me,
Cleanse me and save me,
Wash all my sins away.

3 Lord, make me, from this hour,
Thy loving child to be;
Kept by Thy power,
Kept by Thy power,
From all that grieveth Thee:

4 Till in the snowy dress
Of Thy redeemed I stand,
Faultless and stainless,
Faultless and stainless,
Safe in that happy land!

Mary A. S. Deck

565 The Beautiful City.　　　P.M.　　　O. F. PRESBREY.

CHORUS.

Not half has ev - er been told, . . . Not half has ev - er been told, . .
been told,　　　　　　　　　　　　　　　　　　　　　　　　been told,

Repeat Chorus p

Not half of that ci - ty's bright glo - ry　To mortals has ev - er been told. . .

565 *The building of the wall of it was of jasper: and the city was pure gold,*
*like unto clear glass.—*REV. xxi. 18.

1.

I HAVE read of a beautiful city,
  Far away in the kingdom of God ;
I have read how its walls are of jasper,
  How its streets are all golden and broad :
In the midst of the street is life's river,
  Clear as crystal, and pure to behold ;
But not half of that city's bright glory
  To mortals has even been told.
    Not half has ever been told, etc.

2.

I have read of bright mansions in heaven,
  Which the Saviour has gone to prepare ;
And the saints who on earth have been faith-
  Rest for ever with Christ over there : [ful
There no sin ever enters, nor sorrow,
  The inhabitants never grow old ;
But not half of the joys that await them
  To mortals has ever been told.

3.

I have read of white robes for the righteous,
  Of bright crowns which the glorified wear,
When our Father shall bid them, "Come
  And My glory eternally share": [enter ;
How the righteous are evermore blessèd,
  As they walk through the streets of pure
But not half of the wonderful story [gold :
  To mortals has ever been told.

4.

I have read of a Christ so forgiving,
  That vile sinners may ask and receive
Peace and pardon for every transgression,
  If when asking they only believe :
I have read how He'll guide and protect us,
  If for safety we enter His fold ;
But not half of His goodness and mercy
  To mortals has ever been told.

J. B. Atchinson.

St. Edmund.   6.4.6.4.6.6.6.4.   Sir ARTHUR S. SULLIVAN.

By permission of Novello and Company, Limited.

566 *I am a stranger with Thee, and a sojourner, as all my fathers were.—*
PSALM xxxix. 12.

1 I'M but a stranger here,
    Heaven is my home ;
  Only a sojourner,
    Heaven is my home :
  Danger and sorrow stand
  Round me on every hand ;
  Heaven is my Fatherland,
    Heaven is my home.

2 What though the tempest rage,
    Heaven is my home !
  Short is my pilgrimage,
    Heaven is my home :
  And time's wild, wintry blast
  Soon will be over-past :
  I shall reach home at last,
    Heaven is my home.

3 There at my Saviour's side,
    Heaven is my home !
  I shall be glorified,
    Heaven is my home :
  There are the good and blest,
  Those I love most and best,
  And there I too shall rest,
    Heaven is my home.

4 Therefore I'll murmur not,
    Heaven is my home ;
  Whate'er my earthly lot,
    Heaven is my home :
  For I shall surely stand
  There at my Lord's right hand ;
  Heaven is my Fatherland,
    Heaven is my home.

T. R. Taylor.

Ewing.   7.6.7.6., D.   A. EWING.

567   *And I John saw the holy city, new Jerusalem.*—REV. xxi. 2.

1 JERUSALEM the golden,
    With milk and honey blest,
Beneath thy contemplation
    Sink heart and voice opprest:
I know not, oh, I know not,
    What joys await us there,
What radiancy of glory,
    What bliss beyond compare.

2 They stand, those halls of Zion,
    All jubilant with song;
And bright with many an angel,
    And all the martyr-throng:
The Prince is ever in them,
    The daylight is serene,
The pastures of the blessèd
    Are decked in glorious sheen.

3 There is the throne of David:
    And there, from care released,
The shout of them that triumph,
    The song of them that feast:
And they who with their Leader
    Have conquer'd in the fight,
For ever and for ever
    Are clothed in robes of white.

4 Oh, sweet and blessèd country,
    The home of God's elect!
Oh, sweet and blessèd country
    That eager hearts expect!
Jesus, in mercy bring us
    To that dear land of rest,
Who art, with God the Father,
    And Spirit, ever blest.

                   Tr. *J. M. Neale.*

St. Philip.   10.10.10.4.   Sir J. Barnby.

Al - le - lu - ia, Al - le - lu - ia!

568   *Compassed about with so great a cloud of witnesses.*—Heb. xii. 1.

1 For all the saints, who from their labours rest,
Who Thee by faith before the world confessed,
Thy Name, O Jesus, be for ever blessed.
      Alleluia!

2 Thou wast their Rock, their Fortress, and their Might;
Thou, Lord, their Captain in the well-fought fight;
Thou, in the darkness drear, their one true Light.
      Alleluia!

3 Oh, may Thy soldiers, faithful, true, and bold,
Fight as the saints, who nobly fought of old,
And win, with them, the victor's crown of gold.
      Alleluia!

4 Oh, blest communion, fellowship divine!
We feebly struggle, they in glory shine!
Yet all are one in Thee, for all are Thine.
      Alleluia!

5 And when the strife is fierce, the warfare long,
Steals on the ear the distant triumph-song,
And hearts are brave again, and arms are strong.
      Alleluia!

6 The golden evening brightens in the west:
Soon, soon to faithful warriors cometh rest;
Sweet is the calm of Paradise the blest.
      Alleluia!

7 But lo! there breaks a yet more glorious day;
The saints triumphant rise in bright array;
The King of Glory passes on His way.
      Alleluia!

8 From earth's wide bounds, from ocean's farthest coast,
Through gates of pearl streams in the countless host,
Singing to Father, Son, and Holy Ghost—
      Alleluia!   *W. W. How.*

Newcastle. 8.6.8.8.6. H. L. MORLEY.

569 *God is Light.*—1 JOHN i. 5.

1 ETERNAL Light! Eternal Light!
  How pure the soul must be
When, placed within Thy searching sight,
It shrinks not, but with calm delight
Can live, and look on Thee!

2 The spirits that surround Thy throne
  May bear the burning bliss;
But that is surely theirs alone,
Since they have never, never known
A fallen world like this.

3 Oh, how shall I, whose native sphere
Is dark, whose mind is dim,
Before the Ineffable appear,

And on my naked spirit bear
  The uncreated beam?

4 There is a way for man to rise
  To that sublime abode;
An Offering and a Sacrifice,
A Holy Spirit's energies,
  An Advocate with God:

5 These, these prepare us for the sight
  Of holiness above;
The sons of ignorance and night
May dwell in the Eternal Light,
  Through the Eternal Love.

T. Binney.

570 Let us Sing of This Love. P.M. WEBSTER.

Joyfully.

CHORUS.

In the sweet "by - and - by" We shall meet on that beau - ti - ful shore;

In the sweet "by-and-by" We shall meet on that beau-ti-ful shore.

570 *Eye hath not seen, nor ear heard . . . the things which God hath prepared for them that love Him.*—1 Cor. ii. 9.

1 Let us sing of His love once again—
Of the love that can never decay,
Of the blood of the Lamb who was slain,
Till we praise Him again in that day.

2 There is cleansing and healing for all
Who will wash in the life-giving flood,
There is life everlasting and joy
At the right hand of God through the blood.

3 Even now while we taste of His love,
We are filled with delight at His Name;
But what will it be when above
We shall join in the song of the Lamb?
F. Bottome.

Beatitudo. C.M. J. B. Dykes.

571 *These are they which came out of great tribulation, and have washed their robes, and made them white in the blood of the Lamb.*—Rev. vii. 14.

1 How bright these glorious spirits shine!
Whence all their white array?
How came they to the blissful seats
Of everlasting day?

2 Lo! these are they from sufferings great,
Who came to realms of light;
And in the blood of Christ have washed
Those robes that shine so bright.

3 Now with triumphal palms they stand
Before the throne on high,
And serve the God they love, amidst
The glories of the sky.

4 Hunger and thirst are felt no more,
Nor suns with scorching ray;

God is their Sun, whose cheering beams
Diffuse eternal day.

5 The Lamb, which dwells amidst the throne,
Shall o'er them still preside,
Feed them with nourishment divine,
And all their footsteps guide.

6 'Midst pastures green He'll lead His flock,
Where living streams appear;
And God the Lord from every eye
Shall wipe off every tear.

7 To Father, Son, and Holy Ghost,
The God Whom we adore,
Be glory, as it was, is now,
And shall be evermore.
Isaac Watts and W. Cameron.

SECTION IX.—The Bible.

Lathbury.   6.4.6.4., D.   W. F. SHERWIN.

572

He took the loaves, and He blessed them, and brake and gave to the disciples.—LUKE ix. 16.

1 BREAK Thou the Bread of Life,
  Dear Lord, to me,
As Thou didst break the bread
  Beside the sea;
Beyond the sacred page
  I seek Thee, Lord,
My spirit longs for Thee,
  Thou Living Word.

2 Thou art the Bread of Life,
  O Lord, to me,
Thy Holy Word the truth
  That saveth me;
Give me to eat and live
  With Thee above,
Teach me to love Thy truth,
  For Thou art love.

3 Oh, send Thy Spirit, Lord,
  Now unto me,
That He may touch my eyes
  And make me see;
Show me the truth concealed
  Within Thy Word,
And in Thy Book revealed,
  I see Thee, Lord.

4 Bless Thou the Bread of Life
  To me, to me,
As Thou didst bless the loaves
  By Galilee;
Then shall all bondage cease,
  All fetters fall,
And I shall find my peace,
  My All in all.

Mary A. Lathbury.

573 Endsleigh.   7.6.7.6., D.

Alternative Tune, ANGELS' STORY, *No. 627.*

573   *Thy Word was unto me the joy and rejoicing of mine heart.*—JER. xv. 16.

1 WE love the blessèd Bible,
　　The glorious Word of God;
　The lamp for those who travel
　　O'er all life's dreary road;
　The watchword in life's battle,
　　The chart on life's dark sea;
　The everlasting Bible,
　　It shall our teacher be.

2 Who would not love the Bible,
　　So beautiful and wise!
　Its teachings charm the simple,
　　And all point to the skies;
　Its stories all so mighty
　　Of men so brave to see,
　Divinely-given Bible,
　　It shall our teacher be.

3 But most we love the Bible,
　　For there we children learn
　How Christ took on our childhood.
　　Our hearts to Him to turn;
　And how He bowed to sorrow,
　　That we His face might see;
　The Bible, oh! the Bible—
　　It shall our teacher be.

4 Then we will hold the Bible—
　　The glorious Book of God;
　We'll ne'er forsake the Bible,
　　Through all life's future road.
　And when we shall be dying,
　　Whenever that may be,
　The comfort of the Bible
　　Shall still our solace be.
　　　　　　E. Paxton Hood (altd.).

Fore Street.　　　　S.M.　　　　R. HUDSON POPE

Alternative Tunes, NARENZA, *No.* 41, *and* RHODES, *No.* 85.

574   *Thy Word is a lamp . . . and a light unto my paths.*—PSALM cxix. 105.

1 WE thank Thee, Lord, indeed,
　　That Thou Thy Word hast given,
　To light our path in this dark world,
　　And safely guide to Heaven.

2 To warn of sinful steps,
　　And point our road each day,
　To keep us in the one safe path,
　　The strait and narrow way.

3 Bless those who with us read
　　Thy wondrous Book of Light,
　That all of us with one desire
　　May strive to do the right.

4 As Thy commands we seek
　　Within Thy Word each day,
　Teach us what Thou wilt have us do,
　　Then teach us to obey.

5 Oh, give us minds to learn,
　　And hearts to know Thy will,
　And make us willing, cheerful, strong,
　　Thy bidding to fulfil!

6 We feel our weakness, Lord,
　　But knowing Thou art near,
　When we are weak, then we are strong,
　　We need not, will not, fear.
　　　　　　R. Hudson Pope.

Cling to the Bible! 11.10.11.10. J. R Murray.

CHORUS.

Cling to the Bi - ble!

Cling to the Bi - ble! Cling to the Bi - ble! Our lamp and our guide!

575 *Take heed unto thyself, and unto the doctrine; continue in them.*—1 Tim. iv. 16.

1 Cling to the Bible, though all else be taken;
   Lose not its precepts so precious and pure;
   Souls that are sleeping its tidings awaken:
   Life from the dead in its promises sure.
      Cling to the Bible! etc.

2 Cling to the Bible!—this jewel and treasure
   Brings life eternal, and saves fallen man;
   Surely its value no mortal can measure:
   Seek for its blessing, O soul, while you can!

3 Lamp for the feet that in by-ways have wandered,
   Guide for the youth that would otherwise fall;
   Hope for the sinner whose life has been squandered;
   Staff for the aged, and best Book for all!

                              M. J. Smith.

Quam Dilecta. 6.6.6.6. H. L. JENNER.

576 *Continue ye in My love.*—JOHN xv. 9.

1 ONCE more before we part,
  We bless the Saviour's Name;
  Let every tongue and heart
    Join to extol the Lamb.

2 We on Thy holy Word
  Would feed, and live, and grow;

Go on to know Thee, Lord,
  And practice what we know.

3 Lord, in Thy grace we came,
  Thy blessing still impart;
  We met in Thine own Name,
    And in Thy Name we part.

Horsley. C.M. WM. HORSLEY.

577 *Alternative Tune,* ST. FLAVIAN, *No.* 356.
So they read in the book in the law of God.—NEHEMIAH viii. 8.

1 WE seek Thee, Lord, for in Thy Word
    Such tender love we see;
  With beckoning hand Thou still dost stand,
    And bid us come to Thee.

2 Close to Thine arm, from care and harm,
    Once more the children press;
  Oh, let Thy grace in every place
    Our Scripture Union bless!

3 Thy help we plead, that as we read
    True light our souls may fill,
  Till every heart be taught its part
    In God's own loving will.

4 One hope we claim, one steadfast aim,
    Though scattered far and wide—

One path to share, one cross to bear,
    As brethren side by side.

5 From far around, with gladsome sound,
    Our pilgrim song is heard,
  While through the night is gleaming bright
    The lantern of God's Word.

6 With this their guide, through paths un-
    Thy children's steps have trod;   [tried
  Till little feet have reached the street
    Before the throne of God.

7 Grant us at last, our journey past,
    To meet from every land,
  Through Thy dear love in heaven to prove,
    One grand united band!

Alice E. Rhodes.

Lynton. C.M. A. J. JAMOUNEAU.

By permission of the Epworth Press.
Alternative Tune, ST. FLAVIAN, *No.* 356.

578 *The entrance of Thy words giveth light.*—PSALM cxix. 130.

1 THE Spirit breathes upon the Word,
    And brings the truth to sight ;
  Precepts and promises afford
    A sanctifying light.

2 A glory gilds the sacred page,
    Majestic, like the sun :
  It gives a light to every age ;
    It gives, but borrows none.

3 The hand that gave it still supplies
    The gracious light and heat :

His truths upon the nations rise—
    They rise, but never set.

4 Let everlasting thanks be Thine,
    For such a bright display
  As makes a world of darkness shine
    With beams of heavenly day.

5 My soul rejoices to pursue
    The steps of Him I love,
  Till glory breaks upon my view,
    In brighter worlds above.

W. Cowper.

Southwell. C.M. H. S. IRONS.

Alternative Tunes, BEATITUDO, *No.* 571, *and* EVAN, *No.* 587.

579 *How sweet are Thy words.*—PSALM cxix. 103.

1 FATHER of mercies, in Thy Word
    What endless glory shines !
  For ever be Thy Name adored
    For these celestial lines.

2 Here springs of consolation rise
    To cheer the fainting mind,
  And thirsty souls receive supplies,
    And sweet refreshment find.

3 Here the Redeemer's welcome voice
    Spreads heavenly peace around ;

And life and everlasting joys
    Attend the blissful sound.

4 Oh, may these hallowed pages be
    My ever dear delight !
  And still new beauties may I see,
    And still increasing light.

5 Divine Instructor, gracious Lord,
    Be Thou for ever near ;
  Teach me to love Thy sacred Word,
    And view my Saviour here.

Anne Steele.

Culbach.   7.7.7.7.   German.

Alternative Tune, EPHRAIM, No. 9.

580   *Thy Word was unto me the joy and rejoicing of mine heart.*—JER. xv. 16.

1 HOLY Bible, Book divine,
Precious treasure, thou art mine;
Mine, to tell me whence I came,
Mine, to tell me what I am.

2 Mine, to chide me when I rove,
Mine, to show a Saviour's love;
Mine, thou art to guide and guard,
Mine, to punish or reward;

3 Mine, to comfort in distress,
Suffering in this wilderness;
Mine, to show, by living faith,
Man can triumph over death;

4 Mine, to tell of joys to come,
And the rebel sinner's doom;
Holy Bible, Book divine,
Precious treasure, thou art mine!

J. Burton, Sen.

Farrant.   C.M.   R. FARRANT.

581   *The Lord shall open unto thee His good treasure.*—DEUT. xxviii. 12.

1 THY Word is like a garden, Lord,
With flowers bright and fair,
And every one that seeks may pluck
A lovely nosegay there.

2 Thy Word is like a deep, deep mine,
And jewels rich and rare
Are hidden in its mighty depths
For every searcher there.

3 Thy Word is like the starry host:
A thousand rays of light
Are seen to guide the traveller,
And make his pathway bright.

4 Thy Word is like a glorious choir,
And loud its anthems ring:

Though many tongues and parts unite,
It is one song they sing.

5 Thy Word is like an armoury,
Where soldiers may repair,
And find for life's long battle-day
All needful weapons there.

6 Oh! may I love Thy precious Word,
May I explore its mine!
May I its fragrant flowers glean,
May light upon me shine!

7 Oh! may I find my armour there,—
Thy Word my trusty sword;
I'll learn to fight with every foe
The battle of the Lord.

Edwin Hodder.

Oh, Wonderful Word!   P.M.   Ira D. Sankey.

The Word of the Lord endureth for ever.—1 Peter i. 25.

582

1.
Oh, wonderful, wonderful Word of the Lord!
  True wisdom its pages unfold;
And though we may read them a thousand
    times o'er,
  They never, no, never grow old.
Each line hath a treasure, each promise a
  That all if they will may secure; [pearl,
And we know that when time and the world
    pass away,
  God's Word shall for ever endure.

2.
Oh, wonderful, wonderful Word of the Lord!
  The lamp that our Father above
So kindly has lighted to teach us the way
  That leads to the arms of His love,
Its warnings, its counsels, are faithful and
  Its judgments are perfect and pure; [just;
And we know that when time and the world
    pass away,
  God's Word shall for ever endure.

3.
Oh, wonderful, wonderful Word of the Lord!
  Our only salvation is there;
It carries conviction down deep in the heart,
  And shows us ourselves as we are.
It tells of a Saviour, and points to the cross,
  Where pardon we now may secure;
For we know that when time and the world
    pass away,
  God's Word shall for ever endure.

4.
Oh, wonderful, wonderful Word of the Lord!
  The hope of our friends in the past;
Its truth where so firmly they anchored their
  Through ages eternal shall last. [trust,
Oh, wonderful, wonderful Word of the Lord!
  Unchanging, abiding, and sure;
For we know that when time and the world
    pass away,
  God's Word shall for ever endure.

Julia Sterling.

Guard the Bible Well.　　P.M.　　W. H. DOANE.

CHORUS.

Rouse then, Christians! Rally for the Bi - ble! Work on, pray on, spread the truth abroad;

Stand then like men, in the cause triumphant, For the Bi - ble is the Word of God.

583 *Keep that which is committed to thy trust.—*1 TIM. vi. 20.

1 GUARD the Bible well, all its foes repel,
　　The sweet story tell of the Lord:
　Guard what God revealed, as our sun and shield
　Never, never yield His holy Word.
　　Rouse then, Christians! etc.

2 Book of love divine, precious Word of Thine,
　　Let it ever shine all abroad;
　In the Spirit's might we must win the fight
　For this Gospel light, the truth of God.

3 Shout the Bible song, swell the mighty throng!
　　In the cause be strong of the right;
　Look to God in prayer when the foe you dare,
　And for ever wear His armour bright.

4 Oh, ye Christian band, for this Bible stand!
　　By the Lord's command, ne'er give o'er;
　Lead the army on, till the strife is done,
　And the cause is won for evermore.
　　　　　　　　　　　T. McDougall.

Ravensbaw. 6.6.6.6. German.

584 *The Word of God which liveth and abideth for ever.*—1 PETER i. 23.

1 LORD, Thy Word abideth,
  And our footsteps guideth;
  Who its truth believeth
  Light and joy receiveth.

2 When our foes are near us,
  Then Thy Word doth cheer us,
  Word of consolation,
  Message of salvation.

3 When the storms are o'er us,
  And dark clouds before us,
  Then its light directeth,
  And our way protecteth.

4 Who can tell the pleasure,
  Who recount the treasure,
  By Thy Word imparted
  To the simple-hearted?

5 Word of mercy, giving
  Succour to the living;
  Word of life, supplying
  Comfort to the dying.

6 Oh, that we discerning
  Its most holy learning,
  Lord, may love and fear Thee,
  Evermore be near Thee!
    Sir H. W. Baker.

8.7.8.4.

585 Filey. *I have given them Thy word.*—JOHN xvii. 14. L. MASON.

1. Book of grace and Book of glo-ry! Gift of God to age and youth,

Wondrous is thy sa-cred sto-ry, | 1st time. Bright, bright with truth! | 2nd time. Bright, bright with truth!

2 Book of love! in accents tender
  Speaking unto such as we;
  May it lead us, Lord, to render
  All, all to Thee.

3 Book of hope! the spirit sighing,
  Sweetest comfort finds in thee,
  As it hears the Saviour crying,
  "Come, come to Me!"

4 Book of peace! when nights of sorrow
  Fall upon us drearily,
  Thou wilt bring a shining morrow,
  Full, full of thee.

5 Book of life! when we, reposing,
  Bid farewell to friends we love,
  Give us, for the life then closing,
  Life, life above. *T. Mackellar.*

Staincliffe. L.M. R. W. Dixon.

Alternative Tune, Tallis' Canon, *No. 604.*

586 *All scripture is given by inspiration of God, and is profitable for doctrine, for reproof, for correction, for instruction in righteousness.*—2 Tim. iii. 16.

1 There is a lamp whose steady light
  Guides the poor traveller in the night:
  'Tis God's own Word! Its beaming ray
  Can turn the midnight into day.

2 There is a storehouse of rich fare,
  Supplied with plenty and to spare:
  'Tis God's own Word! It spreads a feast
  For every hungering, thirsty guest.

3 There is a chart whose tracings show
  The onward course, when tempests blow:
  'Tis God's own Word! There, there are found
  Directions for the homeward bound.

4 There is a tree whose leaves impart
  Health to the burdened, contrite heart:
  'Tis God's own Word! It cures of sin,
  And makes the guilty conscience clean.

5 Give me this lamp to light my road,
  This storehouse for my daily food;
  Give me this chart for life's rough sea,
  These healing leaves, this heavenly tree.

H. J. Betts.

Evan. C.M. W. H. Havergal.

Alternative Tune, St. Fulbert, *No. 492.*

587 *A lamp unto my feet, and a light unto my path.*—Psalm cxix. 105.

1 Lamp of our feet, whereby we trace
  Our path when wont to stray;
  Stream, from the fount of heavenly grace;
  Brook, by the traveller's way:

2 Bread of our souls, whereon we feed;
  True manna from on high;
  Our guide and chart, wherein we read
  Of realms beyond the sky:

3 Pillar of fire, through watches dark,
  And radiant cloud by day:
  When waves would whelm our tossing bark,
  Our anchor and our stay:

4 Word of the everlasting God,
  Will of His glorious Son,
  Without thee how could earth be trod,
  Or heaven itself be won?

5 Yet to unfold thy hidden worth,
  Thy mysteries to reveal,
  That Spirit which first gave thee forth,
  Thy volume must unseal.

6 Lord, grant that we aright may learn
  The wisdom it imparts,
  And to its heavenly teaching turn,
  With simple, childlike hearts.

B. Barton.

St. Anselm.   7.6.7.6., D.   Sir J. Barnby.

Alternative Tune, BENTLEY, *No.* 309.

588   *Let the word of Christ dwell in you richly.*—COL. iii. 16.

1 O WORD of God Incarnate!
O Wisdom from on high!
O Truth unchanged, unchanging,
O Light of our dark sky;
We praise Thee for the radiance
That from the hallowed page,
A lantern to our footsteps,
Shines on from age to age.

2 The church from her dear Master
Received the gift divine,
And still that light she lifteth
O'er all the earth to shine,
It is the golden casket
Where gems of truth are stored;
It is the heaven-drawn picture
Of Christ, the living Word.

3 It floateth like a banner
Before God's host unfurled;
It shineth like a beacon
Above the darkling world;
It is the chart and compass
That o'er life's surging sea,
'Mid mists and rocks and quicksands,
Still guide, O Christ, to Thee.

W. W. How.

Lilies. P.M. W. B. BRADBURY.

589

I have rejoiced in the way of Thy testimonies, as much as in all
*riches.—*Psalm cxix. 14.

1.

Thank God for the Bible! 'tis there that we
The story of Christ and His love: [find
How He came down to earth from His
   beautiful home
In the mansions of glory above:
   Thanks to Him we will bring,
   Praise to Him we will sing;
For He came down to earth from His
   beautiful home
In the mansions of glory above.

2.

While He lived on this earth, to the sick and
   the blind,
And to mourners His blessings were given;
And He said, "Let the little ones come unto
   Me,
   For of such is the kingdom of heaven."
   Jesus calls us to come,
   He's prepared us a home,   [Me,
For He said, "Let the little ones come unto
For of such is the kingdom of heaven."

3.

In the Bible we read of a beautiful land,
   Where sorrow and pain never come;
For Jesus is there with a heavenly band,
   And 'tis there He's prepared us a home.
   Jesus calls—shall we stay?
   No! we'll gladly obey;
For Jesus is there with a heavenly band,
   And 'tis there He's prepared us a home.

4.

Thank God for the Bible! its truth o'er the
   earth
   We'll scatter with bountiful hand;
But we never can tell what a Bible is worth,
   Till we go to that beautiful land.
   There our thanks we will bring,
   There with angels we'll sing,
And its worth we can tell, when with Jesus
   we dwell,
   In heaven, that beautiful land.

Anon.

Section X.—Morning Hymns.

Silksworth. 7.5.7.5.7.7. Charles Vincent.

590 *Thy sun shall no more go down.*—Isa. lx. 20.

1 Every morning the red sun
  Rises warm and bright;
But the evening cometh on,
  And the dark cold night:
There's a bright land far away,
Where 'tis never-ending day.

2 Every spring the sweet young flowers
  Open bright and gay,
Till the chilly autumn hours
  Wither them away:
There's a land we have not seen,
Where the trees are always green.

3 Little birds sing songs of praise
  All the summer long;
But in colder, shorter days

They forget their song.
  There's a place where angels sing
Ceaseless praises to their King.

4 Christ our Lord is ever near
  Those who follow Him;
But we cannot see Him here,
  For our eyes are dim:
There's a happy glorious place,
Where men always see His face.

5 Who shall go to that fair land?
  All who love the right;
Holy children there shall stand,
  In their robes of white:
For that heaven, so bright and blest,
Is our everlasting rest.

Mrs. C. F. Alexander.

St. Timothy. C.M. Sir H. W. Baker.

Alternative Tune, Farrant, *No.* 581.

591 *Whatsoever ye do, do all to the glory of God.*—1 Cor. x. 31.

1 My Father, for another night
  Of quiet sleep and rest,
For all the joy of morning light,
  Thy holy Name be blest.

2 Now with the new-born day I give
  Myself anew to Thee,
That as Thou willest I may live,
  And what Thou willest be.

3 Whate'er I do, things great or small,
  Whate'er I speak or frame,
Thy glory may I seek in all,
  Do all in Jesus' Name.

4 My Father, for His sake, I pray,
  Thy child accept and bless;
And lead me by Thy grace to-day
  In paths of righteousness.

Sir H. W. Baker.

Morning Hymn. L.M. F. H. Barthelemon.

Alternative Tune, MELCOMBE, No. 104.

592

I myself will awake early.—PSALM cviii. 2.

AWAKE, my soul, and with the sun
Thy daily stage of duty run;
Shake off dull sloth, and joyful rise
To pay thy morning sacrifice.

2 All praise to Thee, who safe hast kept,
And hast refreshed me while I slept;
Grant, Lord, when I from death shall wake,
I may of endless light partake.

3 Lord, I my vows to Thee renew:
Disperse my sins as morning dew;

Guard my first springs of thought and will,
And with Thyself my spirit fill.

4 Direct, control, suggest this day
All I design, or do, or say;
That all my powers with all their might,
In Thy sole glory may unite.

5 Praise God, from whom all blessings flow;
Praise Him, all creatures here below;
Praise Him above, ye heavenly host;
Praise Father, Son, and Holy Ghost.

T. Ken.

Irish. C.M. ISAAC SMITH.

593 *This is the day which the Lord hath made.*—PSALM cxviii. 24.

1 THIS is the day the Lord hath made,
He calls the hours His own;
Let heaven rejoice, let earth be glad,
And praise surround the throne.

2 To-day He rose and left the dead,
And Satan's empire fell;
To-day the saints His triumphs spread,
And all His wonders tell.

3 Hosanna to the anointed King,
To David's holy Son!

Make haste to help us, Lord, and bring
Salvation from Thy throne.

4 Blest be the Lord, who comes to men
With messages of grace;
Who comes, in God His Father's Name,
To save our sinful race.

5 Hosanna in the highest strains
The church on earth can raise;
The highest heavens in which He reigns
Shall give Him nobler praise.

Isaac Watts.

Q*

Lymington. 7.6.7.6., D. R. JACKSON.

Alternative Tune, DAY OF REST, *No.* 363.

594 *Call the Sabbath a delight.*—ISA. lviii. 13.

1 O DAY of rest and gladness,
  O day of joy and light,
  O balm of care and sadness,
  Most beautiful, most bright;
  On thee the high and lowly,
  Before the eternal throne,
  Sing Holy, Holy, Holy,
  To the great Three in One.

2 On thee, at the creation,
  The light first had its birth;
  On thee, for our salvation,
  Christ rose from depths of earth;
  On thee our Lord victorious
  The Spirit sent from heaven;
  And thus on thee most glorious
  A triple light was given.

3 Thou art a cooling fountain
  In life's dry, dreary sand,
  From thee, like Pisgah's mountain,
  We view our promised land;

  A day of sweet refection,
  A day of holy love,
  A day of resurrection
  From earth to things above.

4 To-day on weary nations
  The heavenly manna falls,
  To holy convocations
  The silver trumpet calls,
  Where Gospel-light is glowing
  With pure and radiant beams,
  And living water flowing
  With soul refreshing streams.

5 New graces ever gaining
  From this our day of rest,
  We reach the rest remaining
  To spirits of the blest.
  To Holy Ghost be praises,
  To Father and to Son;
  The church her voice upraises
  To Thee, blest Three in One.

  C. Wordsworth.

Ascalon. 6.6.8.6.6.8.

595

Peace be within thee.—PSALM cxxii. 8.

1 How pleased and blest was I
   To hear the people cry,
"Come, let us seek our God to-day!"
   Yes, with a cheerful zeal
   We haste to Zion's hill,
And there our vows and homage pay.

2 Zion, thrice happy place,
   Adorned with wondrous grace,
And walls of strength embrace thee round;
   In thee our tribes appear,
   To pray and praise, and hear
The sacred Gospel's joyful sound.

3 There David's greater Son
   Hath fixed His royal throne;
He sits for grace and judgment there.

He bids the saints be glad,
He makes the sinner sad,
And humble souls rejoice with fear.

4 May peace attend thy gate,
   And joy within thee wait,
To bless the soul of every guest:
   The man that seeks thy peace,
   And wishes thine increase,
A thousand blessings on him rest.

5 My tongue repeats her vows,
   Peace to this sacred house!
For there my friends and kindred dwell;
   And, since my glorious God
   Makes thee His blest abode,
My soul shall ever love thee well.

Isaac Watts.

596 Spain. 6.6.6.6., D.   *I was in the Spirit on the Lord's day.*—REV. i. 10.

1. { Je - sus, we love to meet   On this Thy ho-ly day:
We worship round Thy seat   On this Thy ho-ly day: } Thou tender, heav'nly Friend,

To Thee our pray'rs ascend; O'er our young spirits bend   On this Thy ho-ly day.

2 We dare not trifle now
   On this Thy holy day:
In silent awe we bow
   On this Thy holy day:
Check every wandering thought,
And let us all be taught
To serve Thee as we ought
   On this Thy holy day.

3 We listen to Thy Word
   On this Thy holy day:
Bless all that we have heard
   On this Thy holy day:
Go with us when we part,
And to each youthful heart
Thy saving grace impart
   On this Thy holy day.

E. Parson.

Section XI.—Evening Hymns.

Christ's Own Peace.

597

Tranquilly. ♩ = 80.

P.M.

H. Ernest Nichol.

Chorus. ♩. = 48.

Light that groweth not pale With day's de - crease, Love that

nev-er can fail Till life shall cease; Joy no tri-al can mar,

Hope that shineth a-far, Faith se - rene as a star, And Christ's own peace.

597

The night also is Thine.—PSALM lxxiv. 16.

1 LORD, it is eventide: the light of day is waning;
    Far o'er the golden land earth's voices faint and fall;
Lowly we pray to Thee for strength and love sustaining,
    Lowly we ask of Thee Thy peace upon us all.
        Oh, grant unto our souls—
        Light that groweth not pale, etc.

2 Lord, it is eventide: we turn to Thee for healing,
    Like those of Galilee who came at close of day;
Speak to our waiting souls, their hidden founts unsealing;
    Touch us with hands divine that take our sin away.
        Oh, grant unto our souls—

3 Saviour, Thou knowest all, the trial and temptation,
    Knowest the wilfulness and waywardness of youth;
Help us to cling to Thee, our strength and our salvation,
    Help us to find in Thee the one eternal Truth.
        Oh, grant unto our souls—

4 Lord, it is eventide: our hearts await Thy giving,
    Wait for that peace divine that none can take away,
Peace that shall lift our souls to loftier heights of living,
    Till we abide with Thee in everlasting day.
        Oh, grant unto our souls—   *Colin Sterne.*

St. Mattbias.   8.8.8.8.8.8.   W. H. MONK.

598   *The Lord is my light.*—PSALM xxvii. 1.

1 SWEET Saviour, bless us ere we go;
    Thy Word into our minds instil,
And make our lukewarm hearts to glow
    With lowly love and fervent will.
Through life's long day and death's dark
    O gentle Jesus! be our Light.   [night,

2 The day is done, its hours have run,
    And Thou has taken count of all,
The scanty triumphs grace hath won,
    The broken vow, the frequent fall.
Through life's long day and death's dark
    O gentle Jesus! be our Light.   [night,

3 Grant us, dear Lord, from evil ways
    True absolution and release;
And bless us, more than in past days,

With purity and inward peace.
Through life's long day and death's dark
    O gentle Jesus! be our Light.   [night,

4 Do more than pardon; give us joy,
    Sweet fear, and sober liberty,
And simple hearts without alloy
    That only long to be like Thee.
Through life's long day and death's dark
    O gentle Jesus! be our Light.   [night,

5 For all we love, the poor, the sad,
    The sinful, unto Thee we call;
O let Thy mercy make us glad:
    Thou art our Jesus, and our All.
Through life's long day and death's dark
    O gentle Jesus! be our Light.   [night,
                            F. W. Faber.

Abends. [FIRST TUNE.] L.M. Sir H. S. Oakeley.

Hursley. [SECOND TUNE.] L.M. P. Ritter.

599 *The darkness and the light are both alike to Thee.*—PSALM cxxxix. 12.

1 SUN of my soul, Thou Saviour dear,
It is not night if Thou be near;
Oh, may no earth-born cloud arise
To hide Thee from Thy servant's eyes!

2 When the soft dews of kindly sleep
My wearied eyelids gently steep,
Be my last thought, how sweet to rest
For ever on my Saviour's breast!

3 Abide with me from morn till eve,
For without Thee I cannot live;
Abide with me when night is nigh,
For without Thee I dare not die.

4 If some poor wandering child of Thine
Have spurned to-day the voice divine,
Now, Lord, the gracious work begin;
Let him no more lie down in sin.

5 Watch by the sick; enrich the poor
With blessings from Thy boundless store;
Be every mourner's sleep to-night,
Like infant's slumbers, pure and light.

6 Come near and bless us when we wake,
Ere through the world our way we take;
Till, in the ocean of Thy love,
We lose ourselves in heaven above.

J. Keble.

600 St. Anatolius. 7.6.7.6.8.8. A. H. Brown.

By permission of the Oxford University Press.

600   *Thou, Lord, only makest me dwell in safety.*—PSALM iv. 8.

1 THE day is past and over;
    All thanks, O Lord, to Thee;
    I pray Thee now that sinless
    The hours of dark may be:
    O Jesus, keep me in Thy sight,
    And guard me through the coming night

2 The joys of day are over;
    I lift my heart to Thee,
    And ask Thee that offenceless
    The hours of dark may be:
    O Jesus, keep me in Thy sight,
    And guard me through the coming night.

3 The toils of day are over;
    I raise the hymn to Thee,
    And ask that free from peril
    The hours of dark may be:
    O Jesus, keep me in Thy sight,
    And guard me through the coming night.

4 Be Thou my soul's preserver,
    For Thou alone dost know
    How many are the perils
    Through which I have to go:
    O loving Jesus, hear my call,
    And guard and save me from them all.

J. M. Neale.

Eventide.   10.10 10.10.   W. H. MONK.

601   *Abide with us: for it is toward evening.*—LUKE xxiv. 29.

1 ABIDE with me, fast falls the eventide;
    The darkness deepens; Lord, with me abide;
    When other helpers fail, and comforts flee,
    Help of the helpless, oh, abide with me.

2 Swift to its close ebbs out life's little day;
    Earth's joys grow dim, its glories pass away;
    Change and decay in all around I see;
    O Thou, who changest not, abide with me.

3 I need Thy presence every passing hour:
    What but Thy grace can foil the tempter's power?
    Who like Thyself my guide and stay can be?
    Through cloud and sunshine, Lord, abide with me.

4 I fear no foe, with Thee at hand to bless,
    Ills have no weight, and tears no bitterness:
    Where is death's sting? where, grave, thy victory?
    I triumph still, if Thou abide with me.

5 Reveal Thyself before my closing eyes,
    Shine through the gloom, and point me to the skies:
    Heaven's morning breaks, and earth's vain shadows flee:
    In life, in death, O Lord, abide with me.   *H. F. Lyte.*

Angelus. L.M. G. JOSEPH.

Alternative Tune, EDEN, *No.* 190.

602 *When the even was come . . . He healed all that were sick.*—MATT. viii. 16.

1 AT even, ere the sun was set,
  The sick, O Lord, around Thee lay;
  Oh, in what divers pains they met!
  Oh, with what joy they went away!

2 Once more 'tis even-tide, and we
  Oppressed with various ills draw near:
  What if Thy form we cannot see?
  We know and feel that Thou art here.

3 O Saviour Christ, our woes dispel:
  For some are sick; and some are sad;
  And some have never loved Thee well;
  And some have lost the love they had;

4 And some have found the world is vain,
  Yet from the world they break not free;
  And some have friends who give them pain,
  Yet have not sought a Friend in Thee.

5 And none, O Lord, have perfect rest,
  For none are wholly free from sin;
  And they who fain would serve Thee best
  Are conscious most of wrong within.

6 O Saviour Christ, Thou too art Man;
  Thou hast been troubled, tempted, tried;
  Thy kind but searching glance can scan
  The very wounds that shame would hide.

7 Thy touch has still its ancient power;
  No word from Thee can fruitless fall;
  Hear, in this solemn evening hour,
  And in Thy mercy heal us all.
                            H. Twells.

603 Ellers. 10.10.10.10. E. J. HOPKINS.

603

Peace I leave with you, My peace I give unto you.—JOHN xiv. 27.

1 SAVIOUR, again to Thy dear Name we raise
 With one accord our parting hymn of praise;
 We stand to bless Thee ere our worship cease,
 Then, lowly kneeling, wait Thy word of peace.

2 Grant us Thy peace upon our homeward way;
 With Thee begun, with Thee shall end the day:
 Guard Thou the lips from sin, the hearts from shame,
 That in this house have called upon Thy Name.

3 Grant us Thy peace, Lord, through the coming night,
 Turn Thou for us its darkness into light;
 From harm and danger keep Thy children free,
 For dark and light are both alike to Thee.

4 Grant us Thy peace throughout our earthly life,
 Our balm in sorrow, and our stay in strife;
 Then, when Thy voice shall bid our conflict cease,
 Call us, O Lord, to Thine eternal peace.

J. Ellerton.

Tallis' Canon.   L.M.   T. TALLIS.

604

*In the night His song shall be with me, and my prayer unto the God of
my life.*—PSALM xlii. 8.

1 GLORY to Thee, my God, this night,
 For all the blessings of the light;
 Keep me, oh, keep me, King of kings,
 Beneath Thine own almighty wings.

2 Forgive me, Lord, for Thy dear Son,
 The ill that I this day have done;
 That with the world, myself, and Thee,
 I, ere I sleep, at peace may be.

3 Teach me to live, that I may dread
 The grave as little as my bed;
 Teach me to die, that so I may
 Rise glorious at the last great day.

4 Oh, may my soul on Thee repose,
 And may sweet sleep mine eyelids close,—
 Sleep that may me more vigorous make
 To serve my God when I awake.

5 Praise God, from whom all blessings flow;
 Praise Him, all creatures here below;
 Praise Him above, ye heavenly host;
 Praise Father, Son, and Holy Ghost.

T. Ken.

Eudoxia. [FIRST TUNE.]   6.5.6.5.   S. BARING-GOULD.

Copyright. By permission of A. W. Ridley & Co.

Lyndhurst. [SECOND TUNE.]   6.5.6.5., D.   F. W. BLUNT.

By permission of Novello and Company, Limited.

605

When thou liest down, thou shalt not be afraid : yea, thou shalt lie down,
and thy sleep shall be sweet.—PROV. iii. 24.

1 **Now** the day is over,
Night is drawing nigh,
Shadows of the evening
Steal across the sky.

2 Now the darkness gathers,
Stars their watches keep,
Birds and beasts and flowers
Soon will be asleep.

3 Jesus, give the weary
Calm and sweet repose ;
With Thy tenderest blessing
May mine eyelids close.

4 Grant to little children
Visions bright of Thee ;
Guard the sailors tossing
On the deep blue sea.

5 Comfort every sufferer
Watching late in pain ;
Those who plan some evil
From their sin restrain.

6 Through the long night watches
May Thine angels spread
Their white wings above me,
Watching round my bed.

7 When the morning wakens,
Then may I arise
Pure and fresh and sinless
In Thy holy eyes.

8 Glory to the Father,
Glory to the Son,
And to Thee, blest Spirit,
Whilst all ages run.

S. Baring-Gould.

St. Clement. 9.8.9.8. C. C. SCHOLEFIELD.

606 *From the rising of the sun even unto the going down of the same My Name shall be great among the Gentiles.*—MAL. i. 11.

1 THE day Thou gavest, Lord, is ended,
  The darkness falls at Thy behest;
To Thee our morning hymns ascended,
  Thy praise shall sanctify our rest.

2 We thank Thee that Thy church unsleeping,
  While earth rolls onward into light,
Through all the world her watch is keeping,
  And rests not now by day or night.

3 As o'er each continent and island
  The dawn leads on another day,
The voice of prayer is never silent,
  Nor dies the strain of praise away.

4 The sun that bids us rest is waking
  Our brethren 'neath the western sky;
And hour by hour fresh lips are making
  Thy wondrous doings heard on high.

5 So be it, Lord; Thy throne shall never,
  Like earth's proud empires, pass away;
Thy kingdom stands, and grows for ever,
  Till all Thy creatures own Thy sway.

J. Ellerton.

Evening Prayer. 8.7.8.7. GEO. C. STEBBINS.

607 *Let . . . the lifting up of my hands be as the evening sacrifice.*—PSALM cxli. 2.

1 SAVIOUR, breathe an evening blessing,
  Ere repose our spirits seal;
Sin and want we come confessing;
  Thou canst save, and Thou canst heal.

2 Though destruction walk around us,
  Though the arrows past us fly,
Angel-guards from Thee surround us;
  We are safe if Thou art nigh.

3 Though the night be dark and dreary,
  Darkness cannot hide from Thee;
Thou art He, who, never weary,
  Watchest where Thy people be.

4 Should swift death this night o'ertake us,
  And our couch become our tomb,
May the morn in heaven awake us,
  Clad in light and deathless bloom.

J. Edmeston.

Dismissal.   8.7.8.7.8.7.   W. L. VINER.

608   *They went unto their tents joyful and glad of heart.*—1 KINGS viii. 66.

1 LORD, dismiss us with Thy blessing,
   Fill our hearts with joy and peace:
Let us each, Thy love possessing,
   Triumph in redeeming grace:
     Oh, refresh us!
   Travelling through this wilderness.

2 Thanks we give, and adoration,
   For Thy Gospel's joyful sound;
May the fruits of Thy salvation

In our hearts and lives abound:
   May Thy presence
With us evermore be found!

3 So, whene'er the signal 's given
   Us from earth to call away;
Borne on angels' wings to heaven,
   Glad the summons to obey,
     May we ever
Reign with Christ in endless day!

J. Fawcett.

609 Sherwin.   7.7.7.7.4., with Chorus.   WILLIAM F. SHERWIN.

CHORUS.

Holy, Holy, Ho-ly, Lord God of Hosts!

Heav'n and earth are full of Thee; Heav'n and earth are praising Thee, O Lord, most high.

609

Holy, holy, holy, Lord God Almighty.—REV. iv. 8.

1 DAY is dying in the west,
Heaven is touching earth with rest,
Wait and worship while the night
Sets her evening lamps alight
Through all the sky.
Holy, Holy, Holy, etc.

2 Lord of life, beneath the dome
Of the universe, Thy home,
Gather us, who seek Thy face,
To the fold of Thy embrace,
For Thou art nigh.

3 While the deepening shadows fall,
Heart of love, enfolding all,
Through the glory and the grace
Of the stars that veil Thy face,
Our hearts ascend.

4 When for ever from our sight
Pass the stars, the day, the night,
Lord of angels, on our eyes
Let eternal morning rise,
And shadows end.
Mary A. Lathbury.

Evening Hymn.   8.8.7.8.8.7.   WILLIAM JACKSON.

610

Deliver us from evil.—LUKE xi. 4.

1 FATHER, in high heaven dwelling,
May our evening song be telling
Of Thy mercy large and free :
Through the day Thy love hath fed us,
Through the day Thy care hath led us,
With divinest charity.

2 This day's sins, O pardon, Saviour,
Evil thoughts, perverse behaviour,
Envy, pride, and vanity :
From the world, the flesh, deliver,
Save us now, and save us ever,
O Thou Lamb of Calvary !

3 From enticements of the devil,
From the might of spirits evil,
Be our shield and panoply :
Let Thy power this night defend us,
And a heavenly peace attend us,
And angelic company.

4 Whilst the night-dews are distilling,
Holy Ghost, each heart be filling
With Thine own serenity :
Softly let the eyes be closing,
Loving souls on Thee reposing,
Ever blessèd Trinity !   *G. Rawson.*

Section XII.—Foreign Missions.

Benson.   *v. 2*   P.M.   M. D. KINGHAM.

When cover the

611   *The earth shall be filled with the knowledge of the glory of the Lord, as the waters cover the sea.*—HAB. ii. 14.

1 GOD is working His purpose out, as year succeeds to year;
   God is working His purpose out, and the time is drawing near—
   Nearer and nearer draws the time, the time that shall surely be,
   When the earth shall be filled with the glory of God, as the waters cover the sea.

2 From utmost East to utmost West, where'er man's foot hath trod,
   By the mouth of many messengers goes forth the voice of God;
   Give ear to Me, ye continents—ye isles, give ear to Me,
   That the earth may be filled with the glory of God, as the waters cover the sea.

3 What can we do to work God's work, to prosper and increase
   The brotherhood of all mankind—the reign of the Prince of Peace?
   What can we do to hasten the time—the time that shall surely be,
   When the earth shall be filled with the glory of God, as the waters cover the sea?

4 March we forth in the strength of God with the banner of Christ unfurled,
   That the light of the glorious Gospel of truth may shine throughout the world:
   Fight we the fight with sorrow and sin, to set their captives free,
   That the earth may be filled with the glory of God, as the waters cover the sea.

5 All we can do is nothing worth, unless God blesses the deed;
   Vainly we hope for the harvest, till God gives life to the seed;
   Yet nearer and nearer draws the time—the time that shall surely be,
   When the earth shall be filled with the glory of God, as the waters cover the sea.

                                              A. C. Ainger.

Bishopgarth. 8.7.8.7., D. Sir Arthur S. Sullivan.
Stately.

By permission of Novello and Company, Limited.

612 *Go ye therefore, and teach all nations.*—Matt. xxviii. 19.

1 "For My sake and the Gospel's, go
   And tell redemption's story;"
His heralds answer, "Be it so,
   And Thine, Lord, all the glory!"
They preach His birth, His life, His cross,
   The love of His atonement,
For whom they count the world but loss,
   His Easter, His enthronement.

2 Hark, hark, the trump of jubilee
   Proclaims to every nation,
From pole to pole, by land and sea,
   Glad tidings of salvation.
As nearer draws the day of doom,
   While still the battle rages,
The heavenly Day-spring, through the
   Breaks on the night of ages. [gloom,

3 Still on and on the anthems spread
   Of hallelujah voices,
In concert with the holy dead,
   The warrior Church rejoices:
Their snow-white robes are washed in blood,
   Their golden harps are ringing;
Earth and the Paradise of God
   One triumph-song are singing.

4 He comes, whose Advent trumpet drowns
   The last of time's evangels—
Emmanuel crowned with many crowns,
   The Lord of saints and angels:
O Life, Light, Love, the great I AM,
   Triune, who changest never;
The throne of God and of the Lamb
   Is Thine, and Thine for ever!

                              E. H. Bickersteth.

Moel Llys.　　　　　　　7.5.7.5.7.7.　　　　　　SARAH G. STOCK.

613　　　*Sing unto the Lord, all the earth.*—PSALM xcvi. 1.

1 LET the song go round the earth,
　　Jesus Christ is Lord!
Sound His praises, tell His worth,
　　Be His Name adored;
Every clime and every tongue
Join the grand, the glorious song!

2 Let the song go round the earth!
　　From the eastern sea,
Where the daylight has its birth,
　　Glad, and bright, and free:
China's millions join the strains,
Waft them on to India's plains.

3 Let the song go round the earth!
　　Lands where Islam's sway
Darkly broods o'er home and hearth,
　　Cast their bonds away!
Let His praise from Afric's shore
Rise and swell her wide lands o'er!

4 Let the song go round the earth!
　　Where the summer smiles;
Let the notes of holy mirth
　　Break from distant isles!
Inland forests dark and dim,
Snow-bound coasts give back the hymn.

5 Let the song go round the earth!
　　Jesus Christ is King!
With the story of His worth
　　Let the whole world ring!
Him creation all adore
Evermore and evermore!

　　　　　　　Sarah G. Stock.

614 The Hope of the World.　8.7.8.7., D.　　　J. S. DOBBS.

614 *He shall gather the lambs with His arm.*—ISA. xl. 11.

1 JESUS is calling the children
  Into His loving embrace,
Calling by words sweet and gentle,
  And by the love in His face:
From every land 'neath the sunrise,
  Homes full of sadness or joy,
Jesus is calling the children,
  Calling to each girl and boy.

2 See how in Africa's sunshine
  Quickly "Black Brother" has heard,
And how the children of China
  Eagerly wait for His Word;
Trustfully venture the children
  From the far isles of the sea,
While the brown maiden of India
  Lovingly rests on His knee.

3 No one can count all the children,
  Yet Jesus' love is the same,
Seeking to bless those who love Him,
  And those who know not His Name:
Joyful the day and so happy,
  When the wide circle complete,
From all the world little children
  Nestle in love at His feet.

Amy Gordon.

St. Agnes.   C.M.   J. B. DYKES.

615 *He shall speak peace unto the heathen.*—ZECHARIAH ix. 10.

1 OUR Saviour's voice is soft and sweet
  When, bending from above,
He bids us gather round His feet
  And calls us by His love.

2 But while our youthful hearts rejoice
  That thus He bids us come,
"Jesus!" we cry with pleading voice,
  "Bring heathen wanderers home."

3 They never heard the Saviour's name,
  They have not learned His way:
They do not know His grace, who came
  To take their sins away.

4 Dear Saviour, let the joyful sound,
  In distant lands be heard;
And, oh, wherever sin is found,
  Send forth Thy pardoning word!

5 And if our lips may breathe a prayer,
  Though raised in trembling fear,
Oh, let Thy grace our hearts prepare
  And choose some heralds here!

E. Parson.

Coming, Coming, Yes, they are.   P.M.

E. HUSBAND.

Andantino.

1. Com-ing, com-ing, yes, they are, Com-ing, com-ing, from a - far;
2. Com-ing, com-ing, yes, they are, Com-ing, com-ing, from a - far;

From the wild and scorch-ing des - ert, Af - ric's sons of col - our deep;
From the fields and crowd-ed cit - ies, Chi - na gath - ers to His feet;

Je - sus' love has drawn and won them, At His cross they bow and weep.
In His love Shem's gen - tle chil-dren Now have found a safe re - treat.

616

Behold, these shall come from far.—ISA. xlix. 12.

3 Coming, coming, yes, they are,
Coming, coming, from afar;
From the Indies and the Ganges,
Steady flows the living stream,
To love's ocean, to His bosom,
Calvary their wondering theme

4 Coming, coming, yes, they are,
Coming, coming, from afar;
From the steppes of Russia dreary,
From Slavonia's scattered lands,
They are yielding soul and spirit
Into Jesus' loving hands.

5 Coming, coming, yes, they are,
Coming, coming, from afar;
From the frozen realms of midnight,
Over many a weary mile,
To exchange their soul's long winter
For the summer of His smile.

6 Coming, coming, yes, they are,
Coming, coming, from afar;
All to meet in plains of glory,
All to sing His praises sweet;
What a chorus, what a meeting,
With the family complete!

J. Wakefield MacGill.

617 St. Simon.   8.7.8.7., D.   Melody from a French Paroissien.

Alternative Tune, DEERHURST, No. 557.

617   *I heard the voice of the Lord, saying, Whom shall I send, and who will
go for Us ? Then said I, Here am I; send me.*—ISA. vi. 8.

1 HARK! the voice of Jesus crying:
    "Who will go and work to-day?
Fields are white and harvest waiting;
    Who will bear the sheaves away?"
Loud and strong the Master calleth,
    Rich reward He offers thee;
Who will answer, gladly saying,
    "Here am I, send me, send me"?

2 If you cannot speak like angels,
    If you cannot preach like Paul,
You can tell the love of Jesus,
    You can say He died for all.
If you cannot rouse the wicked
    With the Judgment's dread alarms,
You can lead the little children
    To the Saviour's waiting arms.

3 If, among the older people,
    You may not be apt to teach,
"Feed My lambs," said Christ our Shepherd,
    "Place the food within their reach."
And it may be that the children
    You have led with trembling hand
Will be found among your jewels,
    When you reach the better land.

4 Let none hear you idly saying,
    "There is nothing I can do,"
While the souls of men are dying,
    And the Master calls for you.
Take the task He gives you gladly,
    Let His work your pleasure be;
Answer quickly when He calleth,
    "Here am I, send me, send me!"
                                    D. March.

MOSCOW.   6.6.4.6.6.6.4.   F. GIARDINI.

618   *And God said, Let there be light: and there was light.*—GENESIS i. 3.

1 THOU, whose almighty Word
    Chaos and darkness heard,
        And took their flight,
    Hear us, we humbly pray,
    And where the Gospel day
    Sheds not its golden ray,
        Let there be light.

2 Thou, who didst come to bring
    On Thy redeeming wing
        Healing and sight,
    Health to the sick in mind,
    Sight to the inly blind,
    Oh, now to all mankind,
        Let there be light.

3 Spirit of truth and love,
    Life-giving, holy Dove,
        Speed forth Thy flight;
    Move on the waters' face,
    Bearing the lamp of grace,
    And in earth's darkest place
        Let there be light.

4 Holy and blessèd Three,
    Glorious Trinity,
        Wisdom, Love, Might;
    Boundless as ocean's tide,
    Rolling in fullest pride,
    Through the world, far and wide,
        Let there be light.   *J. Marriott.*

619 Message.   P.M.   H. ERNEST NICHOL.

UNISON.

HARMONY.

cr. For the darkness shall turn to dawn - ing, And the dawning to noon-day bright, ..

f And Christ's great kingdom shall come on earth, The king-dom of Love and Light.

UNISON.   HARMONY.

cr. For the darkness shall turn to dawn - ing, And the dawn-ing to noon-day bright, ..

rall.

ff And Christ's great kingdom shall come on earth, The king-dom of Love and Light.

619 *The people that walked in darkness have seen a great light.*—Isa. ix. 2.

1 We've a story to tell to the nations,
   That shall turn their hearts to the right:
   A story of truth and sweetness,
   A story of peace and light:
   For the darkness, etc.

2 We've a song to be sung to the nations,
   That shall lift their hearts to the Lord:
   A song that shall conquer evil,
   And shatter the spear and sword:

3 We've a message to give to the nations,
   That the Lord who reigneth above
   Hath sent us His Son to save us,
   And show us that God is love:

4 We've a Saviour to show to the nations,
   Who the path of sorrow has trod,
   That all of the world's great peoples
   Might come to the truth of God:

   Colin Sterne.

Jesus Saves!   **P.M.**   Wm. J. Kirkpatrick.

620 *All the ends of the earth shall see the salvation of our God.*—Isa. lii. 10.

1 We have heard the joyful sound:
   Jesus saves! Jesus saves!
   Tell the message all around:
   Jesus saves! Jesus saves!
   Bear the news to every land,
   Climb the steeps and cross the waves;
   Onward!—'tis our Lord's command:
   Jesus saves! Jesus saves!

2 Waft it on the rolling tide:
   Jesus saves! Jesus saves!
   Say to sinners far and wide,
   Jesus saves! Jesus saves!
   Sing, ye islands of the sea;
   Echo back, ye ocean caves;
   Earth shall keep her jubilee:
   Jesus saves! Jesus saves!

3 Sing above the toil and strife,
   Jesus saves! Jesus saves!
   By His death and endless life
   Jesus saves! Jesus saves!
   Sing it softly through the gloom,
   When the heart for mercy craves;
   Sing in triumph o'er the tomb,
   Jesus saves! Jesus saves!

4 Give the winds a mighty voice:
   Jesus saves! Jesus saves!
   Let the nations now rejoice,
   Jesus saves! Jesus saves!
   Shout salvation full and free
   To every strand that ocean laves;
   This our song of victory,
   Jesus saves! Jesus saves!

   Priscilla J. Owens.

621 The Whole Wide World. 7.6.7.6., D., with Refrain. J. H. MAUNDER

REFRAIN. UNISON. HARMONY.

The whole wide world, the whole wide world—Pro-claim the Gos-pel tidings through the

whole wide world; Lift up the cross for Je-sus, His ban-ner be un-

-furl'd— Till ev-'ry tongue con-fess Him through the whole wide world!

621

Go ye therefore, and teach all nations.—MATT. xxviii. 19.

1 THE whole wide world for Jesus—
   This shall our watchword be,
Upon the highest mountain,
   Down by the widest sea—
The whole wide world for Jesus!
   To Him all men shall bow,
In city or in prairie—
   The world for Jesus now!
      The whole wide world, etc.

2 The whole wide world for Jesus,
   Inspires us with the thought
That every son of Adam
   Has by His blood been bought;
The whole wide world for Jesus!
   Oh, faint not by the way!
The cross shall surely conquer
   In this our glorious day.

3 The whole wide world for Jesus—
   The marching order sound—
Go ye, and preach the Gospel
   Wherever man is found;
The whole wide world for Jesus!
   Our banner is unfurled—
We battle now for Jesus,
   And faith demands the world!

4 The whole wide world for Jesus—
   In the Father's house above
Are many wondrous mansions—
   Mansions of light and love;
The whole wide world for Jesus!
   Ride forth, O conquering King,
Through all the mighty nations
   The world to glory bring!
                    Mrs. C. Johnson.

Missionary.   7.6.7.6., D.   LOWELL MASON.

622

All flesh shall see the salvation of God.—LUKE iii. 6.

1 FROM Greenland's icy mountains,
   From India's coral strand;
Where Afric's sunny fountains
   Roll down their golden sand;
From many an ancient river,
   From many a palmy plain,
They call us to deliver
   Their land from error's chain.

2 What, though the spicy breezes
   Blow soft o'er Ceylon's isle;
Though every prospect pleases,
   And only man is vile!
In vain with lavish kindness
   The gifts of God are strown;
The heathen in his blindness,
   Bows down to wood and stone.

3 Can we, whose souls are lighted
   With wisdom from on high—
Can we, to men benighted,
   The lamp of life deny?
Salvation! oh, salvation!
   The joyful sound proclaim,
Till each remotest nation
   Has learned Messiah's Name.

4 Waft, waft, ye winds, His story;
   And you, ye waters, roll,
Till like a sea of glory,
   It spreads from pole to pole,
Till o'er our ransomed nature
   The Lamb for sinners slain,
Redeemer, King, Creator,
   In bliss returns to reign. *R. Heber.*

Go Ye into All the World. 11.10.11.10., with Chorus.

JAMES McGRANAHAN.

CHORUS.

"All power is giv-en un-to Me! All power is giv-en un-to Me!

Go ye in-to all the world and preach the Gos-pel; and lo! I am with you al-way."

Words and Music by permission of Mrs. H. C. Dixon.

623   *All power is given unto Me in heaven and in earth.—*MATT. xxviii. 18.

1 FAR, far away in heathen darkness dwelling,
    Millions of souls for ever may be lost;
Who, who will go—Salvation's story telling—
    Looking to Jesus, counting not the cost?
        "All power is given unto Me!" etc.

2 See, o'er the world, wide open doors inviting;
    Soldiers of Christ, arise and enter in!
Christians, awake! your forces all uniting,
    Send forth the Gospel, break the chains of sin!

3 "Why will ye die?" the voice of God is calling;
    "Why will ye die?" re-echo in His Name;
Jesus hath died to save from death appalling;
    Life and salvation therefore go proclaim.

4 God speed the day when those of every nation,
    "Glory to God" triumphantly shall sing;
Ransomed, redeemed, rejoicing in salvation,
    Shout "Hallelujah, for the Lord is King!"

                                        G. M. J.

Jubilee.   9.8.9.8., D.   J. H. MAUNDER.

624   *My Name shall be great among the Gentiles.*—MAL. i. 11. (R.V.)

1 I HEAR ten thousand voices singing
  Their praises to the Lord on high;
Far distant shores and hills are ringing
  With anthems of their nations' joy,—
"Praise ye the Lord! for He has given
  To lands in darkness hid, His light;
As morning rays light up the heaven,
  His Word has chased away our night."

2 On China's shores I hear His praises,
  From lips that once kissed idol stones;
Soon as His banner He upraises,
  The Spirit moves the breathless bones—
"Speed, speed Thy Word o'er land and ocean;
  The Lord in triumph has gone forth:
The nations hear with strange emotion,
  From East to West, from South to North."

3 The song has sounded o'er the waters,
  And India's plains re-echo joy;
Beneath the moon sit India's daughters,
  Soft singing, as the wheel they ply—
"Thanks to Thee, Lord! for hopes of glory,
  For peace on earth to us revealed;
Our cherished idols fell before Thee,
  Thy Spirit has our pardon sealed."   *H. W. Fox.*

R

625 Galilee. [FIRST TUNE.]   L.M.   P. Armes.

Rimington. [SECOND TUNE.]   L.M.   F. Duckworth.

Composer's Copyright. Used by permission.

Kirkstone. [THIRD TUNE.]   L.M.   P. W. G.

Copyright.
Alternative Tune, OMBERSLEY, *No.* 391.

625

The kingdoms of this world are become the kingdoms of our Lord, and of His Christ; and He shall reign for ever and ever.—REV. xi. 15.

1 JESUS shall reign where'er the sun
Doth his successive journeys run;
His kingdom stretch from shore to shore,
Till moons shall wax and wane no more.

2 For Him shall endless prayer be made,
And princes throng to crown His head;
His Name like sweet perfume shall rise
With every morning sacrifice.

3 People and realms of every tongue
Dwell on His love with sweetest song,
And infant voices shall proclaim
Their early blessings on His Name.

4 Blessings abound where'er He reigns:
The prisoner leaps to loose his chains,
The weary find eternal rest,
And all the sons of want are blest.

5 Let every creature rise and bring
Peculiar honours to our King;
Angels, descend with songs again,
And, earth, repeat the loud Amen.

Isaac Watts.

Missionary Prayer.　　　7.6.7.6.8.8.　　　E. K. BRINKWORTH.

Music Copyright. By permission of the National Sunday School Union.

626

A doer of the work . . . shall be blessed.—JAMES i. 25.

1 LORD Jesus, Thou that lovest
Each little child like me,
Oh, take my life and use it,
And let me shine for Thee;
Oh, give me little tasks to do,
To show how much I love Thee too.

2 I know in distant countries,
Beyond the deep blue sea,
Are many little children
Thou lovest just like me;
But they have never heard Thy Name,
And do not know that Jesus came.

3 Lord, let me send Thy message
Across the deep blue sea,
To tell those little children
What Thou hast done for me;
Oh, show me, Lord, what I can do,
That they may know and love Thee too.

M. Wood.

Section XIII.—Hymns for Younger Children.

Fleury. [FIRST TUNE.]   7.6.7.6., D., with Refrain.   From Rossini.

1. I love to hear the sto - ry, Which an - gel voi - ces tell, . .

D.S.—love to hear the sto - ry, Which an - gel voi - ces tell,

How once the King of glo - ry Came down on earth to dwell. . .

How once the King of glo - ry Came down on earth to dwell. . .

I am both weak and sin - ful, But this I sure - ly know,—

The Lord came down to save me, Be - cause He loved me so. . . I

627

I have loved thee with an everlasting love.—Jer. xxxi. 3.

2 I'm glad my blessèd Saviour
Was once a child like me,
To show how pure and holy
His little ones might be:
And if I try to follow
His footsteps here below,
He never will forget me,
Because He loves me so.

3 To sing His love and mercy
My sweetest songs I'll raise;
And though I cannot see Him,
I know He hears my praise:
For He has kindly promised
That even I may go
To sing among His angels,
Because He loves me so.

Mrs. E. H. Miller.

7.6.7.6., D., without Refrain.

Angels' Story. [SECOND TUNE.]   A. H. Mann.

Surrep Chapel. 12.11.12.11. J. S. TYLER.

628   *Jesus said, Suffer little children, and forbid them not, to come unto Me.—*
MATT. xix. 14.

1 HE smiled as He stretched out His arms in glad welcome,
   While little ones hastened to press round His knee,
While He laid His kind hand on each little fair forehead,
   Saying, "Suffer the children to come unto Me."

2 "Send **not** from My presence the children: I love them,
   And they shall be merry and joyous and free;
But bring them where blessings of heaven are dropping,
   Oh, suffer the children to come unto Me."

3 We come then, dear Saviour, by words and by prayers,
   Oh, Thine, Thine alone may the little ones be;
Still stretch out Thy kind arms, still give us a welcome,
   Say, "Suffer the children to come unto Me."

4 And when our young feet touch the waters of Jordan,
   Oh, then may Thy children be dear unto Thee;
Take our hands, lift us up to the palaces golden,
   Say, "Suffer the children to come unto Me."

Marianne Farningham.

Bentley   7.6.7.6., D.   J. P. HULLAH.

629   *To obey is better than sacrifice.*—1 SAM. xv. 22.

1 THE wise may bring their learning,
  The rich may bring their wealth;
And some may bring their greatness,
  And some bring strength and health;
We too would bring our treasures
  To offer to the King:
We have no wealth or learning,
  What shall we children bring?

2 We'll bring Him hearts that love Him,
  We'll bring Him thankful praise,
And young souls meekly striving
  To walk in holy ways:

And these shall be the treasures
  We offer to the King,
And these are gifts that even
  The poorest child may bring.

3 We'll bring the little duties
  We have to do each day,
We'll try our best to please Him
  At home, at school, at play:
And better are these treasures
  To offer to our King,
Than richest gifts without them;
  Yet these a child may bring.
                     Anon.

630 Sidcup. [FIRST TUNE.]   L.M.   JAMES A. CRAIG.

Samson. [SECOND TUNE.]   L.M.   HANDEL.

630   *Who went about doing good.*—ACTS x. 38.

1 JESUS, who lived above the sky,
  Came down to be a Man and die;
  And in the Bible we may see
  How very good He used to be.

2 He went about—He was so kind—
  To cure poor people who were blind;
  And many who were sick and lame,
  He pitied them, and did the same.

3 And more than that, He told them too
  The things that God would have them do;
  And was so gentle and so mild,
  He would have listened to a child.

4 But such a cruel death He died:
  He was hung up and crucified!
  And those kind hands that did such good,
  They nailed them to a cross of wood!

5 And so He died: and this is why
  He came to be a Man and die:
  The Bible says He came from heaven
  That we might have our sins forgiven.

6 He knew how wicked man had been,
  And knew that God must punish sin;
  So, out of pity, Jesus said
  He'd bear the punishment instead.
                Ann Gilbert.

St. Oswald.   8.7.8.7.   J. B. DYKES.

Alternative Tune, SEFTON, *No.* 638.

One of these little ones.—MATT. xviii. 14.

631

1 LITTLE children, follow Jesus,
  None so good and kind as He;
  Hear His voice, for children pleading,
  "Suffer them to come to Me."

2 Like a shepherd He will tend you
  As you walk life's narrow way,
  Homeward bear upon His bosom
  Those who from His sweet fold stray.

3 Yes, He knows the little children
  Are as lambs so weak and small;
  And not one must be forsaken,
  Since He died to save them all.

4 Little children, follow Jesus
  Through the world so big and wide;
  Let Him be your tender Shepherd,
  Follow closely at His side.   *Anon.*

Away in a Manger.
CHILDREN IN UNISON.   11.11.11.11.   W. J. KIRKPATRICK.
Softly. Not too quickly.

632

She . . . laid Him in a manger.—LUKE ii. 7.

1 AWAY in a manger, no crib for a bed,
  The little Lord Jesus laid down His sweet head.
  The stars in the bright sky looked down where He lay—
  The little Lord Jesus asleep on the hay.

2 The cattle are lowing, the Baby awakes,
  But little Lord Jesus, no crying He makes.
  I love Thee, Lord Jesus! look down from the sky,
  And stay by my side until morning is nigh.

3 Be near me, Lord Jesus; I ask Thee to stay
  Close by me for ever, and love me, I pray.
  Bless all the dear children in Thy tender care,
  And fit us for heaven to live with Thee there.

            Trans. from *Martin Luther.*

Ellingham.   7.7.7.7.   S. N. GODFREY.

Alternative Tune, SHERBORNE, *No.* 67.

633   *I have given you an example.*—JOHN xiii. 15.

1 LAMB of God, I look to Thee,
  Thou shalt my example be;
  Thou art gentle, meek, and mild;
  Thou wast once a little child.

2 Fain I would be as Thou art;
  Give me Thy obedient heart:
  Thou art pitiful and kind;
  Let me have Thy loving mind.

3 Let me above all fulfil
  God my heavenly Father's will;
  Never His good Spirit grieve,
  Only to His glory live.

4 Loving Jesus, holy Lamb,
  In Thy gracious hands I am:
  Make me, Saviour, what Thou art,
  Live Thyself within my heart.

                C. Wesley.

St. Martin. [FIRST TUNE.] 7.7.7.7. French Melody, 12th cent.

Sheringham. [SECOND TUNE.] 7.7.7.7., D. KATHLEEN ROBSON.

Copyright. By permission of the Composer.

634 *It is good to sing praises unto our God.*—PSALM cxlvii. 1.

1 GOD our Father, now we lift
  Joyful hearts in glowing praise,
For Thy great and lovely gift,
  Childhood's sweet and happy days.

2 From Thy kind and loving hand
  Come the gifts of life so free,
All the beauties of the land,
  All the wonders of the sea.

3 But a fairer gift than all
  Is our gracious Saviour-Friend,
Who from heaven to manger-stall
  Did in wondrous love descend.

4 Oh, how filled with deeds of love
  Was the life of Him who died!
Dwelling now in heights above,
  Still He calls us to His side.

5 Dear Lord Jesus, brighter still
  Youth's fresh hours if Thou art near,
With Thy grace our hearts now fill,
  Driving out all doubt and fear.

6 Keep us Thine, along the years
  As life's mile-stones each are passed,
Through the laughter and the tears
  Lead us to Thy home at last.

Frank H. Humby.

Copyright

R*

Athens. [FIRST TUNE.]   P.M.   Greek Air

635

Then were there brought unto Him little children.—MATT. xix. 13.

1. I . . think when I read that sweet sto-ry of old, When Jesus was here among men,

How He call'd lit-tle children, as lambs to His fold, I should like to have been with them then.

I . . wish that His hands had been placed on my head, That His arm had been thrown around me,

And that I might have seen His kind look when He said, "Let the lit-tle ones come un-to Me."

Huddleston. [SECOND TUNE.]   P.M.   ARTHUR BERRIDGE.

1. I think when I read that sweet sto-ry of old, When Je-sus was here among men,

How He call'd little children, as lambs to His fold, I should like to have been with them then.

I . . wish that His hands had been placed on my head, That His arm had been thrown around me,

And that I might have seen His kind look when He said, "Let the lit-tle ones come unto Me."

2 Yet still to His footstool in prayer I may go,
   And ask for a share in His love;
And if I now earnestly seek Him below,
   I shall see Him and hear Him above:
In that beautiful place He has gone to prepare
   For all who are washed and forgiven;
And many dear children are gathering there,
   "For of such is the kingdom of heaven."

3 But thousands and thousands, who wander and fall,
   Never heard of that heavenly home;
I should like them to know there is room for them all,
   And that Jesus has bid them to come.
I long for the joy of that glorious time,
   The sweetest, and brightest, and best;
When the dear little children of every clime
   Shall crowd to His arms and be blest. *Mrs. Jemima Luke.*

Words Copyright. By permission of the National Sunday School Union.

636

*Hereby perceive we the love of God, because He laid down His life
   for us.*—1 JOHN iii. 16.

1 HERE'S a message of love, come down from above,
   To invite little children to heaven;
In God's blessed Book poor sinners may look,
   And see how all sin is forgiven.
For there they may read how Jesus did bleed,
   His life everlasting to give;
He cleanseth the soul, He maketh us whole,
   That with Him in heaven we may live.

2 And then, when they die, He takes them on high,
   To be with Him in heaven above;
For so kind is His heart, that He never will part
   From a child that has tasted His love.
And oh, what delight in heaven so bright,
   When they see the dear Saviour's face,
On His beauty to gaze, and sing to His praise,
   And rejoice in His own boundless grace! *Anon.*

To be sung to ATHENS. No. 635.

Happy Song. P.M. W. B. Bradbury.

637 *He appointed singers unto the Lord, that should praise . . . as they went out before the army.*—2 Chron. xx. 21.

1.
We are march-ing on, with shield and banner bright; We will work for God, and
From the youth-ful ranks our ar-my we prepare, As we ral-ly round our

D.C. We are march-ing on-ward, sing-ing as we go, To the prom-ised land where

bat-tle for the right; We will praise His Name, re-joic-ing in His might, And we'll
bless-ed standard here; And the Sa-viour's cross we ear-ly learn to bear, While we

liv-ing wa-ters flow; Come and join our ranks as pilgrims here be-low, Come and

Fine. f Chorus.

work till Je-sus calls.
work till Je-sus calls. } Then a-wake, then a-wake, Happy song, happy

work till Je-sus calls.

D.C.

song, Shout for joy, shout for joy, As we glad-ly march a-long.

2 We are marching on: our Captain, ever near,
Will protect us still, His gentle voice we hear:
Let the foe advance, we'll never, never fear,
    For we'll work till Jesus calls.
Then awake, awake, our happy, happy song;
We will shout for joy, and gladly march along;
In the Lord of hosts let every heart be strong,
    While we work till Jesus calls.

3 We are marching on the strait and narrow way,
That will lead to life and everlasting day,
To the smiling fields that never will decay:
    But we'll work till Jesus calls.
We are marching on, and pressing towards the prize,
To a glorious crown beyond the glowing skies,
To the radiant fields where pleasure never dies,
    And we'll work till Jesus calls.   *Fanny J. Crosby.*

Sefton. 8.7.8.7. H. A. Crosbie.

Alternative Tune, Stuttgart, *No. 434.*

638 *Jesus called a little child unto Him.*—Matt. xviii. 2.

1 Jesus loves the little children,
  Once He took them on His knee,
  Gently put His arms around them,
  Saying, "Let them come to Me!"

2 Oh! He loves to see them kneeling,
  And, with hands together, pray;
  Loves to hear them call Him Jesus,
  If they mean the words they say.

3 Once He gave His life to buy them
  Back from Satan's evil ways,
  And at last to heaven take them,
  There to sing His worth and praise.

4 If they trust Him as their Saviour,
  He will wash their sins away;
  He will take their hand and lead them
  All along the narrow way.

5 He would have them love each other,
  And be truthful, meek, and mild,
  Doing as their parents bid them,
  As He did when once a Child.

6 Then when He shall come to call them,
  They shall see Him face to face,
  And with saints and angels praise Him
  For His matchless love and grace.
  Anon.

Westcliffe. C.M. J. H. Maunder.
Slowly and solemnly.

Alternative Tune, St. Agnes, *No. 134.*

639 *Thou God seest me.*—Gen. xvi. 13.

1 God is in heaven: Can He hear
  A little prayer like mine?
  Yes, that He can; I need not fear:
  He'll listen unto mine.

2 God is in heaven: Can He see
  When I am doing wrong?
  Yes, that He can; He looks at me
  All day and all night long.

3 God is in heaven: Would He know
  If I should tell a lie?

Yes; though I said it very low,
  He'd hear it in the sky.

4 God is in heaven: Does He care,
  Or is He good to me?
  Yes; all I have to eat or wear,
  'Tis God that gives it me.

5 God is in heaven: May I pray
  To go there when I die?
  Yes; seek Him, trust Him, and one day
  He'll call me to the sky. *Ann Gilbert.*

In Memoriam.   8.6.7.6.7.6.7.6.   Sir J. Stainer.

640   *Jesus . . . took a child, and set him by Him.—*Luke ix. 47.

1 THERE'S a Friend for little children
　　Above the bright blue sky,
　A Friend who never changes,
　　Whose love will never die:
　Unlike our friends by nature,
　　Who change with changing years,
　This Friend is always worthy
　　The precious Name He bears.

2 There's a home for little children
　　Above the bright blue sky,
　Where Jesus reigns in glory—
　　A home of peace and joy:
　No home on earth is like it,
　　Nor can with it compare,
　For every one is happy,
　　Nor could be happier, there.

3 There's a crown for little children
　　Above the bright blue sky,
　And all who look to Jesus
　　Shall wear it by and by;
　A crown of brightest glory
　　Which He will then bestow
　On those who found His favour
　　And loved Him here below.

4 There's a song for little children
　　Above the bright blue sky,
　A song that will not weary,
　　Though sung continually;
　A song which even angels
　　Can never, never sing;
　They know not Christ as Saviour,
　　But worship Him as King.

5 There's a robe for little children
　　Above the bright blue sky;
　A harp of sweetest music
　　And palms of victory;
　And all above is treasured,
　　And found in Christ alone:
　Oh, come, dear little children,
　　That all may be your own.

Albert Midlane.

All for Jesus.   8.7.8.7.   Sir J. Stainer.

Alternative Tune, St. Oswald, *No.* 631.

Early will I seek Thee.—Psalm lxiii. 1.

641

1 Saviour, while my heart is tender,
  I would yield that heart to Thee,
All my powers to Thee surrender,
  Thine and only Thine to be.

2 Take me now, Lord Jesus, take me;
  Let my youthful heart be Thine:
Thy devoted servant make me,
  Fill my soul with love divine.

3 Send me, Lord, where Thou wilt send me,
  Only do Thou guide my way;

May Thy grace through life attend me,
  Gladly then shall I obey.

4 Let me do Thy will, or bear it,
  I would know no will but Thine;
Shouldst Thou take my life, or spare it,
  I that life to Thee resign.

5 Thine I am, O Lord, for ever,
  To Thy service set apart;
Suffer me to leave Thee never,
  Seal Thine image on my heart.

                  J. Burton, Junr.

Chacewater.   6.5.6.5.   A. C. Sharpley.

Alternative Tune, Enon, *No.* 644.

Learn of Me.—Matt. xi. 29.

642

1 Let me learn of Jesus:
  He is kind to me;
Once He died to save me,
  Nailed upon the tree.

2 If I go to Jesus,
  He will hear me pray,
Make me good and holy,
  Take my sins away.

3 Let me think of Jesus:
  He is full of love,

Looking down upon me
  From His throne above.

4 If I trust in Jesus,
  If I do His will,
Then I shall be happy,
  Safe from every ill.

5 Oh, how good is Jesus!
  May He hold my hand,
And at last receive me
  To a better land!

                Fanny J. Crosby.

Sunnyside. [FIRST TUNE.] 6.5.6.5., with Chorus. W. O. GIBB.

CHORUS.

If I come to Je-sus, Happy I shall be, He is gently calling Little ones like me.

Spiers. [SECOND TUNE.] 6.5.6.5., with Chorus.

CHORUS.

If I come to Je-sus, Happy I shall be, He is gently calling Little ones like me.

Alternative Tune, WOODBROOK, *No.* 668.

643   *Incline your ear, and come unto Me.*—ISA. lv. 3.

1 IF I come to Jesus,
   He will make me glad ;
   He will give me pleasure
   When my heart is sad.
   If I come to Jesus, etc.

2 If I come to Jesus,
   He will hear my prayer ;
   For He loves me dearly,
   And my sins did bear.

3 If I come to Jesus,
   He will take my hand ;
   He will kindly lead me
   To a better land.

4 There, with happy children,
   Robed in snowy white,
   I shall see my Saviour,
   In that world so bright.

Fanny J. Crosby.

Enon. 6.5.6.5. O. M. FEILDEN.

644 *The garden of the Lord.*—Isa. li. 3.

1 In our dear Lord's garden,
  Planted here below,
Many tiny flowerets
  In sweet beauty grow.

2 Christ, the loving Gardener,
  Tends these blossoms small,
Loves the little lilies
  And the cedars tall.

3 Nothing is too little
  For His gentle care,
Nothing is too lowly
  In His love to share.

4 Jesus loves the children,
  Children such as we,
Blessed them when their mothers
  Brought them to His knee.

5 Jesus calls the children,
  Bids them come and stand,
In His pleasant garden,
  Watered by His hand.

6 Lord, Thy call we answer;
  Take us in Thy care,
Train us in Thy garden,
  In Thy work to share.

Mrs. E. S. Armitage.

Malvern. *Tenderly.* P.M. Anon.

REFRAIN.

Yes, Lord Jesus; yes, Lord Jesus; yes, Lord Je - sus.

645 *Jesus called a little child unto Him.*—Matt. xviii. 2.

1 "Little child, I call thee to Me,
  I will take thee for My own;
Sin forsaking, Me embracing,
  Choose Me for thy King alone."
    Yes, Lord Jesus; etc.

2 "Little child, I bid thee listen
  Every time I speak to thee;
Do My pleasure, then the treasure
  Of My love I'll give to thee.

3 "Little child, I bid thee follow
  Everywhere that I may lead;
Always cheerful, never fearful,
  Trusting Me in every need.

4 "Little child, remember always
  That the Lord hates every sin;
Then be careful and be prayerful,
  Watch and pray lest wrong begin."
    Anon.

Waltham Street.

UNISON OR DUET.   8.3.8.3., D.   G. B. BLANCHARD.

Smoothly.

1. Lis - ten to .. the voice of Je - sus, Oh, so sweet! ..

As the lit - tle chil - dren gath-er Round His feet; ..

Young ones to .. His knees are climb - ing, There to rest;

Old - er ones stand round Him wait - ing To be blest.

646   *For of such is the kingdom of heaven.*—MATT. xix. 14.

2 When the mothers who had brought them
    Heard men say
"'Tis no place for little children;
    Go away!"
They were sorry,—but their sorrow
    Soon was gone,
For He raised His hands and blessed them,
    Every one.

3 And He said to His disciples,
    "These are Mine;
In the kingdom of My Father
    They shall shine;
Send them not away, but rather
    Bring them near;
Even little ones may love their
    Saviour dear."

4 Still He loves the little children,
    You and me;
And He wants us all to love Him
    Faithfully.
Let us then with hearts and voices
    Gladly say:
"I am Thine, O blessèd Jesus,
    Thine for aye!"

G. B. Blanchard.

Harvest. P.M. JOHN ADCOCK.

647 *The fields . . . are white already to harvest.*—JOHN iv. 35.

1 THE fields are all white,
  And the reapers are few;
  We children are willing,
  But what can we do
To work for our Lord in His harvest?

2 Our hands are so small,
  And our words are so weak,
  We cannot teach others;
  How then shall we seek
To work for our Lord in His harvest?

3 We'll work by our prayers,
  By the gifts we can bring,
  By small self-denials;
  The least little thing
May work for our Lord in His harvest.

4 Until, by and by,
  As the years pass, at length,
  We too may be reapers,
  And go forth in strength
To work for our Lord in His harvest.

Anon.

Nassau. 7.7.7.7.7.7. J. ROSENMÜLLER.

648 *The Prince of life, whom God hath raised from the dead.*—ACTS iii. 15.

1 LITTLE children, join to sing
Glory, glory to our King;
Christ is risen from the dead,
Crowns unfading wreathe His head.
He is Conqueror o'er the grave!
Mighty to redeem and save!

2 Now behold Him high enthroned,
Mercy beaming from His face:
By adoring angels owned,

God of holiness and grace:
Little children, join to sing
Glory, glory to our King.

3 Jesus, on us deign to shine,
Warm our hearts and tune our tongues;
May we with the blest combine,
Share their joy and swell their songs;
And with hearts and voices sing
Glory, glory to our King.

R. Murray McCheyne.

Wells.   7.7.7.7.7.7.   D. BORTNIANSKI.

649   *Look unto Me, and be ye saved.*—ISA. xlv. 22.

1 CHILDREN, you have gone astray,
  Far from God and peace and heaven!
Would you leave that dangerous way?
  Would you have your sins forgiven?
Christ can all your sins forgive:
Look to Jesus, look and live!

2 Children, you have sinful hearts!
  Jesus Christ can make you whole;
He can inward grace impart,

Sanctify and save your soul.
Jesus a new heart can give;
Look to Jesus, look and live!

3 Children, you may shortly die!
  Jesus died your souls to save:
If you to the Saviour fly,
  You shall live beyond the grave.
Life eternal He will give;
Look to Jesus, look and live!

J. Burton, Jun.

Doncaster.   S.M.   S. WESLEY.

Alternative Tune, ST. GEORGE, *No.* 425.
Thou desirest truth in the inward parts.—PSALM li. 6.

650

1 I OFTEN say my prayers,
    But do I ever pray?
  And do the wishes of my heart
    Go with the words I say?

2 I may as well kneel down
    And worship gods of stone,
  As offer to the living God
    A prayer of words alone.

3 For words without the heart
    The Lord will never hear;
  Nor will He to those lips attend
    Whose prayers are not sincere.

4 Lord, teach me what I need,
    And teach me how to pray;
  Nor let me ask Thee for Thy grace
    Not feeling what I say.

J. Burton, Jun.

Derwent.
Not too fast.   8.5.8.3.   C. L. NAYLOR.

Alternative Tune, HARTHAM, *No.* 234.

651   *Thou art the Guide of my youth.*—JER. iii. 4.

1 JESUS, Friend of little children,
    Be a Friend to me;
  Take my hand and ever keep me
    Close to Thee.

2 Show me what my love should cherish,
    What, too, it should shun;
  Lest my feet for poison-flowers
    Swift should run.

3 Teach me how to grow in goodness,
    Daily as I grow;
  Thou hast been a Child, and surely
    Thou dost know.

4 Fill me with Thy gentle meekness,
    Make my heart like Thine;
  Like an altar-lamp then let me
    Burn and shine.

5 Step by step, oh, lead me onward,
    Upward into youth!
  Wiser, stronger still becoming
    In Thy truth.

6 Never leave me, nor forsake me,
    Ever be my Friend;
  For I need Thee from life's dawning
    To its end.

Walter J. Mathams.

Portrush.   6.5.6.5., with Chorus.   H. P. MAIN.

CHORUS.

If we seek Him ear-ly, If we come to-day, We can be His little friends, He has said we may.

652   *Those that seek Me early shall find Me.*—PROVERBS viii. 17.

1 WE are little children,
    Very young indeed,
  But the Saviour's promise
    Each of us may plead.
    If we seek Him early, etc.

2 Little friends of Jesus,
    What a happy thought!
  What a precious promise
    In the Bible taught!

3 Little friends of Jesus,
    Walking by His side,
  With His arm around us,
    Every step to guide.

4 We must love Him dearly,
    With a constant love,
  Then we'll go and see Him,
    In our home above.

Fanny J. Crosby.

Gosben.   6.5 6.5., D.   Miss Davis.

653   *The Good Shepherd giveth His life for the sheep.*—JOHN x. 11.

1 JESUS is our Shepherd,
  Wiping every tear;
Folded in His bosom,
  What have we to fear?
Only let us follow
  Whither He doth lead,
To the thirsty desert
  Or the dewy mead.

2 Jesus is our Shepherd,—
  Well we know His voice!
How its gentle whisper
  Makes our heart rejoice!
Even when He chideth,
  Tender is His tone;
None but He shall guide us,
  We are His alone.

3 Jesus is our Shepherd:
  For the sheep He bled;
Every lamb is sprinkled
  With the blood He shed:
Then on each He setteth
  His own secret sign,
"They that have My spirit,
  These," saith He, "are Mine."

4 Jesus is our Shepherd:
  Guarded by His arm,
Though the wolves may raven,
  None can do us harm;
When we tread death's valley,
  Dark with fearful gloom,
We will fear no evil,
  Victors o'er the tomb.

Hugh Stowell.

654 Marlborough Road.   P.M.

CHORUS.

For I will fol-low Je - sus,

For I will fol-low Je - sus, For I will fol-low Je - sus.. All the way...

654 *Be ye therefore followers of God, as dear children.*—EPH. v. 1.

1 THE world looks very beautiful,
  And full of joy to me ;
The sun shines out in glory
  On everything I see ;
I know I shall be happy
  While in the world I stay,
For I will follow Jesus
    All the way.
      For I will follow Jesus, etc.

2 I'm but a youthful pilgrim ;
  My journey's just begun ;
They say I'll meet with sorrow
  Before my journey's done.
The world is full of trouble,
  And trials too, they say ;
But I will follow Jesus
    All the way.

3 Then, like a little pilgrim,
  Whatever I may meet,
I'll take it—joy or sorrow—
  And lay at Jesus' feet.
He'll comfort me in trouble,
  He'll wipe my tears away ;
With joy I'll follow Jesus
    All the way.

4 Then trials cannot vex me,
  And pain I need not fear,
For when I'm close by Jesus,
  Grief cannot come too near.
Not even death can harm me,
  When death I meet one day ;
To heaven I'll follow Jesus
    All the way.
        Anna B. Warner.

Jewels. *Moderato.*   P.M.   G. F. ROOT.

CHORUS.

Like the stars of the morn-ing, His bright crown a - dorning, They shall shine in their beau-ty, Bright gems for His crown.

655 *They shall be Mine, saith the Lord of hosts, in that day when I make up My jewels.*—MALACHI iii. 17.

1 WHEN He cometh, when He cometh,
  To make up His jewels,
All His jewels, precious jewels,
  His loved and His own.
    Like the stars of the morning, etc.

2 He will gather, He will gather,
  The gems for His kingdom :

All the pure ones, all the bright ones,
  His loved and His own.

3 Little children, little children
  Who love their Redeemer,
Are the jewels, precious jewels,
  His loved and His own.
        W. O. Cushing.

Stories of Jesus. P.M. F. A. CHALLINOR.

Words and Music Copyright. By permission of the National Sunday School Union.

Things . . . concerning Jesus of Nazareth.—LUKE xxiv. 19.

656

1 TELL me the stories of Jesus
  I love to hear;
Things I would ask Him to tell me
  If He were here;
    Scenes by the wayside,
    Tales of the sea;
    Stories of Jesus,
    Tell them to me.

(*Girls.*)
2 First let me hear how the children
  Stood round His knee;
And I shall fancy His blessing
  Resting on me;
    Words full of kindness,
    Deeds full of grace,
    All in the lovelight
    Of Jesus' face.

(*Boys.*)
3 Into the city I'd follow
  The children's band,
Waving a branch of the palm-tree
  High in my hand;
    One of His heralds,
    Yes, I would sing
    Loudest hosannas!
    Jesus is King!

(*All.*)
4 Tell me, in accents of wonder,
  How rolled the sea,
Tossing the boat in a tempest
  On Galilee!
    And how the Master,
    Ready and kind,
    Chided the billows,
    And hushed the wind.

(*Girls.*)
5 Tell how the sparrow that twitters
  On yonder tree,
And the sweet meadow-side lily
  May speak to me—
    Give me their message,
    For I would hear
    How Jesus taught us
    Our Father's care.

(*All*)
6 Show me that scene in the garden,
  Of bitter pain;
And of the cross where my Saviour
  For me was slain—
    Sad ones or bright ones,
    So that they be
    Stories of Jesus,
    Tell them to me. *W. H. Parker.*

Maidstone. 7.7.7.7., with Chorus. W. B. GILBERT.

Je-sus, hear Thy child to-day; Hear, oh, hear me when I pray!

By permission of Novello and Company, Limited.

Hear my prayer, O Lord.—PSALM cii. 1.

657

1 SAVIOUR, bless a little child,
Teach my heart the way to Thee;
Make it gentle, good, and mild;
Loving Saviour, care for me.
Jesus, hear Thy child to-day;
Hear, oh, hear me when I pray!

2 I am young, but Thou hast said
All who will may come to Thee;
Feed my soul with living bread;
Loving Saviour, care for me.

3 Jesus, help me, I am weak;
Let me put my trust in Thee;
Teach me how and what to speak;
Loving Saviour, care for me.

4 I would never go astray,
Never turn aside from Thee;
Keep me in the heavenly way;
Loving Saviour, care for me.
Fanny J. Crosby.

Spohr. 8.6.8.6.8.6. L. SPOHR.

658 *He that is faithful in that which is least is faithful also in much.*—LUKE xvi. 10.

1 I CANNOT do great things for Him
Who did so much for me;
But I would like to show my love,
Lord Jesus, unto Thee:
Faithful in very little things,
O Saviour, may I be.

2 There are small things in daily life
In which I may obey,
And thus may show my love to Thee;
And always—every day—
There are some little loving words
Which I for Thee may say.

3 There are small crosses I may take,
Small burdens I may bear,
Small acts of faith and deeds of love,
Small sorrows I may share;
And little bits of work for Thee
I may do everywhere.

4 I ask Thee, Lord, to give me grace
My little place to fill,
That I may ever walk with Thee
And ever do Thy will;
And in each duty, great or small,
I may be faithful still. *Anon.*

Lubeck. 7.7.7.7. FREYLINGHAUSEN'S *Gesangbuch*, 1704.

Alternative Tunes, BUCKLAND, *No.* 687, *and* ST. MARTIN, *No.* 634.

659 *In all thy ways acknowledge Him, and He shall direct thy paths.*—PROV. iii. 6.

1 FATHER, lead me day by day,
Ever in Thine own sweet way,
Teach me to be pure and true,
Show me what I ought to do.

2 When in danger, make me brave;
Make me know that Thou canst save:
Keep me safe by Thy dear side;
Let me in Thy love abide.

3 When I'm tempted to do wrong,
Make me steadfast, wise, and strong;
And when all alone I stand,
Shield me with Thy mighty hand.

4 When my heart is full of glee,
Help me to remember Thee—
Happy most of all to know
That my Father loves me so.

5 When my work seems hard and dry,
May I press on cheerily;
Help me patiently to bear
Pain and hardship, toil and care.

6 May I do the good I know,
Be Thy loving child below,
Then at last go home to Thee,
Evermore Thy child to be.

Words Copyright. By permission of the National Sunday School Union. *J. Page Hopps.*

Capernaum. 7.7.7.7. R. REDHEAD.

660 *Hear my prayer, O Lord, and give ear unto my cry.*—PSALM xxxix. 12.

1 BLESSÈD Jesus, meek and mild,
Stoop to hear a little child;
At Thy feet I come to pray;
Saviour, turn me not away.

2 Take away my load of sin,
Make me clean and pure within;
Teach me all I need to know;
Be my Shepherd here below.

3 In my childhood may I be
Gentle, meek, and pure, like Thee;
Help me every sin to leave,
Lest Thy loving heart I grieve.

4 Tender Jesus, Thou didst call
To Thine arms the children small;
Lo! I come, and humbly pray,
Saviour, cast me not away. *Anon.*

Jesus Loves Me! 7.7.7.7., with Chorus. W. B. BRADBURY.

CHORUS.

Yes, Jesus loves me, Yes, Jesus loves me, Yes, Jesus loves me, The Bible tells me so.

661 *Unto Him that loveth us, . . . be glory.*—REV. i. 5, 6.

1 JESUS loves me! this I know,
For the Bible tells me so;
Little ones to Him belong,
They are weak, but He is strong.
   Yes, Jesus loves me, etc.

2 Jesus loves me! He who died
Heaven's gate to open wide;
He will wash away my sin,
Let His little child come in.

3 Jesus loves me! loves me still,
When I'm very weak and ill,
From His shining throne on high
Comes to watch me where I lie.

4 Jesus loves me! He will stay
Close beside me all the way;
If I love Him, when I die
He will take me home on high.
   Anna B. Warner.

Canonbury. 6.5.6.5., with Chorus.

CHORUS.

Jesus loves our pil-grim band, He will lead us by the hand, Lead us to the better land, Happy home on high.

662 *They shall ask the way to Zion with their faces thitherward.*—JER. l. 5.

1 I'M a little pilgrim,
And a stranger here;
Though this world is pleasant,
Sin is always near.
   Jesus loves our pilgrim band, etc.

2 Mine's a better country,
Where there is no sin;
Where the tones of sorrow
Never enter in.

3 But a little pilgrim
Must have garments clean,

If he'd wear the white robes
And with Christ be seen.

4 Jesus, cleanse and save me;
Teach me to obey:
Holy Spirit, guide me
On my heavenly way.

5 I'm a little pilgrim,
And a stranger here;
But my home in heaven
Cometh ever near.
   J. Curwen.

Warwick Lane.   7.7.7.3.   W. P. HAMMOND.

663   *Sing praises unto our King.*—PSALM xlvii. 6.

1 COME, ye children, sweetly sing
Praises to your Saviour-King;
Hearts and voices gladly bring:
    Praise His Name!

2 Jesus is the children's Friend,
Loving, faithful, to the end;
Richest gifts from Him descend,
    Joy and peace.

3 Once from heaven to earth He came,
Suffered death, contempt, and blame,
Died upon a cross of shame,
    Crowned with thorns.

4 'Twas our sinful souls to save
Thus His precious blood He gave!

Ransomed now from sin's dark grave
    We may sing.

5 Blessèd Jesus, loving, kind,
We would early seek and find;
And our souls in covenant bind,
    Thine to be.

6 For our sins we deeply grieve,
But Thy promise we believe—
"Him that cometh I receive:"
    Lord, we come.

7 Help us love Thee more and more,
Serve Thee truly evermore,
Till Thy mercy we adore
    In heaven above.

Etta Campbell.

Sharon.   8.7.8.7.   W. BOYCE.

664   *I will both lay me down in peace, and sleep.*—PSALM iv. 8.

1 JESUS, tender Shepherd, hear me,
    Bless Thy little lamb to-night;
Through the darkness be Thou near me,
    Keep me safe till morning light.

2 All this day Thy hand has led me,
    And I thank Thee for Thy care;

Thou hast clothed me, warmed, and fed me,
    Listen to my evening prayer.

3 Let my sins be all forgiven,
    Bless the friends I love so well;
Take me, when I die, to heaven,
    Happy there with Thee to dwell.

Mrs. M. L. Duncan.

Walmsley. *Tenderly.*   8.4.8.4., with Chorus.   R. G. THOMPSON.

CHORUS.

Gent - ly to lead them,
Gent - ly to lead them,
Gent-ly, gent-ly to lead them,

Guard.. them and feed them, Je - sus to His
Guard them and feed them, Je-sus is call - ing, is calling the lambs, the
to His
Guard them, guard them and feed them, the

fold; .. Gent - ly to lead them, Guard.. them and feed them,
fold; Gent - ly to lead them, Guard them and feed them,
lambs to His fold; Gent - ly to lead them, Guard them and feed them,
fold; ..
lambs to His fold; Gently, gently to lead them, Guard them, guard them and feed them,

Je - sus
Je - sus is call - ing, is call-ing the lambs to His fold. ..

665   *Jesus called them unto Him.*—LUKE xviii. 16.

1 JESUS is calling the children
  Unto His side;
Stretching His arms to receive them,
  Op'ning them wide.
    Gently to lead them, etc.

2 Jesus is calling the children
  Why do they stay
Out in the wilderness wandering,
  Going astray?

3 Jesus is calling the children
  Echo the call

Tell them He waits for their coming,
  Wanting them all.

4 Jesus is calling the children,
  Calling to-day;
Hasten, each one, for the blessing,
  Do not delay!

5 Jesus is calling the children,
  Here, Lord, are we;
Safe in the Good Shepherd's keeping
  Ever to be.
            R. Walmsley.

Salem.   P.M.   German Air.
Arr. by A. Rhodes.

666   *Suffer little children to come unto Me.*—Luke xviii. 16.

1   When mothers of Salem
    Their children brought to Jesus,
The stern disciples drove them back,
    And bade them depart:
    But Jesus saw them ere they fled,
    And sweetly smiled, and kindly said,
"Suffer little children to come unto Me."

2   "For I will receive them,
    And fold them in My bosom;
I'll be a Shepherd to those lambs,
    Oh, drive them not away!
For if their hearts to Me they give,
They shall with Me in glory live:
Suffer little children to come unto Me."

3   How kind was our Saviour
    To bid those children welcome!
But there are many thousands who
    Have never heard His Name;
    The Bible they have never read;
    They know not that the Saviour said,
"Suffer little children to come unto Me."

4   Oh, soon may the heathen
    Of every tribe and nation
Fulfil Thy blessèd word, and cast
    Their idols all away;
    Oh, shine upon them from above,
    And show Thyself a God of love;
Teach the little children to come unto Thee.

W. M. Hutchings.

667 Woolacombe.   8.7.8.7., with Chorus.   W. J. Kirkpatrick.

CHORUS.

We are little friends, we are loving friends, We are happy, happy lit-tle friends of Jesus; We are little friends, we are loving friends; We are happy all day long.

667   *Let the children of Zion be joyful in their King.*—PSALM cxlix. 2.

1 Do you know what makes us happy,
  When so many hearts are sad?
We are little friends of Jesus,
  That is why we are so glad.
    We are little friends, etc.

2 Jesus loves the children dearly,
  In His Word He tells them so;

Once He took them up and blessed them,
  Many, many years ago.

3 We are little lambs of Jesus;
  He, our Shepherd kind and dear,
Speaks, and though we do not see Him,
  In our hearts His voice we hear.

S. Martin.

Woodbrook.   6.5.6.5., D.   JOHN ADCOCK.

Alternative Tune, HATHERLEY, *No.* 223.

668   *I am His.*—SONG OF SOLOMON ii. 16.

1 I BELONG to Jesus—
    'Twas a happy day
  When His blood most precious
    Washed my sins away;
  When His Holy Spirit
    Changed my heart of stone,
  Set His mark upon me,
    Sealed me for His own.

2 I belong to Jesus—
    So I'll try to spend
  All my life in pleasing
    My almighty Friend.
  Since He is so holy,
    I must watch and pray
  That I may grow like Him
    More and more each day.

3 I belong to Jesus—
    Therefore I can sing,
  For I'm safe and happy
    Underneath His wing;
  But so many round me
    Are all dark and cold,
  I must try to bring them
    Into Jesus' fold.

4 I belong to Jesus—
    Soon He will be here;
  If I love and trust Him,
    What have I to fear?
  Round about Him gathered
    Will His people be:
  And I'm sure that Jesus
    Will remember me.

Ellen H. Willis.

Albano.   C.M.   V. Novello.

669   *He came to Nazareth, and was subject unto them.*—Luke ii. 51.

1 I love to think, though I am young,
    My Saviour was a child;
That Jesus walked this earth along,
    With feet all undefiled.

2 He kept His Father's word of truth,
    As I am taught to do;
And while He walked the paths of youth,
    He walked in wisdom too.

3 I love to think that He who spake
    And made the blind to see,
And called the sleeping dead to wake,
    Was once a child like me:

4 That He who wore the thorny crown,
    And tasted death's despair,
Had a kind mother like my own,
    And knew her love and care.

5 I know 'twas all for love of me
    That He became a child,
And left the heavens, so fair to see,
    And trod earth's pathway wild.

6 Then, Saviour, who wast once a Child,
    A child may come to Thee;
And, oh! in all Thy mercy mild,
    Dear Saviour, come to me.
                   E. Paxton Hood.

Sawley.   C.M.   J. Walch.

Org.

Org.

670   *And the child Samuel grew on, and was in favour both with the Lord,*
                      and also with men.—1 Sam. ii. 26.

1 God make my life a little light
    Within the world to glow;
A little flame that burneth bright,
    Wherever I may go.

2 God make my life a little flower
    That giveth joy to all,
Content to bloom in native bower,
    Although the place be small.

3 God make my life a little song
    That comforteth the sad;

That helpeth others to be strong,
    And makes the singer glad.

4 God make my life a little staff
    Whereon the weak may rest,
That so what health and strength I have
    May serve my neighbours best.

5 God make my life a little hymn
    Of tenderness and praise;
Of faith—that never waxeth dim,
    In all His wondrous ways.

      M. Betham-Edwards.

North Coates.   6.5.6.5.   T. R. MATTHEWS.

By permission of Novello and Company, Limited.

671   *O satisfy us early with Thy mercy; that we may rejoice and be glad all our days.*—PSALM xc. 14.

1 JESUS, high in glory,
  Lend a listening ear;
When we bow before Thee,
  Children's praises hear.

2 Though Thou art so holy,
  Heaven's almighty King,
Thou wilt stoop to listen
  While Thy praise we sing.

3 We are little children,
  Weak and apt to stray;
Saviour, guide and keep us
  In the heavenly way.

4 Save us, Lord, from sinning,
  Watch us day by day:
Help us now to love Thee,
  Take our sins away.

5 Then when Thou shalt call us
  To our heavenly home,
We will gladly answer,
  "Saviour, Lord, we come."

6 In the many mansions,
  From all sin set free,
Loud shall be our praises,
  When Thy face we see.

Harriett B. McKeever.

Derby.   6.5.6.5.   F. FILITZ.

672   *Lord, save us.*—MATT. viii. 25.

1 JESUS, meek and gentle,
  Son of God most High,
Pitying, loving Saviour,
  Hear Thy children's cry!

2 Pardon our offences,
  Loose our captive chains,
Break down every idol
  Which our soul detains.

3 Give us holy freedom,
  Fill our hearts with love.

Draw us, Holy Jesus,
  To the realms above.

4 Lead us on our journey,
  Be Thyself the Way
Through this earthly darkness
  To eternal day.

5 Jesus, meek and gentle,
  Son of God most High,
Pitying, loving Saviour,
  Hear Thy children's cry!

G. R. Prynne.

S

Rickmansworth. 8.3.8.3. W. F. HURNDALL.

Copyright by W. Garrett Horder.

673 *He shall feed His flock like a shepherd.*—ISAIAH xl. 11.

1 JESUS, the children are calling;
    O draw near!
Fold the young lambs in Thy bosom,
    Shepherd dear.

2 Slow are our footsteps and failing,
    Oft we fall:
Jesus, the children are calling;
    Hear their call!

3 Cold is our love, Lord, and narrow;
    Large is Thine,
Faithful, and strong and tender:
    So be mine!

4 Gently, Lord, lead Thou our mothers;
    Weary they;
Bless all our sisters and brothers
    Night and day.

5 Fathers themselves are God's children;
    Teach them still:
Let the good Spirit show all men
    God's wise will.

6 Now to the Father, Son, Spirit,
    Three in One,
Bountiful God of our fathers,
    Praise be done!

Annie Matheson.

Words Copyright. By permission of the National Sunday School Union.

Innocents. 7.7.7.7. Composed or adapted by JOSEPH SMITH.

674 *I am but a little child.*—1 KINGS iii. 7.

1 GENTLE Jesus, meek and mild,
Look upon a little child;
Pity my simplicity,
Suffer me to come to Thee.

2 Fain I would to Thee be brought;
Blessèd Lord, forbid it not;
In the kingdom of Thy grace,
Give a little child a place.

3 Lamb of God, I look to Thee;
Thou shalt my example be;
Thou art gentle, meek, and mild;
Thou wast once a little Child.

4 Fain I would be as Thou art;
Give me Thy obedient heart;
Thou art pitiful and kind,
Let me have Thy loving mind.

5 Loving Jesus, gentle Lamb,
In Thy gracious hands I am;
Make me, Saviour, what Thou art,
Live Thyself within my heart.

C. Wesley.

Excelsior.   7.6.7.6., Trochaic.   JOSIAH BOOTH.

Copyright. Inserted by permission of the Composer.

675 *I will direct my prayer unto Thee, and will look up.*—PSALM v. 3.

1 LOOKING upward every day,
　Sunshine on our faces;
Pressing onward every day
　Toward the heavenly places.

2 Growing every day in awe,
　For Thy Name is holy;
Learning every day to love
　With a love more lowly.

3 Walking every day more close
　To our Elder Brother;
Growing every day more true
　Unto one another.

4 Every day more gratefully
　Kindnesses receiving,
Every day more readily
　Injuries forgiving.

5 Leaving every day behind
　Something which might hinder;
Running swifter every day,
　Growing purer, kinder.

6 Lord, so pray we every day,
　Hear us in Thy pity,
That we enter in at last
　To the Holy City.

Words Copyright. By permission of the National Sunday School Union. *Mary Butler.*

Capetown.   7.7.7.5.   F. FILITZ.

rall.

676 *Satisfy us early with Thy mercy.*—PSALM xc. 14.

1 GENTLE Saviour, ever nigh,
Though adored by hosts on high
Thou wilt listen to the cry
　Of a little child.

2 Cleanse my heart from every sin,
Make me pure and good within;
Ere the cares of life begin
　Save a little child.

3 Give me strength to do the right
Day by day from morn till night;

Make my life sincere and bright;
　Bless a little child.

4 When my feet are prone to stray
From the strait and narrow way,
In that dark and evil day
　Keep a little child.

5 Bless me all life's journey through;
Let Thy grace my heart renew;
Make me holy, wise, and true,
　Thine obedient child.

Words Copyright. By permission of the National Sunday School Union. *Henry Putnam.*

Palestine. C.M., with Chorus. W. GAWLER'S Hymns and Psalms.

CHORUS.

The voice with-in, the voice with-in, Oh, may I have a care; It speaks to warn from ev-'ry sin, And God has placed it there.

677

Holding faith, and a good conscience.—1 TIM. i. 19.

1 THE still small voice that speaks within,
  I hear it when at play
I speak the loud and angry word
  That drives my friend away.
    The voice within, etc.

2 If falsehood whispers to my heart
  To tell a coward lie,
To hide some careless thing I've done,
  I hear the sad voice nigh.

3 If selfishness would bid me keep
  What I should gladly share,
I hear again the inner voice,
  And then with shame forbear.

4 I thank Thee, Father, for this friend,
  Whom I would always heed;
Oh, may I hear the slightest tone
  In every time of need!

Frances Fagan.

678 Missionary. 7.6.8.6., D. LOWELL MASON.

678 *To be conformed to the image of His Son.*—ROM. viii. 29.

1 I WANT to be like Jesus,
    So lowly and so meek,
For no one marked an angry word
    That ever heard Him speak:
I want to be like Jesus,
    So frequently in prayer,
Alone upon the mountain top;
    He met His Father there.

2 I want to be like Jesus:
    I never, never find
That He, though persecuted, was
    To anyone unkind:

I want to be like Jesus,
    Engaged in doing good,
So that of me it may be said,
    "She hath done what she could."

3 I want to be like Jesus,
    Who kindly said to all,
"Let little children come to Me;"
    I would obey the call:
But oh! I'm not like Jesus,
    As anyone may see;
O gentle Saviour, send Thy grace,
    And make me like to Thee!

W. M. Whittemore.

I'll be a Sunbeam.   P.M.   E. O. EXCELL (arr.).

CHORUS.

A sun-beam, a sun-beam, Jesus wants me for a sun-beam, A sun-beam, a sun-beam, I'll be a sunbeam for Him.

679 *As the light of the morning, when the sun riseth.*—2 SAM. xxiii. 4.

1 JESUS wants me for a sunbeam,
    To shine for Him each day;
In every way try to please Him,
    At home, at school, at play.
    A sunbeam, etc.

2 Jesus wants me to be loving,
    And kind to all I see;
Showing how pleasant and happy
    His little one can be.

3 I will ask Jesus to help me,
    To keep my heart from sin;
Ever reflecting His goodness,
    And always shine for Him.

4 I'll be a sunbeam for Jesus,
    I can, if I but try,
Serving Him moment by moment,
    Then live with Him on high.

Nellie Talbot.

Child Service. 7.6.8.8.6. H. Elliot Button.

By permission of Novello and Company, Limited.

680 *Whatsoever thy hand findeth to do, do it with thy might.*—ECCLES. ix. 10.

1 Oh, what can little hands do
  To please the King of heaven?
The little hands some work may try
To help the poor in misery:
  Such grace to mine be given.

2 Oh, what can little lips do
  To please the King of heaven?
The little lips can praise and pray,
And gentle words of kindness say:
  Such grace to mine be given.

3 Oh, what can little eyes do
  To please the King of heaven?
The little eyes can upward look,

And learn to read God's holy Book:
  Such grace to mine be given.

4 Oh, what can little hearts do
  To please the King of heaven?
Our hearts, if God His Spirit send,
Can love and trust their Saviour Friend:
  Such grace to mine be given.

5 Though small is all that we can do
  To please the King of heaven;
When hearts and hands and lips unite
To serve the Saviour with delight,
  They're precious in His sight.
          Grace W. Hisdale.

Derby. 6.5.6.5. F. Filitz.

Alternative Tune, ENON, *No.* 644.
Christ died for our sins.—1 COR. xv. 3.

681

1 JESUS, tender Saviour,
    Hast Thou died for me?
  Make me very thankful
    In my heart to Thee.

2 When the sad, sad story
    Of Thy grief I read,
  Make me very sorry
    For my sins indeed.

3 Now I know Thou livest,
    And dost plead for me:
  Make me very thankful
    In my prayers to Thee.

4 Soon I hope in glory,
    At Thy side to stand;
  Make me fit to meet Thee
    In that happy land. *Anon.*

Alstone.   L.M.   C. E. WILLING.

682   *Even a child is known by his doings, whether his work be pure, and whether it be right.*—PROV. xx. 11.

1 WE are but little children weak,
  Nor born in any high estate;
What can we do for Jesus' sake,
  Who is so high, and good, and great?

2 When deep within our swelling hearts
  The thoughts of pride and anger rise;
When bitter words are on our tongues,
  And tears of passion in our eyes:

3 Then we may stay the angry blow,
  Then we may check the hasty word;

Give gentle answers back again,
  And fight a battle for our Lord.

4 With smiles of peace, and looks of love,
  Light in our dwellings we may make;
Bid kind good humour brighten there—
  And still do all for Jesus' sake.

5 There's not a child so small and weak
  But has his little cross to take,
His little work of love and praise
  That he may do for Jesus' sake.

Mrs. C. F. Alexander.

Franconia.   S.M.   German.

683   *All have sinned and come short of the glory of God.*—ROMANS iii. 23.

1   I'M not too young to sin,
   I'm not too young to die,
I'm not too little to begin
  A life of faith and joy.

2   I'm not too young to know
   The Saviour's love to me
In coming down to earth below
  To die upon the tree.

3   I'm not too young to love,
   I'm not too young to pray,
To look to Jesus up above,
  And all His Word obey.

4   Jesus, I love Thy Name;
   From evil set me free,
And ever keep Thy little lamb,
  Who puts his trust in Thee.

Anon. and (vv. 2 and 3) Geo. Goodman.

Jesus Bids us Shine.   P.M.   E. O. EXCELL.

684 *Let your light so shine before men, that they may see your good works, and glorify your Father which is in heaven.*—MATT. v. 16.

1 JESUS bids us shine
  With a pure, clear light;
Like a little candle
  Burning in the night.
In this world of darkness,
  So we must shine—
You in your small corner,
  And I in mine.

2 Jesus bids us shine,
  First of all for Him;
Well He sees and knows it
  If our light grows dim.

He looks down from heaven,
  To see us shine—
You in your small corner,
  And I in mine.

3 Jesus bids us shine,
  Then, for all around;
Many kinds of darkness
  In this world abound—
Sin and want and sorrow;
  So we must shine—
You in your small corner,
  And I in mine.   *Susan Warner.*

Trinity Chapel.   10.10.10.10., Dactylic, with Chorus.
685   *I have loved you, saith the Lord.*—MAL. i. 2.   P. P. BLISS.

2 Though I forget Him, and wander away,
  Still He doth love me wherever I stray;
  Back to His dear, loving arms would I flee,
  When I remember that Jesus loves me.
    I am so glad that Jesus loves me, etc.

3 Oh, if there's only one song I can sing
  When in His beauty I see the great King!

This shall my song in eternity be,
  "Oh, what a wonder that Jesus loves me!"
4 Jesus loves me, and I know I love Him,
  Love brought Him down my poor soul to redeem;
Yes, it was love made Him die on the tree:
  Oh, I am certain that Jesus loves me!
    (*Last two verses at top of next page.*)

5 If one should ask of me, how can I tell?
  Glory to Jesus, I know very well!
  God's Holy Spirit with mine doth agree,
  Constantly witnessing—Jesus loves me.

6 In this assurance I find sweetest rest,
  Trusting in Jesus, I know I am blest;
  Satan, dismayed, from my soul now doth flee,
  When I just tell Him that Jesus loves me.
  P. P. Bliss.

Lead Me to Jesus.   P.M.   W. H. Doane.

Quickly haste and come where happy children meet. Hither come and sing the Saviour's praises sweet:

Rest from thy pleasures, rest from thy play, Come to our meeting, come a-way.

686

And he brought him to Jesus.—JOHN i. 42.

1 LEAD me to Jesus, lead me to Jesus;
    Help me to love Him, help me to pray;
  He is my Saviour: I would believe Him;
    I would be like Him—show me the way.
      Quickly haste and come, etc.

2 Lead me to Jesus; He will receive me;
    He is so loving, gentle, and mild—
  Calling the children, bidding them welcome;
    Surely He calls me—I am a child.

3 Tell me of Jesus, tell of His mercy,
    Is there a fountain flowing so free?
  All who are willing drink of its waters—
    Say, is that fountain flowing for me?

4 Lord, I am coming: Jesus, my Saviour,
    Pity my weakness; make me Thy child:
  I would receive Thee, trust and believe Thee;
    I would be like Thee—gentle and mild.
      Fanny J. Crosby.

s*

Buckland.   7.7.7.7.   L. G. HAYNE.

687   *My sheep hear My voice, and I know them, and they follow Me: and I give unto them eternal life.*—JOHN x. 27, 28.

1 LOVING Shepherd of Thy sheep,
  Keep Thy lamb, in safety keep;
  Nothing can Thy power withstand,
  None can pluck me from Thy hand.

2 Loving Saviour, Thou didst give
  Thine own life that we might live,
  And the hands outstretched to bless
  Bear the cruel nails' impress.

3 I would praise Thee every day,
  Gladly all Thy will obey,

Like Thy blessèd ones above,
Happy in Thy precious love.

4 Loving Shepherd, ever near,
  Teach Thy lamb Thy voice to hear,
  Suffer not my steps to stray
  From the strait and narrow way.

5 Where Thou leadest I would go,
  Walking in Thy steps below,
  Till before my Father's throne
  I shall know as I am known.
             Jane E. Leeson.

Humility.   7.7.7.5.   S. RAPHAEL.
Smoothly. UNISON.

688   *And they brought young children to Him, that He should touch them.*—MARK x. 13.

1 JESUS, when He left the sky,
  And for sinners came to die,
  In His mercy passed not by
    Little ones like me.

2 Mothers then the Saviour sought
  In the places where He taught,
  And to Him their children brought—
    Little ones like me.

3 Did the Saviour say them nay?
  No! He kindly bade them stay,

Suffered none to turn away
  Little ones like me.

4 'Twas for them His life He gave,
  To redeem them from the grave;
  Jesus able is to save
    Little ones like me.

5 Children then should love Him now,
  Strive His holy will to do:
  Pray to Him and praise Him too—
    Little ones like me.   *M. Rumsey.*

Section XIV.—Special Occasions.

Melita.

8.8.8.8.8.8.

J. B. Dykes.

689

Thou rulest the raging of the sea.—Psalm lxxxix. 9.

1 Eternal Father, strong to save,
Whose arm hath bound the restless wave,
Who bidd'st the mighty ocean deep
Its own appointed limits keep:
   Oh, hear us when we cry to Thee
   For those in peril on the sea!

2 O Christ, whose voice the waters heard,
And hushed their raging at Thy word,
Who walkedst on the foaming deep,
And calm amid the storm didst sleep:
   Oh, hear us when we cry to Thee
   For those in peril on the sea!

3 O Holy Spirit, who didst brood
Upon the waters dark and rude,
And bid their angry tumult cease,
And give, for wild confusion, peace:
   Oh, hear us when we cry to Thee
   For those in peril on the sea!

4 O Trinity of love and power,
Our brethren shield in danger's hour;
From rock and tempest, fire and foe,
Protect them wheresoe'er they go:
   Thus evermore shall rise to Thee
   Glad hymns of praise from land and sea.

W. Whiting.

Hermas.　　　　　6.5., 12 lines.　　　　FRANCES R. HAVERGAL.

690　　　*Thou shalt guide me with Thy counsel.*—PSALM lxxiii. 24.

1 JESUS, blessèd Saviour,
　　Help us now to raise
Songs of glad thanksgiving,
　　Songs of holy praise.
Oh, how kind and gracious
　　Thou hast always been!
Oh, how many blessings
　　Every day has seen!
　　Jesus, blessèd Saviour,
　　　　Now our praises hear,
　　For Thy grace and favour
　　　　Crowning all the year.

2 Jesus, holy Saviour,
　　Only Thou canst tell
How we often stumbled,
　　How we often fell!
All our sins (so many!),
　　Saviour, Thou dost know:
In Thy blood most precious
　　Wash us white as snow.
　　Jesus, blessèd Saviour,
　　　　Keep us in Thy fear,
　　Let Thy grace and favour
　　　　Pardon all the year.

3 Jesus, loving Saviour,
　　Only Thou dost know
All that may befall us
　　As we onward go;
So we humbly pray Thee,
　　Take us by the hand,
Lead us ever upward
　　To the better land.
　　Jesus, blessèd Saviour,
　　　　Keep us ever near,
　　Let Thy grace and favour
　　　　Shield us all the year.

4 Jesus, precious Saviour,
　　Make us all Thine own,
Make us Thine for ever,
　　Make us Thine alone.
Let each day, each moment
　　Of this glad new year,
Be for Jesus only,
　　Jesus, Saviour dear.
　　Then, O blessèd Saviour,
　　　　Never need we fear:
　　For Thy grace and favour
　　　　Crown our bright New Year.
　　　　　　　Frances R. Havergal.

Deva. 6.5.6.5., D., with Refrain. E. J. HOPKINS.

REFRAIN.

Onward then and fear not,

Children of the day! For His Word shall nev-er, Nev-er pass a-way!

Alternative Tune, PILGRIMS OF THE NIGHT, *No.* 97.

691 *He hath said, I will never leave thee, nor forsake thee.*—HEB. xiii. 5.

1 STANDING at the portal
  Of the opening year,
Words of comfort meet us,
  Hushing every fear;
Spoken through the silence
  By our Father's voice,
Tender, strong, and faithful,
  Making us rejoice.
    Onward then and fear not, etc.

2 I, the Lord, am with thee,
  Be thou not afraid,
I will help and strengthen,
  Be thou not dismayed!
Yea, I will uphold thee
  With My own right hand,
Thou art called and chosen
  In My sight to stand.

3 For the year before us,
  Oh, what rich supplies!
For the poor and needy
  Living streams shall rise;
For the sad and sinful
  Shall His grace abound;
For the faint and feeble
  Perfect strength be found.

4 He will never fail us,
  He will not forsake;
His eternal covenant
  He will never break.
Resting on His promise,
  What have we to fear?
God is all-sufficient
  For the coming year.

Frances R. Havergal

Father, let me Dedicate. 7.5.7.5., D. Sir G. A. Macfarren.

692 *That God in all things may be glorified.*—1 Peter iv. 11.

1 FATHER, let me dedicate
All this year to Thee,
In whatever worldly state
Thou wilt have me be:
Not from sorrow, pain, or care,
Freedom dare I claim;
This alone shall be my prayer,
"Glorify Thy Name."

2 Can a child presume to choose
Where or how to live?
Can a Father's love refuse
All the best to give?
More Thou givest every day
Than the best can claim,
Nor withholdest aught that may
Glorify Thy Name.

3 If in mercy Thou wilt spare
Joys that yet are mine;
If on life, serene and fair,
Brighter rays may shine:
Let my glad heart, while it sings,
Thee in all proclaim,
And, whate'er the future brings,
"Glorify Thy Name."

4 If Thou callest to the cross,
And its shadow come,
Turning all my gain to loss,
Shrouding heart and home;
Let me think how Thy dear Son
To His glory came,
And in deepest woe pray on,
"Glorify Thy Name."

L. Tuttiett.

St. George's Chapel. 7.7.7.7., D. Sir G. J. ELVEY.

693 *Thou shalt keep . . . the feast of harvest.*—EXOD. xxiii. 15, 16.

1 COME, ye thankful people, come,
  Raise the song of harvest home:
  All is safely gathered in,
  Ere the winter storms begin;
  God our Maker doth provide
  For our wants to be supplied;
  Come to God's own temple, come,
  Raise the song of harvest-home!

2 All the world is God's own field,
  Fruit unto His praise to yield;
  Wheat and tares together sown,
  Unto joy or sorrow grown;
  First the blade, and then the ear,
  Then the full corn shall appear;
  Lord of harvest, grant that we
  Wholesome grain and pure may be.

3 For the Lord our God shall come,
  And shall take His harvest home;
  From His field shall in that day
  All offences purge away;
  Give His angels charge at last
  In the fire the tares to cast;
  But the fruitful ears to store
  In His garner evermore.

4 Even so, Lord, quickly come
  To Thy final Harvest-home,
  Gather Thou Thy people in,
  Free from sorrow, free from sin;
  There for ever purified,
  In Thy presence to abide:
  Come, with all Thine angels, come;
  Raise the glorious Harvest-home.

H. Alford.

Dresden.　　　　7.6.7.6., D., with Refrain.　　　J. A. P. SCHULTZE.

REFRAIN.

694　*The eyes of all wait upon Thee; and Thou givest them their meat in due season.*—PSALM cxlv. 15.

1 WE plough the fields, and scatter
　The good seed on the land,
But it is fed and water'd
　By God's almighty hand;
He sends the snow in winter,
　The warmth to swell the grain,
The breezes, and the sunshine,
　The soft refreshing rain.
　　All good gifts around us
　　Are sent from heav'n above;
　Then thank the Lord, O thank the
　　For all His love.　　　[Lord,

2 He only is the Maker
　Of all things near and far;

He paints the wayside flower,
　He lights the evening star.
The winds and waves obey Him,
　By Him the birds are fed;
Much more to us, His children,
　He gives our daily bread.

3 We thank Thee then, O Father,
　For all things bright and good,
The seed-time and the harvest,
　Our life, our health, our food.
Accept the gifts we offer
　For all Thy love imparts,
And, what Thou most desirest,
　Our humble, thankful hearts.

M. Claudius, tr. Miss Jane M. Campbell.

Springfield. 11.10.11.10., Dactyllic. H. I. GAUNTLETT.

695 *Of Thine own have we given Thee.*—1 CHRON. xxix. 14.

1 HERE, Lord, we offer Thee all that is fairest,
Bloom from the garden, and flowers from
the field; [carest
Gifts for the stricken ones, knowing Thou
More for the love than the wealth that
we yield.

2 Send, Lord, by these to the sick and the
dying; [peace;
Speak to their hearts with a message of
Comfort the sad, who in weakness are lying;
Grant the departing a gentle release.

3 Raise, Lord, to health again those who have
sickened,
Fair be their lives as the roses in bloom;
Give of Thy grace to the souls Thou hast
quickened, [gloom.
Gladness for sorrow, and brightness for

4 We, Lord, like flowers, must bloom and
must wither, [must die;
We, like these blossoms, must fade and
Gather us, Lord, to Thy bosom for ever,
Grant us a place in Thy house in the sky.

A. G. W. Blunt.

St. John. 6.6.6.6.8.8. W. H. HAVERGAL.

696 *If thou turn to the Lord thy God . . . He will not forsake thee.*—
DEUT. iv. 30, 31.

1 To Thee, our God, we fly
For mercy and for grace:
O hear our lowly cry,
And hide not Thou Thy face.
O Lord, stretch forth Thy mighty hand,
And guard and bless our Fatherland.

2 Arise, O Lord of hosts;
Be jealous for Thy Name;
And drive from out our coasts
The sins that put to shame.
O Lord, stretch forth Thy mighty hand,
And guard and bless our Fatherland.

3 The powers ordained by Thee
With heavenly wisdom bless;
May they Thy servants be,
And rule in righteousness.
O Lord, stretch forth Thy mighty hand,
And guard and bless our Fatherland.

4 Give peace, Lord, in our time;
O let no foe draw nigh,
Nor lawless deed of crime
Insult Thy majesty.
O Lord, stretch forth Thy mighty hand,
And guard and bless our Fatherland.

W. W. How.

National Anthem.   6.6.4.6.6.6.4.

697   *And all the people shouted, and said, God save the King.*—1 SAM. x. 24.

1 GOD save our gracious King,
Long live our noble King,
God save the King:
Send him victorious,
Happy and glorious,
Long to reign over us:
God save the King!

2 Thy choicest gifts in store
On him be pleased to pour;
Long may he reign:
May he defend our laws,
And ever give us cause
To sing with heart and voice,
God save the King!

698   *God be merciful unto us, and bless us.*—PSALM lxvii. 1.

1 GOD bless our native land,
May heaven's protecting hand
Still guard her shore;
May peace her sway extend,
Foe be transformed to friend,
And Britain's power depend
On war no more.

2 Through changes time shall bring,
O Lord, preserve the King;
Long may he reign.
His heart inspire and move
With wisdom from above;
And in a nation's love
His throne maintain.

3 May just and righteous laws
Uphold the public cause
And bless our isle.
Home of the brave and free,
The land of liberty,
We pray that still on thee
Kind heaven may smile!

4 And not this land alone,
But be Thy mercies known
From shore to shore;
Lord, make the nations see
That men should brothers be,
And form one family
The wide world o'er.

W. E. Hickson.

God be with you! P.M. W. G. TOMER.

Till we meet, . . Till we meet, Till we meet at Je - sus' feet;

Till we meet, . . Till we meet, God be with you till we meet a - gain!

699 *Now, brethren, I commend you to God, and to the word of His grace.—* ACTS xx. 32.

1 GOD be with you till we meet again!
By His counsels guide, uphold you,
With His sheep securely fold you;
God be with you till we meet again!
  Till we meet, etc.

2 God be with you till we meet again!
'Neath His wings securely hide you,
Daily manna still provide you;
God be with you till we meet again!

3 God be with you till we meet again!
When life's perils thick confound you,
Put His loving arms around you;
God be with you till we meet again!

4 God be with you till we meet again!
Keep love's banner floating o'er you,
Smite death's threatening wave before you,
God be with you till we meet again.

J. E. Rankin.

Section XV.—Vespers, Dorology, and Benediction.

Vespers.   S.M.   Anon. Arr. from Beethoven.

700   *The Lord is my light and my salvation.*—Psalm xxvii. 1.

Lord, keep us safe this night,
Secure from all our fears;
May angels guard us while we sleep,
Till morning light appears.   *J. Leland.*

Vespera.   8.7.8.7.7.7.   Sir J. Barnby.

By permission of Novello and Company, Limited.

701   *Thou shalt lie down, and none shall make thee afraid.*—Job xi. 19.

Through the day Thy love has spared us,
Now we lay us down to rest;
Through the silent watches guard us;
Let no foe our peace molest:
Jesus, Thou our Guardian be;
Sweet it is to trust in Thee!   *T. Kelly.*

DOXOLOGY.

L.M.

Old Hundredth.

G. Franc.

702

Praise Him, all ye people.—PSALM cxvii. 1.

PRAISE God, from whom all blessings flow;
Praise Him, all creatures here below;
Praise Him above, ye heavenly host;
Praise Father, Son, and Holy Ghost.

T. Ken.

BENEDICTION.

NUMBERS vi. 24—26.

P.M.

C. M. VON WEBER (adapted).

703

The Lord bless and keep thee, Make His face shine; Un- to thee gra-cious be,

Both thee and thine. Lift up His coun-ten-ance, Send thee re - lease..

From sin be - set-ting thee, And give thee peace. A - men, A-men, A - men.

Geo. Goodman.

INDEX OF FIRST LINES

Index of First Lines

Index of First Lines

METRICAL INDEX.

METRICAL INDEX.

7777D	No.
Everlasting Love	386
Hollingside	361
St. George's Chapel	693
Sheringham	634
Tichfield..	379

7s (10 lines).
Mendelssohn	119

78784
St. Albinus	167

8383
Rickmansworth	673

8383D
Waltham Street	646

8484
Victoria Street..	296

8484 (with refrain).
Walmsley	665

848484
Wentworth	59

84884
God holds the key	351

84848884
Oh, how He loves	327
Southgate	316

8583
Art thou longing	233
Bullinger	417
Cairnbrook 73, 255	
Derwent..	651
Hartham	234
St. Helen's	435
Stephanos	235

8583 (with refrain).
Precious, precious blood of Jesus	147

86767676
In Memoriam	640

8684
St. Cuthbert	187

868686
St. Silas	368
Spohr 141, 439, 658	

86886
Newcastle	569
Rest	402

8784
Filey	585

8785
St. Leonards	551

8787
All for Jesus	641
Batty	373
Cross of Jesus	94
Dominus Regit Me	390
Evening Prayer	607
Lucerne	412
St. Andrew	467
St. Oswald .. 276, 631	
Sefton	638
Sharon 550, 664	
Sicilian Mariners .. 373, 470	
Stuttgart	434

8787 (with refrain).	No.
Arch Street	83
Channels Only	421
Daybreak	494
Have you any room for Jesus	216
My Redeemer	8
Refuge	320
The Saviour with me..	343
Trusting More	273
Woolacombe	667

87873
Etiam et Mihi	259
Even Me..	259

87874447
Helmsley	179

878747
Heber (Evangel)	430
Rousseau	253
St. Raphael	312

878766667
Ein' Feste Burg	322

878777
Gounod	457
Irby	120
Requiem	367
Vespera	701

878787
Ephesus	52
Dismissal	608
Kensington New	110
Mannheim	355
Praise, my Soul	32
Regent Square	175
St. Christian	164
St. Werburgh	337
The Good Shepherd ..	335
Triumph	32

8787D
All the Way	293
Alleluia (Wesley)	30
Amicus Divinus	449
Austria	27
Bethany	362
Bishopgarth	612
Constance	449
Converse	64
Courage, Brother	354
Deerhurst	557
Ebenezer	138
Golden Sheaves	436
Hyfrydol	158
Lux Eoi	542
Petros	339
St. Asaph	536
St. Hilda	14
St. Simon	617
Scopas	122
The Blessed Name	26
The Hope of the World ..	614
Vocation	242

8787D (with refrain).
The Sweetest Story	123

8787887
The Golden Chain	493

87887
St. Jude	485

886886
Innsbruck	480
Ravendale	480

887887	No.
Evening Hymn..	610

8883
Aescendune	490
St. Aëlred	299

8884
Almsgiving	89
Memorial	399
Southport	84
Sunset	442
Victory	165

8885
St. Aubin	476

8886
Agnus Dei	227
Cambridge	489
Just as I am	226
Silverstone	411
Trust	405

8886 (with refrain).
More than tongue can tell ..	153

8887
Ewhurst	471

8888 (Amphibrachic).
Celeste 280, 281	

88886
St. Margaret	398

888888
Credo (Stainer)	124
Melita	689
St. Catherine 251, 290	
St. Chrysostom	458
St. Matthias	598
Stella	380

9696
Llanthony Abbey	375
Whitchester	375

9898
St. Clement	606

9898 (with refrain).
Redemption	268
The Wonderful Story.. ..	145

9898D
Jubilee	624
Park Langley	131

10.4.10.4
Submission	298

10.4.10.4.10.10
Lux Benigna	295
Sandon	295

10.10
Pax Tecum	338

10.10. (with refrain).
Yet there is room	224

10.10.10.4
Austalis	50
Kandersteg	50
St. Philip	568

10.10.10.6 (with refrain).
Verily, Verily	245

METRICAL INDEX.

ALPHABETICAL INDEX OF TUNES.

ALPHABETICAL INDEX OF TUNES.

CHURCH SEASONS AND SPECIAL OCCASIONS.

T

FLOWER SERVICES	97, 99, 101, 103, 106, 108, 644, 695.
HOME AND FOREIGN MISSIONS	21, 35, 55, 423, 424, 426-436, 439, 440, 509, 546, 611-626, 647.
OLD AND NEW YEAR	40, 91, 337, 355, 368, 390, 391, 414, 470, 501, 520, 534, 671, 690-692.
NATIONAL	696, 697, 698.
FOR THOSE AT SEA	73, 689.
VALEDICTORY	77, 430, 699.

INDEX OF SCRIPTURE REFERENCES

Index of Scripture References

Index of Scripture References

Novello, Printers, London